ALBERTA

A NATURAL HISTORY

ALBERTA

A Natural History

EDITOR-IN-CHIEF / W. G. HARDY

PUBLISHED BY THE PATRONS

DISTRIBUTED TO THE TRADE
BY M. G. HURTIG, PUBLISHERS,
EDMONTON, ALBERTA

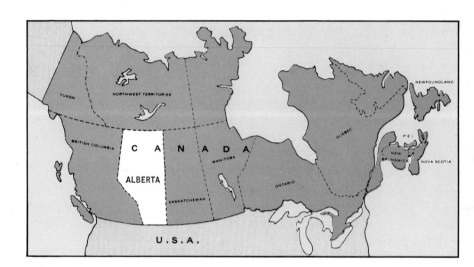

1st Printing September 1967, 23,000 copies
2nd Printing November 1967, 20,000 copies
3rd Printing September 1971, 10,000 copies
4th Printing January 1975, 10,000 copies

The body text, picture captions and headings of this book are set in Melior type. The book is printed Web Offset on Georgian Smooth paper. Printed and bound by the Evergreen Press Limited, Vancouver. Printed in Canada.

Editors

W. G. HARDY, C.M., M.A., Ph.D., F.I.A.L., LL.D., *Editor-in-Chief*

MARGARET COLEMAN JOHNSON, *Assistant Editor*
CYRIL G. HAMPSON, B.A., Ph.D., *Chief Associate Editor*

Associate Editors

ROBERT GREEN, B.Sc., Ph.D., *Technical Illustrations*
CYRIL G. HAMPSON, B.A., Ph.D., *Photography*
MARY G. HAMPSON, *Photographic Assistant*
BRIAN HITCHON, B.Sc., Ph.D., *Project Originator and Consultant*
MARGARET COLEMAN JOHNSON, *Executive Secretary*
IAN C. MacDONALD, M.Ed., *Editorial Consultant*
W. MILLS PARKER, *Project Co-ordinator*
J. DEWEY SOPER, LL.D., *Consultant in Mammalogy*

Production Committee

Robert Green, Cyril G. Hampson, W. G. Hardy
Margaret Coleman Johnson, W. Mills Parker

Technical and Advisory Committee

Dr. Charles D. Bird, Dr. William A. Fuller, Dr. Robert Green
Dr. Cyril G. Hampson, Dr. W. George Hardy, M. G. Hurtig
Ian C. MacDonald (Chairman), *W. Mills Parker*
Dr. Charles R. Stelck (Vice-Chairman)

EDITORS,
PATRONS
AND SPONSORS

Patrons

Canadian Utilities Limited; Canadian Western Natural Gas Company Limited; Northwestern Utilities Limited; Alberta Power Limited

Sponsoring Natural History and Learned Societies

Alberta Geographic Society
Alberta Society of Petroleum Geologists
Archaeological Society of Alberta (Edmonton, Calgary, Lethbridge)
Calgary Bird Club
Calgary Zoological Society
Canadian Society of Wildlife and Fishery Biologists (Alberta Chapter)
Edmonton Bird Club
Edmonton Geological Society
Edmonton Zoological Society
Entomological Society of Alberta
Historical Society of Alberta
Natural History Club
Royal Astronomical Society of Canada (Edmonton and Calgary Centres)

CONTENTS

PART I — THE LAND

CHAPTER ONE: NIGHT SKIES OVER ALBERTA
Franklin C. Loehde, B.Sc., B.Ed.   5

CHAPTER TWO: THE RECORD OF THE ROCKS
Charles R. Stelck, M.Sc., Ph.D., F.R.S.C. 21

CHAPTER THREE: CLIMATE AND WEATHER PATTERNS
Richmond W. Longley, B.Sc., M.A. 53

CHAPTER FOUR: MOUNTAINS AND PLAINS
Robert Green, B.Sc., Ph.D.
Arleigh H. Laycock, M.Sc., Ph.D. 69

PART II — FLORA AND FAUNA

CHAPTER FIVE: THE PRAIRIE WORLD
Robert Webb, B.Sc.
Alexander Johnston, B.S.A., M.S.
J. Dewey Soper, LL.D. 93

CHAPTER SIX: THE CYPRESS HILLS
Charles D. Bird, B.Sc., Ph.D.
Ian A. R. Halladay, B.Sc. 117

CHAPTER SEVEN: THE ASPEN PARKLAND
Charles D. Bird, B.Sc., Ph.D.
Ralph D. Bird, M.Sc., Ph.D. 135

CHAPTER EIGHT: THE BOREAL FOREST
Taiga
George H. La Roi, M.Sc., Ph.D. 151

Summer Animals
Cyril G. Hampson, B.A., Ph.D. 169

Winter in the Northern Forest
William A. Fuller, M. Sc., Ph.D. 172

Man and the Forest
Edo Nyland, B.S.F. 184

CHAPTER NINE: MOUNTAIN HABITATS
  David A. Boag, M.Sc., Ph.D.
  W. George Evans, M.Sc., Ph.D. 193

CHAPTER TEN: AQUATIC LIFE
  Aquatic Habitats
  Rodney J. Paterson, B.A. 221

  Aquatic Plant Life
  Lorene L. Kennedy, M.Sc., Ph.D. 227

  Aquatic Invertebrate Life
  R. C. B. Hartland-Rowe, B.Sc., Ph.D. 239

  The Angler's Domain
  Martin J. Paetz, M.Sc. 248

  Water Conservation
  Rodney J. Paterson, B.A. 256

CHAPTER ELEVEN: THE STUDY OF NATURAL HISTORY
  M. T. Myres, M.A., Ph.D. 265

PART III — MAN

CHAPTER TWELVE: THE FIRST PEOPLE
  Alan Bryan, M.A., Ph.D. 277

CHAPTER THIRTEEN: EARLY NATURAL HISTORY
EXPLORATIONS
  Brian Hitchon, B.Sc., Ph.D. 295

CHAPTER FOURTEEN: THE IMPACT OF THE WHITE MAN
  James G. MacGregor, B.A., B.Sc. 303

CREDITS 320

BIOGRAPHICAL SKETCHES 321

FURTHER READING 323

INDEX 328

EDITOR'S ACKNOWLEDGMENTS

IN THIS BOOK the reader will find an authoritative account of the main features of the natural history of Alberta, phrased in non-technical language and complemented by photographs, maps, diagrams and marginal drawings. Its principal objective is to interest a wide audience in the fascinating world of nature.

Such a presentation has long been needed for schools, libraries and the reading public. It was Dr. Brian Hitchon, however, who originated the concept of this volume as a Centennial project and served in its early stages as Chairman of the Operating and Technical Committee of the Participating Societies. Through his enthusiasm and that of his prime collaborator, Ian C. MacDonald, the project received the support of Natural History and Learned Societies in Alberta, and of the Patrons. Without the strenuous and persistent efforts of Dr. Hitchon and Mr. MacDonald ALBERTA — A NATURAL HISTORY would never have moved from an idea to a realistic undertaking.

The putting together of the book was the work of many minds. Its general arrangement and the tenor of its contents were hammered out in meetings of representatives of the sponsoring Societies. Everyone, however, is especially indebted to the twenty-five authors. Each is a specialist in his subject matter, and each has contributed generously of his time, effort and patience to make his technical knowledge available to non-specialists.

Besides a deep appreciation of the vital contribution of the authors, my own particular thanks are due to the Production Committee. Margaret Coleman Johnson brought to her Assistant Editorship a lively intelligence and a long experience as an author and as a teacher of creative writing. The Director of Photography, Dr. Cyril G. Hampson, internationally known for his photographic masterpieces of wildlife, made available his personal collection of some 20,000 photographic studies. In his rôle as Director of Photography he was ably assisted by his wife, Mary G. Hampson. As Director of Technical Illustrations, Dr. Robert Green gave conscientious supervision to those Alberta cartographers and artists who have contributed to this book. Throughout the varying phases and difficulties of the undertaking W. Mills Parker served with energy and versatility as Project Co-ordinator for the Patrons. There were others who, from time to time, assisted during certain stages of the project — but from the inception of the actual composition of the volume to its completion, the Production Committee provided the necessary sustained effort.

All those connected with the publication of this book, and all who read it are deeply indebted to the Patrons — Canadian Utilities Limited; Canadian Western Natural Gas Company Limited; Northwestern Utilities Limited; Alberta Power Limited. Their support was unremitting and their generosity has made ALBERTA — A NATURAL HISTORY a volume within the reach of everyone.

ALBERTA'S NATURAL ENVIRONMENT is a treasure house of merging and yet distinctive worlds. In its parklands, foothills, mountains and deep forests are secluded haunts, often made beautiful by snow-bright peaks, forgotten valleys, encompassing trees, mirrored lakes or undulating hills and unexpected streams. Here modern man, in a realization that he is still a part of nature, can restore his soul.

There are other riches for those who gaze about them with discerning eyes. Rock strata and fossil remains, when understood, take the observer back to the genesis of the province and to the story of the long aeons during which its structure and contours were moulded and life was developed from form to form until man's arrival. If one looks to the distant stars, he realizes a challenge to humanity's significance. Most of all, perhaps, in every area of Alberta, on land or in the "aqueous cosmos", is a pulsating life adapted to its particular environment. As the pages of this volume and the appended lists of Further Reading make clear, whether the observer's interest be in anthropology, astronomy, geography, geology or living things, any of these fields can be investigated and enjoyed.

It is this natural heritage that conservationists wish to preserve. In today's Alberta, over-population, serious encroachment on the habitats of plant and animal life, and the pollution of air, soil and water may seem remote possibilities. A half century hence, they may be problems crowding in upon us.

Today, more than ever before, civilized man is the somewhat blundering master of his natural environment and, in consequence, he must learn to manage it. This is as true in Alberta as elsewhere. One purpose of this volume therefore is to suggest "wise conservation" and an understanding of the complex interrelationships and inexorable laws of the natural world. Above all else, however, the authors of its articles are seeking to interest the reader in Alberta's world of nature.

ALBERTA'S WORLD OF NATURE

PART I/THE LAND

THE LAND

THE PHYSICAL CHARACTERISTICS of Alberta exert a strong influence on the nature of its flora and fauna. In the pages that follow we see the wide skies in which, night after winter night, the aurora borealis dances and spirals and across which meteors often flash. We read of the records left in the rocks during the two and a half billion years in which, through alternating infloodings of ocean waters and upliftings of land surface, the basic structure of the province was built and oil, natural gas, coal and other resources stored within it. The variations of a climate which helps determine the types of life that flourish in Alberta are described. So is the diversity of a landscape which ranges from rolling plains to mountain ramparts and from treeless prairie through the aspen groves and cultivated fields of the parklands to the depths of the northern forests.

In these first four chapters we perceive how important it is to understand the province's physical background, if we wish to comprehend the wide variety of its plant and animal life.

Title Picture Part I — Freshfield Glacier, Banff National Park — by G. Hunter.

C.T.

CHAPTER ONE

Night Skies over Alberta

ON MARCH 4th, 1960, at 1:06 A.M., a meteoric fireball seared its way through the atmosphere above central Alberta. Its passage to Earth lasted only a few seconds. During those seconds hundreds of people gazed in amazement at an intense blue-white light dripping orange sparks. Moments later, over an area of 2,000 square miles, its sound shock-wave rattled windows, shook the foundations of homes and startled families from sleep.

This fireball, the Bruderheim meteorite, travelled at 26 miles per second, accelerated earthward by the force of gravity. Its 660 pounds of stone and iron rained down in boulders near the town of Bruderheim, 40 miles northeast of Edmonton, the capital city of Alberta. Some of these boulders weighed more than 60 pounds and, upon striking the ground, split open to reveal a gray, stony texture, stippled with nodules of metal. These nodules, consisting chiefly of pure iron, soon oxidized to form red flecks on the exposed surfaces of the pieces of rock. One astonished farmer reported finding large fragments of the charred meteorite only a few feet from his front porch.

Visual sightings of the Bruderheim fireball ranged from that reported by a pilot flying over the city of Calgary to those of residents of Alberta and of the mountain areas of British Columbia. Team work by Alberta scientists soon resulted in co-ordination of the many sightings. Within hours most of the larger pieces had been collected, and detailed investigations had been begun by R. E. Folinsbee of the Department of Geology of the University of Alberta and L. A. Bayrock of the Research Council of Alberta. Truly a remarkable phenomenon, the Bruderheim meteorite was one of the few instances of immediate scientific examination of a celestial object just hours after its fall to Earth from outer space.

FRANKLIN C. LOEHDE

Title picture – Andromeda galaxy

5

Meteors and meteorites

Meteorites – the term given to meteors that reach the Earth in large enough pieces to be recognized – are comparatively rare, because even large meteors usually disintegrate and burn up during their passage through the atmosphere. In Alberta, from 1910 to 1964, only seven meteorites have been seen to fall to Earth or have been found – such as the fragment turned up by a ploughshare near Mayerthorpe in 1964, or the Peace River meteorite which was seen to fall in the spring of 1963. A few fragments of this Peace River meteorite were recovered and studied for radioactivity by H. W. Taylor, at that time a member of the Department of Physics of the University of Alberta.

Even though meteorites are of infrequent occurrence, Alberta's evening sky, particularly in autumn, is often pierced by the darting flashes of shooting stars or meteors, which are quickly extinguished in the blackness of the heavens. Every day thousands of particles from outer space, some no bigger than flecks of dust, are captured by Earth's gravitational pull. This celestial debris, some of it from the formation of the solar system billions of years ago, enters our atmosphere at speeds up to 50 miles per second. Such rapid penetration heats the debris to incandescence and the particles are soon consumed in fire. The very fine dust that remains is carried around the world by winds in the upper atmosphere until eventually it settles, far from the original entry point.

Because the long clear winter nights in Alberta are ideal for the study of meteors, the then Federal Department of Mines and Technical Surveys established meteor observatories in 1952 at Meanook and Newbrook. Both stations are located about 90 miles north of Edmonton, and are equipped with some of the finest "fast" cameras. They are "fast" because, despite the swiftness of the meteor across the heavens, the sensitivity of the lens and film are such that a record of the path of a meteor can be made. The cameras use a rotating shutter so that the meteor's path, as photographed on the film, is chopped into segments, each segment representing a short interval of time. In this way the actual speed of the meteor can be calculated. It was at the Newbrook station, too, that the first photograph in North America was taken of Sputnik I – the first man-made satellite in orbit.

The chemical composition of meteorites is similar to that of rocks on Earth, and so from a study of meteorites valuable information can be obtained about the origin of Earth and the composition of the universe. Measurement of the radioactivity of meteorites also provides supporting evidence of the age of the universe. Compared to the tremendous expense of building and launching a space vehicle, meteorites are aptly termed the "poor man's space probe".

No less important, but perhaps more stirring to the imagination, are the recent findings of chemists who have studied the coal-like material present in the rare "carbonaceous" meteorites, such as the one which fell in 1864 near the village of Orgueil in France. Complex chemical compounds, similar to those found in living things on earth today, have been detected in extremely small amounts in this type of meteorite. Thus in 1964, G. W. Hodgson and B. L. Baker of the Research Council of Alberta, after examining a fragment of the Orgueil meteorite, published a report of the discovery of indigenous or innate traces of a residue of chlorophyll (the colouring-matter of the green parts of plants). Such evidence from carbonaceous meteorites seems to indicate that life on other planets may be a possibility. Scientists, however, are cautious in the conclusions they draw from the study of meteorites because they recognize that a meteorite may have been contaminated with soil after falling to Earth.

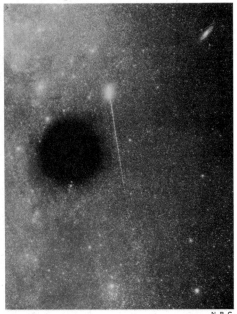

c.h.

Fragment, about six inches wide, of Bruderheim meteorite.

n.r.c.

Perseid meteor. Note the Andromeda Galaxy in upper righthand corner.

Therefore, it is of utmost importance that falls to Earth are quickly recovered and reported to scientists.

The aurora borealis

Almost synonymous with Canada are the rippling bands of light that flit over its northern skies. The aurora borealis or northern lights are a constant source of fascination to those who live where these dancing upper atmospheric lights can be observed.

The zone of greatest auroral activity passes through the extreme northeast portion of Alberta where the dazzling phenomenon may be seen on about 300 nights a year. Southwest of a line extending from Peace River town to Edmonton, the number of displays that can be expected annually drops to about 160. In southern Alberta, residents are fortunate if on 30 nights in a year they can observe an auroral display. Usually the display begins as a faint glow on the northeastern horizon. Later in the evening, this glow rises in the sky, brightens, and takes on a greenish hue. Shortly afterward, a dark lower border appears, giving the impression of a greenish-yellow rainbow. This quiescent form may continue for hours and then, without warning, it may suddenly turn upon itself like a glowing celestial serpent and produce a dazzling curtain of light, with a brilliant red and yellow border. Rays extending from the curtain may dart skyward and rotate like a gigantic pinwheel.

The early Eskimos believed that the "keoeeit", the great white light that appears in the heavens before there is any daylight, was a procession of torches held by the spirits leading the recently departed dead

Aurora borealis over northern Alberta

B.F.

to the heavenly land. Early Scandinavians explained the northern lights as the reflection of sunlight off the icebergs in the Arctic Ocean.

Today, however, a scientific thesis best accounts for this interesting phenomenon. About 110 miles above Earth, where American and Russian astronauts move about in space, the atmosphere is as rarified as that inside the tubing of a neon sign. It is in this environment that the northern lights are born. Far from Earth, the great furnace of the sun is continually ejecting the waste products of its nuclear sources of energy. The nuclei of atoms, stripped of their planetary electrons by these nuclear explosions, are shot into space at speeds of 60,000 miles per second. They become trapped in Earth's magnetic field and collect in the upper atmosphere. Drawn earthward by the magnetic field, they bombard the molecules of nitrogen and oxygen of the rarified upper air and cause these atoms to give out the green, yellow and red glow of the northern lights. It is because the magnetic field is more intense near the north and south magnetic poles that the northern lights (aurora borealis) and southern lights (aurora australis) are best seen at high latitudes. In Alberta, both the Meanook and Newbrook meteor observatories are favourably located for auroral studies. The studies made at these observatories of the aurora borealis are valuable, but most of the auroral observations in the province are the work of enthusiastic amateurs.

Astronomical studies in Alberta

The grandfathers of astronomical studies in Alberta were the late J. W. Campbell, formerly Head of the Department of Mathematics at the University of Alberta, and the late Cyril G. Wates of Edmonton, a gifted amateur. It was Dr. Campbell who, in Edmonton in 1932, with the support of others, brought into being the first Alberta centre of the Royal Astronomical Society of Canada. Since that time, this centre has grown in both enthusiasm and membership. A similar centre, with a similar development since its inception, was established in Calgary in 1958.

Mr. Wates' achievement in the construction, mounting and improvement of design of telescopes for amateurs was recognized in 1944 by the Royal Astronomical Society of Canada's award to him of the Chant Medal. This medal is the greatest honour an amateur astronomer in Canada can receive. In the reflecting telescopes he built, Mr. Wates ground, polished and silvered his own mirrors. In 1932, he constructed his own private observatory, and by 1942 he had personally designed and completed his largest telescope, one with a mirror twelve and one-half inches in diameter, equipped with a four-inch field finder and a ball-bearing mounting, and weighing, in all, 750 pounds. This telescope was donated to the University of Alberta which built an observatory to house it and a four-inch refracting telescope belonging to the Department of Mathematics. The building was officially opened on May 20th, 1943. The Wates' telescope, at that time the sixth largest in Canada, remained there until 1954 when the observatory was torn down because of university expansion.

Besides the building of telescopes and the writing of articles on this art, Mr. Wates, along with Dr. Campbell, played a very considerable part in developing an interest in astronomy throughout the province. Many other amateurs have also made contributions. The Chant Medal, for example, was awarded to Earl Milton, formerly of Edmonton, and at that time an amateur astronomer, for his work on Alberta auroral observations during the International Geophysical Year of 1957-58. In 1963, R. Choquette of Calgary, at the age of 17, constructed a radio telescope to listen to sounds emitted from outer space; while in Edmonton, in 1965, R. Broughton designed and built equipment to receive and reproduce

MC. D.

Wates Observatory — the first observatory at the University of Alberta.

pictures from weather satellites. In Calgary, too, a team of amateurs established a moon-watch station to keep track of satellites which are orbiting the earth.

Another outstanding achievement has been the founding of planetaria in Edmonton and Calgary. Largely because of the enthusiasm of the members of the Edmonton Centre – a cross-section of the community – on September 22nd, 1960, the City of Edmonton opened the Queen Elizabeth Planetarium. This was the first planetarium for the public in Canada. A second planetarium, at the suggestion of W. Stilwell, became the Centennial project of the City of Calgary. In these planetaria, in an atmosphere of soft lights and music, the patrons forget the affairs of Earth and become a part of the cosmos.

In astronomy there is in Alberta, as elsewhere, close co-operation between scientists and amateurs. In order to release scientists and the larger telescopes for other activities, such studies as auroral observations, the examination of the horizon for comets just before sunrise and sunset, the making of meteor counts, and the observation of occultations – a term used for the passage of the moon in front of a star – are often carried on by amateurs. On occasion amateurs make important discoveries. For example, although the existence of the ninth planet from the sun, Pluto, had been predicted in 1916 by a scientist, Percival Lowell, it was an amateur astronomer, Clyde Tombaugh, who, on February 18th, 1930, actually photographed that planet. Similarly, in 1966 a young graduate student, Stephen Kilston, found a new comet which now bears his name.

In the sphere of professional astronomical activities, besides the Meanook and Newbrook meteor observation stations, the University of Calgary maintains a cosmic ray station on Sulphur Mountain at Banff. This station studies the high energy particles reaching Earth from outer space.

The most striking astronomical programme in the province, perhaps, is that of the Baker-Nunn Satellite Tracking Camera at the Royal Canadian Air Force's Primrose Evaluation Range, some 25 miles from Cold Lake in northeastern Alberta. This camera, which has been operated by the R.C.A.F. since October, 1962, is valued at $120,000. It can photograph a .303 bullet in flight at a distance of 50 miles, and has taken pictures of the Vanguard I satellite, a six-inch sphere, at a distance of 2,000 miles.

This R.C.A.F. camera is the only one of its kind in Canada. Along with 15 other similar units which are scattered around the globe, it tracks satellites which are orbiting the earth and the objects, such as rocket bodies and nose cones, which accompany the satellites through space. The correlated information from all 16 units is used by scientists to measure the effects of factors such as gravity and the drag of atmospheric dust on the orbits of satellites. It was from data collected by these units that men discovered that Earth is slightly pear-shaped.

Noctilucent clouds

On rare occasions at twilight in the summer, patches of light may be seen over the northern horizon. Unlike the northern lights, with which they are often confused, noctilucent clouds remain motionless for hours and may even last for a few nights. They resemble stilled ripples of sand on a beach in the sky or, at times, feathery arches of blue and yellow hues. The clouds are visible only after the sun has set and the sky has darkened. The first recording of them in Alberta was made in 1933. Rocket probes which have been sent into these clouds reveal them to be similar to the clouds we normally see, which are composed primarily of condensed water vapour.

Tracking camera at R.C.A.F.'s Primrose Evaluation Range, near Cold Lake, Alberta.

Why moisture should be found in such a rarified atmosphere and what the mechanism is that triggers the appearance of the noctilucent clouds are still not fully understood and must await more intensive study. But the amateur astronomer need not wait for the appearance of either meteors or the infrequent noctilucent clouds to enjoy the night skies of Alberta, for the stars are a year-round, celestial spectacle.

The winter sky

On clear winter evenings more bright stars are visible in the skies over Alberta than at any other time of the year. The night canopy is dominated by Orion, the mighty hunter of the sky, with his club held high ready to strike. His quarry is the ferocious celestial bull, Taurus, with his unmistakable V-shaped horns. Each horn-tip is marked by a bluish star, while the sparkling red star Aldebaran, the brightest in the constellation, is a gleaming eye. A good test for sharp eyesight are the Pleiades, which lie on the back of Taurus. Six or seven twinkling stars, forming a pattern resembling a little dipper, may be seen, but a telescope or binoculars will unfold dozens more, all of the same cool blue colour. These stars of the Pleiades are astronomically very young, and are still enveloped in the gases from which they developed and emerged millions of years ago. The brilliant blue star Rigel, with a surface temperature of 25,000 degrees, along with a fainter star, Saiph, represent the legs of Orion, and the giant star Betelgeuse, one of his shoulders. If Betelgeuse were placed where our sun is now, the planets Mercury, Venus, Earth, Mars and Jupiter would all be orbiting within Betelgeuse itself.

Orion may be identified easily by the three famous stars forming his

Noctilucent clouds photographed from Grande Prairie.

B.F.

belt, which are set obliquely between Rigel and Betelgeuse. Hanging immediately below the belt is his sword, consisting of a group of stars within which is embedded the famous Orion Nebula. Visible but faintly to the unaided eye, this greenish-white patch of light is in actuality a huge incandescent mass of swirling gas. It is of special interest because it contains many strange stars which pulsate brightly and unpredictably. There are strong indications that these unusual stars, called variables, have been in existence for only a few million years, which makes them infants on the cosmological scale.

The brightest object in the heavens, except the sun, moon and Venus, is Sirius, the dog star, which may be seen along a line extended southeast from the belt stars of Orion. It is so called because it represents the eye of heaven's large dog, Canis Major. This star usually flares in a vivid array of colours ranging from red to green. In the 19th century astronomers discovered that Sirius meandered almost imperceptibly from its normal path. Someone theorized that this wandering was caused by the gravitational attraction of a heavy but unseen star. Eventually, a large telescope revealed, amid the glare of light from Sirius, a tiny white companion star with a density so great that just one cubic inch of its material weighs many tons. Astronomers now know that these so-called "white-dwarf" stars are doomed to a slow cooling process, which will finally produce a dark cinder, invisible except for its attractional powers.

Skirting the northeastern horizon is the prowler of the north, Ursa Major, or the Great Bear. Canadians know part of this group better as the Big Dipper. Four stars represent the bowl and three stars the handle

The Orion Nebula

C.T.

11

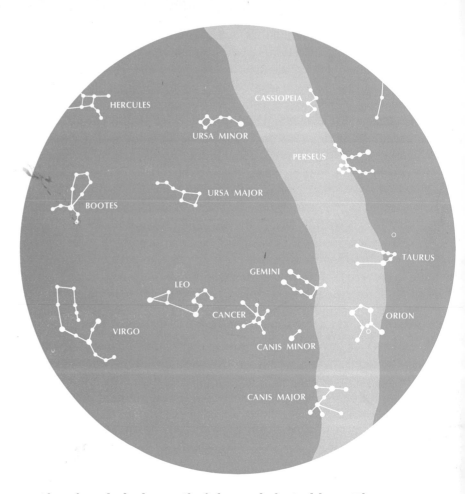

Star map of winter skies

or, if preferred, the long tail of the mythological bear. The two stars at the end of the bowl point towards Polaris, the North Star, which is located directly above our North Pole; thus Polaris seems to remain fixed, while all other stars seem to circle the pole every 24 hours. Polaris itself is part of the constellation of the Small Bear (Ursa Minor), in which it forms the end of the tail. The two cosmic bears are perhaps the most closely linked astronomical objects to be seen in Alberta's skies, because they are always visible, winter or summer.

The spring sky

The advent of spring in Alberta is marked by the appearance in its eastern evening sky of Leo, the Lion. This constellation was held sacred by the ancient Egyptians and bears a remarkable resemblance to a crouching lion, with the white star Regulus, one of the twenty brightest stars in the sky, marking the heart, and Denebola, a star of second magnitude, the tail.

When Leo is nearly due south in the heavens, two bright stars, Spica and Arcturus, make their appearance to the southeast and east, respectively. Arcturus, brighter than Spica, is a pretty yellow sun which by May or June is almost overhead. Light from this distant sun was actually used to open the Chicago World's Fair of 1933 by utilizing a photo-electric cell to capture the light and convert it into enough electricity to throw the switches to the lights of the Fair. Spica seems virtually alone in the southeast, yet, despite this appearance of emptiness, the entire area north of Spica is actually ablaze with stars in galaxies which are so far away that they can be detected only as faint points of light, even with long photographic exposures and large telescopes. These galaxies resemble our own Milky Way and, like giant pinwheels, slowly rotate every 200 million years. If we consider our Milky Way an average galaxy, then each of the tiny points of light seen near Spica is really a galaxy of 100

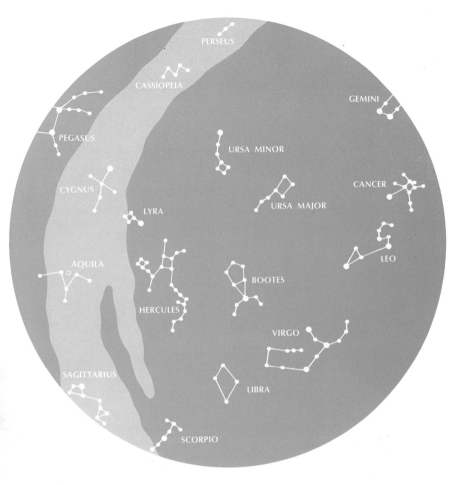

Star map of spring skies

billion stars, each star being like our sun. With a thousand galaxies counted, and 100 billion stars in each, this part of the sky is certainly not empty.

A quick trip northwestward and diagonally across the sky, takes us to Cassiopeia, the Queen. Sometimes called the Lady in the Chair, Cassiopeia looks like a large W above the horizon, and is in the middle of a star-studded part of the Milky Way. To the west of Cassiopeia is a hazy patch of light which, when viewed through binoculars, reveals not one but two jewel-like star clusters. Despite the brilliance of their background, these two clusters easily become favourites of amateur astronomers. Almost 300 stars are closely packed together in these two clusters, and all colours of the rainbow are represented.

The summer sky
When Cassiopeia swings over the northern horizon summer has begun, and the constellations that we associate with warm breezes and green leaves appear. The Summer Triangle is well-known to star gazers, for it dominates the southern skies during July and August. It consists of three bright stars belonging to the constellations Aquila, the Eagle; Lyra, the Harp; and Cygnus, the Swan. All three are part of the Milky Way and have a rich field of fainter stars as a backdrop. Altair, the main star in the Eagle, is located at the southern vertex of the Triangle.

To the northwest and almost overhead is Vega, a brilliant blue star, which is the chief star of Lyra, the Harp, an extremely small but pretty constellation. Besides being the fourth most luminous star in the visible sky, it also takes turns at being our North Star. Because Earth's axis of rotation wobbles slowly, the celestial poles do not remain fixed among the stars. On a day to day basis they move imperceptibly, but over the millennia noticeable changes occur. The ancient Egyptians and the Indian migrants to North America from Asia saw a different North Star.

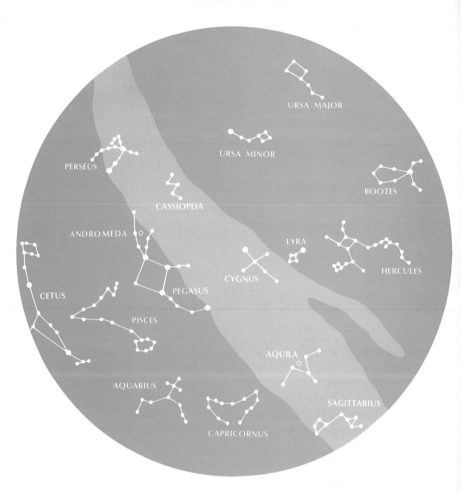

Star map of summer skies

The passages within the Great Pyramid of Cheops were originally aligned with the old North Star of Thuban, a star in Draco, the Dragon, near Ursa Major. About 12,000 years hence, Vega will appear stationary in the sky, with all the other stars revolving around it as they now appear to do about Polaris.

Deneb completes the Triangle, and little imagination is needed to see that it marks the tail of the heavenly swan, Cygnus. Sometimes called the Northern Cross, this constellation has five stars which straddle the Milky Way. Although Deneb is fainter to the naked eye than Vega, it is actually hundreds of times brighter. All stars as we see them today are ghostly images of the past. We are seeing Deneb, for instance, as it looked 1,600 years ago. If it were to disappear now, it would be another 16 centuries before astronomers on earth would be able to detect its disappearance. At the foot of the Cross – or at the head of the Swan – is the star Albireo. Its true beauty is only revealed through a telescope when a pair of sparkling stars can be seen. One is greenish-blue, and the other a golden hue, the two making a delightful pair.

While Cygnus and Lyra are riding high overhead in the middle of summer, slipping over the southern horizon towards the southwest is one of the most dramatic constellations in the heavens. Located in the very centre of our galaxy is Scorpio, the Scorpion. Unfortunately the high northern latitude of Alberta prevents our seeing this constellation to proper advantage. On a clear moonlight night, Scorpio is unmistakable within the bulge of stars in the centre of the Milky Way, and looks exactly like its name. Scorpio's stinger is partially below the horizon, and so viewing requires a very clear and unobstructed horizon.

The autumn sky

The month of October sees the Summer Triangle slip westward to be replaced by the autumn constellations. Because of the increasing number

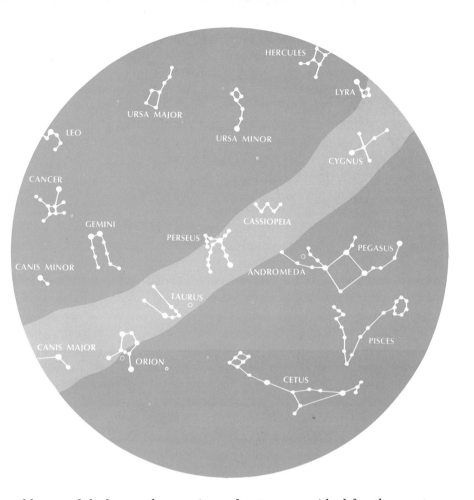

Star map of autumn skies

of hours of darkness, the evenings of autumn are ideal for the amateur astronomer. The very crispness of the air seems to add zest to the stars themselves. By the middle of October Ursa Major has settled into an upright position over the northern horizon. Cassiopeia with its familiar W-shape is to the southeast of the pole star. With Cassiopeia now almost overhead, the full procession of the mythological "Royal Family" begins. As the delightful story goes, the vain Cassiopeia, Queen of ancient Ethiopia, boasted that her daughter, Andromeda, was more beautiful than the sea nymph, Atergatis. This aroused the anger of Neptune, king of the sea, who threatened to destroy Ethiopia unless Cassiopeia sacrificed her daughter to Cetus, the sea monster. Fearing for her country she complied, and so Andromeda was chained to the rocks beside the sea. Before the helpless Andromeda was devoured, however, the hero of the story, Perseus, saw Andromeda's plight and advanced towards Cetus, holding the head of the snake-haired Medusa, whom he had just despatched. Cetus was turned to stone by this sight, and Andromeda and Perseus escaped on the back of the winged horse, Pegasus.

All of these mythological characters are represented in the stars. Pegasus rides high in the southern skies during October, but, unfortunately for Canadians, upside down. Our heroine, Andromeda, chained to the rocks, is found to the west of Pegasus. Apart from the fascinating story of Andromeda's plight, this constellation contains the farthest object in the universe visible to the unaided eye, the famous Andromeda Galaxy. This giant whirlpool of 100 billion stars sent the light which is reaching us now coursing through the void toward the Milky Way and Earth about two million years ago. Far to the south of Andromeda is the monster of the deep, Cetus. He is kept at bay by Perseus, who can be found between Andromeda and her mother. Perseus, with Medusa hanging from his belt, is seen in the middle of the Milky Way with many other

15

bright stars. Medusa is marked by a most unusual star, Algol, named by the Arabs and meaning "the demon". A demon it appears to be, for it will suddenly become much fainter before flaring up again. Astronomers have discovered that Algol has a dark, unseen companion revolving about it, and, for a few hours of its trip about Algol, the dark companion obscures the light of the host star, producing a drop in brightness. A study of Algol for a few nights allows the amateur star-gazer to predict in advance when the sudden fading will occur.

Indian legends about the stars

The Plains Indian enjoyed a wide vista of sky. This direct contact with the heavens certainly influenced the Indian's interpretation of the powerful forces that surrounded him. He placed the abode of the gods in the inaccessible vault of the heavens and, like almost all primitive peoples, enshrined the heroes and heroines of his folk-tales in the skies. Unlike the modern city dweller beneath his perpetual cloak of haze, the native of the open prairie was continually exposed to the myriads of stars with their pulsating colours and the band of eerie light which we call the Milky Way. An idle evening under a clear, dark sky afforded the Indian the opportunity to wend his way through the twisting patterns of the stars, and soon the haphazard arrangement became clearer, more meaningful, in terms of his way of life. Animals could be found everywhere; legendary heroes reappeared with bows drawn ready to down the thundering bison.

Of the few legends which have been preserved, one is the Cree legend of Oo-chay-ka-tak, the Big Dipper.

A Cree Indian living in isolation with his wife and two young sons discovered that his wife was consorting with evil spirits who took the form of snakes hiding in a tree trunk. Repelled by this, the husband chopped off the heads of these snakes and warned his sons of an impending calamity before sending them off to safety. He told them that in the future they would see him in the skies. His wife was furious when she saw that her snakes were dead and departed in a rage to seek vengeance by killing her husband. Hiding in his wigwam, he waited for his wife to poke in her head, whereupon he chopped it off. The trunk of her body chased him through the top opening of the wigwam. The husband escaped to the sky and remains there today as Oo-chay-ka-tak, the Big Dipper.

Those rare phenomena, comets, have produced their share of stories and here is a Blackfoot legend of the Smoking Star.

Smoking Star was a kind spirit of the Blackfoot people. One day he was induced to come to their land and help a destitute old couple who were not well cared for by their son-in-law as the old laws required. After providing them with their wants and ridding the land of all monsters this great spirit began his journey home. On the way he was killed by some Crow Indians who were on the war path. With his death there appeared in the sky a smoking star as a reminder to all of what had happened.

Foundations of astronomy

Astronomers of ancient Babylonia made accurate observations of the sun and moon, identified five planets – Jupiter, Mars, Mercury, Saturn and Venus – distinguished between planets and fixed stars and made a beginning at understanding the precession of the equinoxes. In ancient Egypt, too, priests studied the heavens. Later, a Greek thinker, Thales, predicted the eclipse of May 28th, 585 B.C. He and his successors of the 6th and 5th century B.C., however, were chiefly interested in speculations about the nature and origin of the universe. Then, from the 4th century B.C. onward, Greek scientists, building, in particular, on what they had learned from Babylonian astronomers, made such discoveries

J.M.G.

The comet Mrkos, first seen in 1957. Note the "Big Dipper" above the comet.

as determining that Earth turns daily on its axis and that Mercury and Venus revolve about the sun. One Greek scientist even advanced the heliocentric theory – that the sun, not Earth, is the centre of the universe.

The heliocentric theory was rejected by the other Greek scientists of the day, and the geocentric theory – Earth as the centre of the universe – was the accepted theory and dogma until 1543. In that year, a treatise on celestial orbits by Nicolaus Copernicus of Poland was published. This treatise proved that the sun, not Earth, is the hub of the solar system. Then in 1610, Italy's brilliant Galileo Galilei, with his small telescope, revealed that much of the heavens lay beyond that which could be seen with unaided eyes. As time went by, Johannes Kepler of Germany discovered laws of motion which demonstrated the orderliness of the universe, and England's Isaac Newton described the principle of gravitational attraction. The achievements of these four men laid the foundation for further researches into the nature and age of the universe.

The age of the universe

It has often been said that we now know more of the world in which our ancestors lived than did our ancestors themselves. The present sophisticated techniques of scientists have greatly expanded our estimates of

17

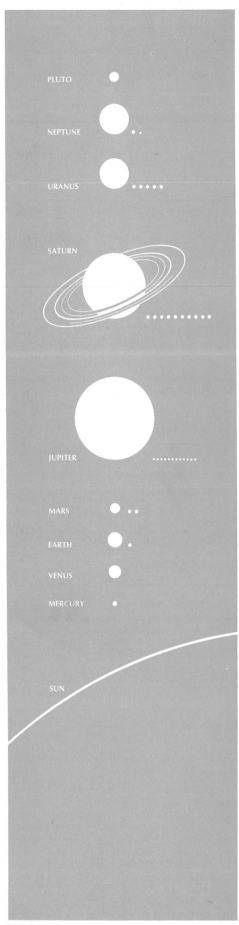

The sun and planets in order of position and proportionate sizes. Note the associated moons. The solar system is thought to be five billion years old.

the antiquity of man's culture as well as of the earth itself. Radioactive dating by geophysicists has revealed that parts of the earth's crust are nearly four billion years old. The actual formation of the earth and her sister planets probably preceded the development of Earth's solid mantle by more than a billion years. A more accurate estimate of the age of the universe itself appears to be a direct result of our ability to peer deeper into the vast reaches of space; for when we look into the universe we perceive light from star systems that left for the earth in aeons past and is only now reaching our telescopes. Therefore the most distant galaxies in our universe also represent the oldest members of this universe. The completion of the 200-inch reflecting telescope on Mount Palomar in California in 1948 greatly increased our ability to look into the depths of both time and space. This giant of telescopes revealed whirlpools of stars so remote that billions of years have elapsed between the time the light left them and reached our little planet. Then, in 1961, the mysterious quasars were discovered.

Before 1961 what are now called quasars were thought to be ordinary stars within our own galaxy, the Milky Way, and relatively close to us in terms of astronomical distance. Then, they were found to be powerful emitters of radio waves. The quasars are now suspected of being very luminous galaxies, receding from the earth's position in space at exceedingly high velocities.

Astronomers have conjectured that the more distant an object is from Earth, the faster it seems to be moving away from us. This "recessional velocity" is revealed by the "red spectral shift" – that is, the shift of colours in the spectrum of a star toward the red end of the colour band and observed in varying degrees for almost all stars. Quasars have the greatest red spectral shift of any objects so far known. If this shift is due to recessional velocity, the quasars are the most distant objects astronomers have as yet detected and are on the very rim of the known universe. According to this theory, one quasar, called 3C9 by astronomers, is speeding away from us at 150,000 miles each second. Furthermore, it would take more than ten billion years for a beam of light, travelling at 186,000 miles a second, to traverse the tremendous distance thought to separate our planet from 3C9. If this and other conjectures are correct, we can obtain an indication of the age of the known universe – that is, how long the universe has been expanding since a presumed initial explosion – as well as an indication of an estimate of the distance of the quasars from Earth.

Astronomical distances

To express the distance thought to separate our planet from quasar 3C9 in miles would be almost meaningless, since it would be 588 followed by 20 zeros. To compute such a distance, or any of the vast distances of outer space, astronomers use "light-years". A light-year is the distance travelled in one year by a beam of light, moving at 186,000 miles a second. This light-year is a distance of 5.88 trillion miles or 588 with 10 zeros. Therefore the quasar 3C9 is said to be ten billion light-years away.

It is difficult to appreciate such astronomical numbers, so let us devise a scale based on the more familiar distance between Edmonton and Calgary, or about 180 miles along the highway. If we let Calgary represent the quasar 3C9, and the city hall in Edmonton our planet Earth, then we need venture only a little more than the thickness of a human hair from the door of the city hall to leap out into space a distance of more than 25 trillion miles to the star, Alpha Centauri, which, except for the sun, is nearest to us. If a rocket travelled 25,000 miles per hour, it would still take nearly 120,000 years for the one-way trip from Earth to this star. Using the same scale of distance and time, the thickness of one sheet of newspaper from the door of the city hall places us near the bright northern star Vega, 27 light years away and also 27 years in the past, because the Vega we see tonight is really an image that was produced during World War II.

Just one foot from the same doorway takes us 10,500 years into the past, equivalent to a distance of 10,500 light-years, which is beyond the limit of the faintest star seen with the unaided eye. Nine feet on our Edmonton to Calgary scale would take us, in terms of light-years, across the whole diameter of our entire 100-billion-star Milky Way. The Andromeda Galaxy, another giant pinwheel of whirling stars like the Milky Way, is at the 20-foot mark. It is two million light-years away, and light from this galaxy left for Earth two million years ago. Red Deer is the half-way point in our journey to the end of the universe. At this five billion light-year distance we are dealing with an antiquity so remote in time as well as distance that the earth would just be forming from the primaeval dust and gas strewn about a newly-emerging star, the sun. Earth would have to cool for nearly three billion years before primitive life would be able to survive under its steamy atmosphere. Travelling at the speed of light, it would take us another five billion years to reach what seems at the moment to be the final outpost, the 3C9 quasar.

This is the extent of the universe as we now perceive it. Vast, in both space and time, it is still practically unexplored even by our telescopes, let alone by man himself.

The origin of the universe

The red spectral shift of the quasars and other stars supports the theory that the universe is expanding. We can make an analogy to this expansion by painting dots on a balloon and then inflating it. As we fill the balloon each dot, or star, will be seen to move both outward and away from all other dots. This concept of the expanding universe has led some scientists to propose that the entire universe was originally formed about ten billion years ago after a cataclysmic cosmic explosion. The temperatures produced near the centre of this explosion probably exceeded one billion degrees, and when the elementary atomic particles cooled down to a few million degrees all the chemical elements were formed, ranging from hydrogen to uranium. It is difficult to visualize what the universe was like before the cosmic explosion, but elaborations of the theory allow for alternating expansions and contractions. At present the universe appears to be expanding rapidly. However, at some unknown date in the future a contraction may take place and eventually the universe would reach a state similar to that at the "beginning" of time and space.

Professor Fred Hoyle of Cambridge University, England, has developed another concept: that the universe has never had a beginning. (In none of the theories does it have an end.) He maintains that the universe is in a continual state of evolution. Matter is continually destroying itself in countless nuclear explosions in the centres of stars and the resulting energy is flooding the cosmos. In other parts of the universe this energy is accumulating, and is being reformed to matter, in a process known as "pair production". Matter, under special conditions, may be formed directly from high energy radiation when it passes near the nuclei of heavy atoms. Both processes are well understood and so add credence to Professor Hoyle's "continuous-creation" theory, as it is sometimes called. All present-day theories still leave many questions unanswered. Only further research into the depths of space will allow a true assessment of their relative merits.

M.W. & P.O.

Mosaic of the Milky Way

The Pleiades

C.H.

CHAPTER TWO

The Record of the Rocks

CHARLES R. STELCK

ALBERTA'S RICH AND VARIED LANDSCAPE sweeps east from snow-clad Rocky Mountain peaks, past stream-carved foothills and across rolling plains to low-lying, rock-girt lakes in its northeast corner. Two and a half billion years of the history of Alberta are inscribed in the rocky framework of this landscape; two and a half billion years during which Alberta's essential body was created, moulded, shaped and re-shaped, and borne from distant latitudes and far meridians to its present dwelling-place. Alberta today is in the cool-temperate zone – but once rich tropical forests flourished here, and an archipelago of coral reefs grew up through tepid seas. These seas – the Pacific Ocean, the Arctic Ocean, and the Gulf of Mexico – all reached shorelines in Alberta in far-off days and left their record.

The oldest records of Alberta are found within its northeastern part, east of the Slave River, where crystalline rocks formed during the Pre-cambrian Era appear at the surface. Precambrian – the vast stretch of time between 3,500 million and 600 million years ago – is the term used by geologists for the period in the earth's history before the first skeleton-bearing animals appeared. It is usually divided into three parts: Azoic, when there was no life; Archaeozoic, with incipient life; and Proterozoic, with primitive living organisms devoid of skeletons.

The Precambrian rocks of Alberta

Precambrian rocks make up the Canadian Shield, the name given to the ancient and rounded rocks which form the nucleus of North America. In Canada, the Shield stretches from Labrador through northern Quebec, northern Ontario, eastern and northern Manitoba, the District of Keewa-tin and northern Saskatchewan to the northeast corner of Alberta. The province's Precambrian rocks, however, although dating from at least

Title picture – Precambrian strata in the Rocky Mountains.

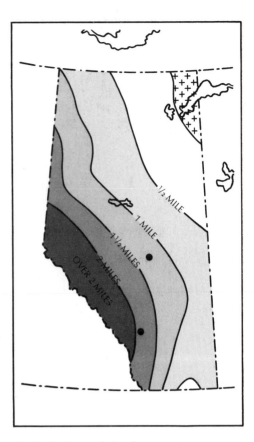

Depth to Precambrian basement

two billion years ago, are not the oldest in the world but belong to Early Proterozoic time.

The Canadian Shield does not end in Alberta's northeast corner, for its crystalline rocks plunge under the plains and mountains to form a basement under the rest of the province. To reach this basement on the western side of Alberta, one must drill down some 20,000 feet or almost four miles. This means that the basement slopes down to the west at a rate of four miles in each 500 miles, so that in central Alberta the Precambrian rocks are approximately two miles beneath our feet. This basement tells us that Alberta has existed as rocky substance for at least two billion years. These two billion years are the span of Alberta's geologic history.

How Alberta's Precambrian rocks were formed

In Alberta's Precambrian rocks are found pebbles worn down from still older rocks. Two of the mountain ranges of which these pebbles may be the miniscule remnants are known to have been built about 2,300 million years ago – one a complex of mountains, named after Lake Superior, that cut across Ontario and over to Montana, the other a range in the Yellowknife area to the north of present-day Alberta.

Between these two ranges lay the Alberta of that day. At what times in that far-off era Alberta was under water or was uplifted as a broad lowland is not known. It seems likely that a continental shelf extended outward from each of the mountain complexes, a deep-water channel being maintained between them from what is now central Alberta to

Canadian Shield, northeast Alberta, showing roots of ancient mountains scored by continental glaciers during the Ice Age.

northernmost Manitoba. In any case, the wearing down of the Montana and Yellowknife Mountains filled the straits between them with sands and muds to a thickness of more than 50,000 feet. When the sands and muds hardened, they became Alberta's oldest rocks. These ancient Precambrian rocks, laid down between 2,300 and 1,900 million years ago, are called Churchillian, after Port Churchill on Hudson Bay, and form the bulk of Alberta's basement.

The occurrence of limestones as part of the rock sequence suggests that there was nonskeletal life in the seas in which Alberta's Churchillian rocks were being formed. (Limestones come into being when plant life uses the carbon dioxide dissolved in water as raw material for food, thus freeing the lime to settle on the bottom.) Then, beginning earlier than 1,600 million years ago, a paced and measured earth convulsion, accompanied by tremendous heat and spouting volcanoes, melted, squeezed and uplifted the Churchillian strata into a vast complex of mountains reaching over most of Alberta and stretching as far as Greenland. Granites intruded the folded sediments which, through heat and pressure, were changed, or metamorphosed, into gneisses.

In those days the mountainous land was still a lifeless waste, but from 2,000 to 1,600 million years ago, one-celled plants and bacteria, which were iron-secreting in some cases and have left iron deposits in Labrador and the Lake Superior region, were floating in the ocean. Some of these very early plants and animals were trapped in sediments and, although severely carbonized or silicified, can be recognized under our microscopes.

Time, with a 700-million-year broom, swept away all but the roots of the Churchillian mountains, the granites and gneisses of which still show the results of the long-ago melting, heating and squeezing. These roots, together with the remnants of the still earlier Montana and Yellowknife ranges, form the bulk of the western part of the Canadian Shield.

Middle Proterozoic times

While the 700-million-year broom was sweeping in long, slow strokes, an ancient Pacific Ocean was rolling lazy, white-crested waves onto the western side of Alberta. Headlands jutted out into the blue sea in Montana and in northern British Columbia so that western Alberta was the coastline of a broad embayment, or large bay. By the time the Churchillian mountains had been raised, the algae in the shallow water of this embayment were depositing more and more lime. Many of the hemispherical colonies of the fossil algae of those days, looking like cabbage heads wherever they are weathered out of the rock, can be seen in such places as Waterton Lakes National Park and west of the Yellowhead Pass. These limy hemispheres, called *Collenia,* grew along the margins of the ancient embayment and marked an Alberta shoreline of 1,100 million years ago. Today, algal colonies similar in design to the *Collenia* in Waterton Lakes National Park develop in intertidal waters – the shoreline between high and low tides – along the coast of Australia.

During this same period there was desert in what is now the Lake Athabasca area so that sands, like those in the northwestern parts of Australia, were laid down in its mountain valleys. Flooding rivers spread the sands widely. Today these sands, hardened to red quartzites, rest flat on the eroded crystalline roots of the Churchillian mountains to the south of Lake Athabasca.

The rivers of this time flowed from east to west to dump their loads of broken sand and coarse rock into Alberta's Pacific embayment. Out in the ocean a few "quiet" volcanoes – that is, there were no violent explosions – poured out their lava flows. The evidence of these volcanoes of

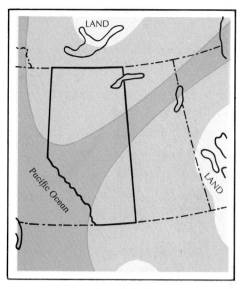

Early Proterozoic seas

C.H.

Collenia, which is the oldest sea-water plant in Alberta.

23

GEOLOGICAL TIME CHART			Millions of Years before Present
CENOZOIC	QUATERNARY		
			1
	TERTIARY	PLIOCENE	
			11
		MIOCENE	
			25
		OLIGOCENE	
			40
		EOCENE	
			60
		PALEOCENE	
			70
MESOZOIC	CRETACEOUS		
			135
	JURASSIC		
			180
	TRIASSIC		
			225
PALAEOZOIC	PERMIAN		270
	CARBONIFEROUS		350
	DEVONIAN		400
	SILURIAN		440
	ORDOVICIAN		500
	CAMBRIAN		600
PROTEROZOIC			2400
ARCHAEOZOIC			3000
AZOIC			3500

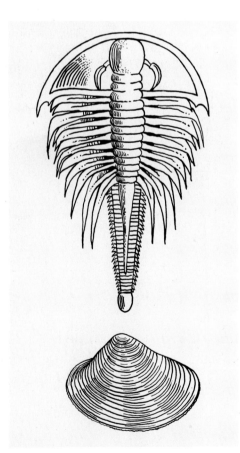

Olenellus, a trilobite. The first animal with a complex skeleton.

Scenella, the first snail on Earth.

1,100 million years ago can be observed today in the dark boulders in the streams of Waterton Lakes National Park and in the equally dark cliffs of its alpine uplands.

For hundreds of millions of years, from 1,600 to 800 million years ago, sediments from the Churchillian mountains were deposited almost continually in the sea on the west side of Alberta. Since in the Waterton embayment the muds were at times exposed to drying in shallow lagoons, mud cracks from some of these sediments can be seen today in the shales of Waterton Lakes National Park. The bay from the Pacific Ocean remained until Late Proterozoic times in the Jasper National Park area where it reached relatively farther eastward. Here, in Miette Valley, from Pyramid Mountain to Old Fort Point, and underlying the townsite of Jasper itself, can be seen sandstones made from the erosional wastes of Alberta's first mountains.

Late Proterozoic times

At this point, there is a gap in the geologic record of Alberta. Continents were high over much of the world. The Pacific Ocean was pushed out of Alberta so that the shoreline lay somewhere to the west in what is now the Cariboo district of British Columbia. But the erosion continued until the Churchillian mountains were reduced to low, rounded hills. Except for faults and breaks caused in later days, and except for its westward tilt, this is how Alberta's basement would look today, if all the later rocks and deposits could be stripped away from it to convert it into a fossil landscape. The Precambrian ended with little further evidence left within Alberta, and the Palaeozoic Era began.

The Palaeozoic Era

The word "palaeozoic" means "ancient life". For convenience, the 375 million years of the Palaeozoic Era – from 600 to 225 million years ago – are divided into six intervals of time. These are known, from the oldest to the youngest, as the Cambrian, Ordovician, Silurian, Devonian, Carboniferous and Permian Periods.

Six hundred million years ago, in Early Cambrian time, the Pacific Ocean returned to Alberta, teeming with life of a much more advanced kind. For the first time, animals with skeletons appear as fossils in the sands and limestones laid down along its shore. Trilobites, looking like big water beetles, primitive sponges with cup shapes, and little ancestors of the sea urchins all sported the latest in skeletons. With them dwelt a host of soft-bodied forms: jelly fish, leeches, worms of many sorts, and minor shrimp-like types, along with primitive bivalves and as yet untwisted snails.

What happened in the Pacific Ocean to cause skeletons to develop is not known, but the first animal to have a skeleton, the trilobite *Olenellus*, is a complex segmented animal, not a simple creature, and a long history of soft-bodied development must have preceded the appearance of its skeleton. As well as can be determined, *Olenellus* represents the ancestor of 95 per cent of all present-day arthropods – insects, crabs, spiders, lobsters, shrimps and centipedes. These arthropods total about three-quarters of our known species of animals. The trilobites themselves reached their greatest number and variety 500 million years ago, and have long since gone from the face of the earth. Their companion, however, the little untwisted snail – *Scenella* is its name – has a very close equivalent, known as *Neopilina*, which is still living in the depths of the Pacific Ocean. All the modern twisted snails and all the clams developed out of the *Scenella*-like forms of the earliest Palaeozoic Era. Snails and clams show their maximum variety today, but the untwisted form lives on with them, unconcerned with modern styles.

THE BEDROCK GEOLOGY OF ALBERTA

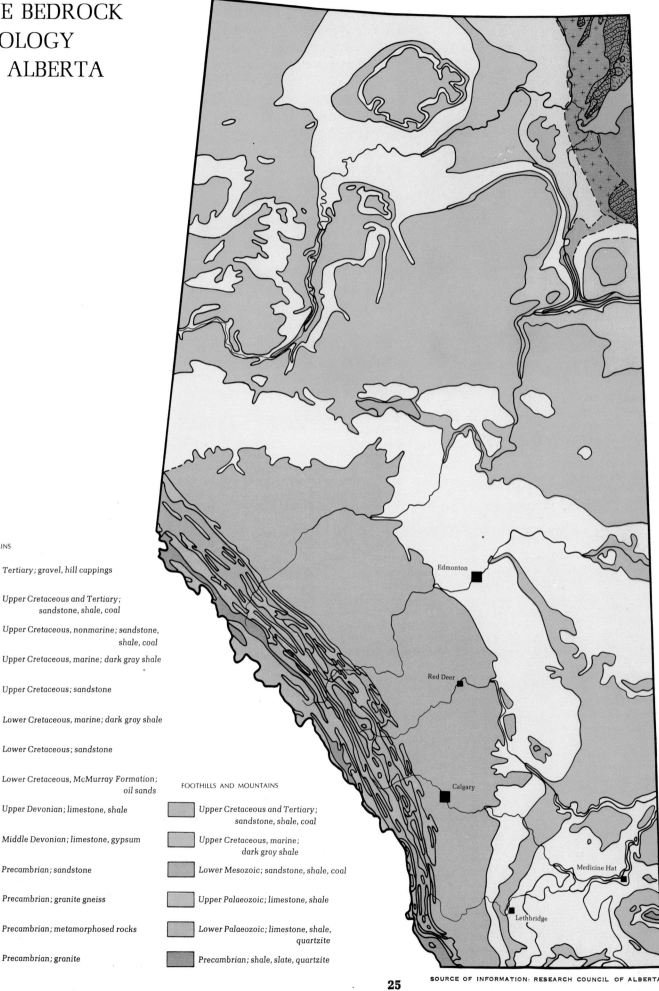

PLAINS

Tertiary; gravel, hill cappings

Upper Cretaceous and Tertiary; sandstone, shale, coal

Upper Cretaceous, nonmarine; sandstone, shale, coal

Upper Cretaceous, marine; dark gray shale

Upper Cretaceous; sandstone

Lower Cretaceous, marine; dark gray shale

Lower Cretaceous; sandstone

Lower Cretaceous, McMurray Formation; oil sands

Upper Devonian; limestone, shale

Middle Devonian; limestone, gypsum

Precambrian; sandstone

Precambrian; granite gneiss

Precambrian; metamorphosed rocks

Precambrian; granite

FOOTHILLS AND MOUNTAINS

Upper Cretaceous and Tertiary; sandstone, shale, coal

Upper Cretaceous, marine; dark gray shale

Lower Mesozoic; sandstone, shale, coal

Upper Palaeozoic; limestone, shale

Lower Palaeozoic; limestone, shale, quartzite

Precambrian; shale, slate, quartzite

Edmonton

Red Deer

Calgary

Medicine Hat

Lethbridge

25

SOURCE OF INFORMATION: RESEARCH COUNCIL OF ALBERTA.

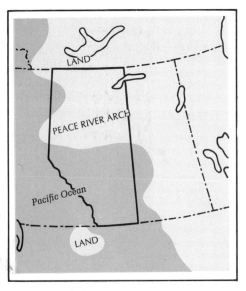

Middle Cambrian seas

This Early Cambrian ocean was much more limy than the Precambrian seas so that a chemical environment favourable to the development of skeletons may have been present. In addition, tremendous thicknesses of limestone were deposited after the initial sandy-beach phases were submerged by the advancing water. These sandy-beach phases can be seen in Banff National Park at the base of Mount Eisenhower and at Lake Louise, and at Mount Edith Cavell in Jasper National Park. When one views Mount Eisenhower, for instance, the present valley floor brings back the old Precambrian land. The sandstone at the base of the mountain is the sandy beach of the Pacific Ocean of 600 million years ago. Then, as the ocean pressed on to the east, deeper waters covered the area now dominated by Mount Eisenhower, and no longer is there sandstone in the upper part of the mountain face, but shales and limestones from the muds and limes laid down in quiet depths below the turbulence of waves.

Middle and Late Cambrian times

By Middle Cambrian time, the whole of Alberta south of Lesser Slave Lake was covered by a tongue of the Pacific Ocean, which had also reached into Saskatchewan. The water was shallow and warm. Limestones were deposited and a tremendous variety of trilobites developed. Other animals with skeletons appeared, and one of the most extensive fossil records ever recovered comes from the Middle Cambrian Stephen Shale deposit near Field, British Columbia, adjacent to the Alberta boundary. Here is the first gazette of life, with skeletal and nonskeletal animals all preserved in fine black shales that must have been laid down in a stagnant hole in the bottom of the sea. This stagnant hole had a pickling effect upon the dead animals of 550 million years ago, while the poisonous waters kept away potential scavengers. Sea weeds, jelly fish, sea cucumbers, trilobites, ancestors of crabs, of crayfish, of shrimps and of

Mount Eisenhower. Rocks of Cambrian age form the cliffs of this "massif", northwest of Banff, Alberta.

C.H

lobsters are represented, and leeches, arrow worms and tentacled marine worms are but little different from their counterparts of today.

The Stephen Shale deposit is unique in that the internal organs and fine external appendages of the long-dead animals, delicately traced in thin, carbonaceous film on the black shale, may often be recognized in some of the fossils. C. D. Walcott, the great palaeontologist of the early 1900's, used to park his private railway car on a siding at Field to work the quarry on the mountain. His studies of the fossils from this quarry marked a radical change in the attitude of palaeontologists. After Walcott's beautifully illustrated descriptions of these fossils of 550 million years ago, palaeontologists had to accept not only the concept of change, but also the realization that, in many ways, certain animals had retained essential similarities across tremendous reaches of time. Strangely enough, the list of animal forms from the Stephen Shale is most closely reflected today in the composition of the modern fauna of the Black Sea.

By the Middle Cambrian period, the severe flooding of Alberta had modified the containing headlands of the embayment. In the southeasternmost part of Alberta, the edge of a large island, called Montania, jutted up from northwestern Montana. This island had originally formed the southern headland of the Alberta embayment. In the Peace River country, the north headland of the Alberta embayment, known as the Peace River arch, formed a broad peninsula thrusting westward into what is now the Dawson Creek area of British Columbia.

North of the Peace River headland, another Pacific embayment penetrated into the Keg River area of Alberta. The Alberta and Keg River embayments developed on the downwarps, or depressed areas, of the granitic phases of the old Precambrian basement.

When embayments of this sort develop and become filled with sediments, they are often spoken of as basins. The pattern of oil exploration in Alberta is controlled by the margins of these basins, since the successive layers of sediments in the basins became piled up like a stack of saucers. Oil is lighter than water and floats up to the margins of the saucers, where it is stored in porous rocks around the edges. Very early in Palaeozoic time these basins were beginning to have outlines, and their impress was carried into the rocks of Alberta for the next 400 million years so that they are reflected in the patterns of oil and gas fields within the province today.

By Late Cambrian time, the seas were reaching over into the Williston basin of southern Saskatchewan and had flooded onto the south flank of the Peace River arch. The western end of the headland may have become an island.

The Ordovician Period

The Upper Cambrian sedimentary rocks of most of southern Alberta are shaly and silty and, at the latitude of Red Deer, the Cambrian rocks grade upwards into the Ordovician sequence with no sign of a break. The same situation is found on the western boundary of Alberta near Field, British Columbia, and as far north as the Smoky River. Along the watershed of the Rocky Mountains the Ordovician shales in this area carry graptolites, a fossil that looks like a pencil marking on the rock. These pencil-like markings have a saw-tooth margin, and a little animal related to the modern hemichordates (tiny creatures intermediate between worms and vertebrate animals) once lived in the colonial skeleton which housed a score or more of these animals. Graptolites are found from the latest Cambrian time until Devonian time, and are used by geologists the world over to correlate rocks of one continent to those of another, since they apparently floated freely in the ancient oceans.

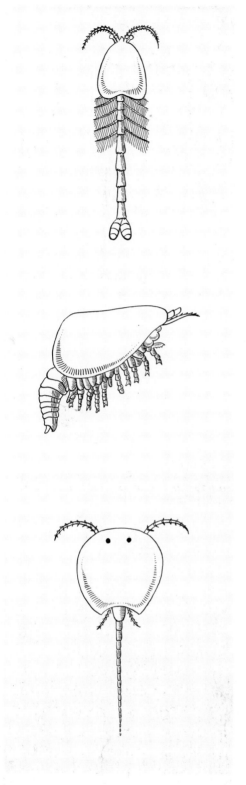

Stephen Shale fossils

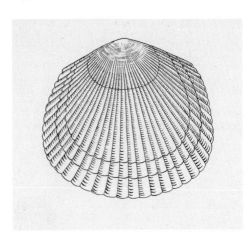

Orthis – an early Palaeozoic brachiopod

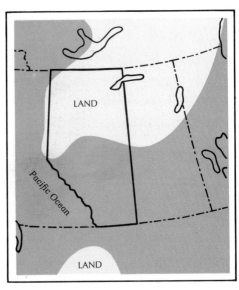

Late Ordovician seas

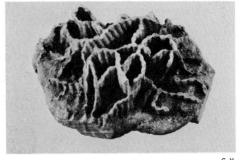

Halysites, a Palaeozoic chain coral.

C.H.

Early Ordovician time saw fewer floodings of Alberta and Saskatchewan. By the Middle Ordovician, the Pacific Ocean had withdrawn and Alberta was left high and dry. The subsequent erosion removed much of the Cambrian and Early Ordovician deposits and left two escarpments of Cambrian rocks. One of these ran north-south through Saskatchewan; the other, the Meadow Lake escarpment, reached west from Saskatchewan to about Edmonton and then swung north toward Lesser Slave Lake. The Montania Island was once again tied to the mainland and the Pacific embayment was limited to the western edge of Alberta, north of Waterton Lakes National Park.

In Late Ordovician time the seas once more swept into Alberta in one of the most wide-spread inundations in the history of the North American continent. Because of subsequent erosion, rocks laid down in the Ordovician Period are only found in Alberta in the mountains or at depth in the southeastern part. Ordovician rocks appear elsewhere, however, and can be seen in the mottled limestones brought from Manitoba's Tyndall quarries for the adornment of Alberta's public buildings. Fossils similar to those in the Tyndall limestones can be recognized in the mountains on the west side of Banff National Park.

Late Ordovician fossils are both abundant and different. In Late Cambrian or Early Ordovician times, except for the primitive sea urchins, most skeletons of animals were made of a horny or protein type of material, such as is found in the horns of cattle or the wings of insects. But when the animals returned with the seas of Late Ordovician time, all were showing off the latest in shells made of calcium carbonate, a harder material. Even the conservative trilobites strengthened their skeletons with it. One of the humble relatives of the jelly fish became attached to the ocean bottom and started to build skeletons of calcium carbonate. Thus it began the long line of corals and hydrocorallines which still live today, and have been vital contributors to rock formation ever since. Bivalves, like the brachiopods and clams, and univalves, such as snails and the chambered nautiloids, developed calcareous skeletons. The bryozoa – pinhead-sized animals that grow in colonies which look like moss – made their appearance at this time.

Another interesting form that appeared was a close relative of the crayfish. Called an ostracode, it manufactured a little bivalve shell into which to retreat when danger threatened. It is one of the most important groups of what are broadly termed microfossils. Microfossils are so tiny that oil-well drills do not break up all of them, and scientific identification may be made under a microscope. Since most animals change slowly with time, each form of an animal can be recognized as belonging to a certain age. Oil men are interested in the age indicated by such fossils, since part of the art of mapping for oilfield discovery is correlating beds of rock of the same age. This allows the geologist to reconstruct maps of the sea margins and depths of water in the past. Old shorelines are favourable areas for oil and gas discovery. Thus these microfossils of long ago are important today.

Other fossils were abundant in the Late Ordovician sea. Among these, we ought to mention the peculiar chain corals, sponges that look like sunflowers, honeycomb corals and the large straight or coiled chambered shells of the primitive nautiloids. These last are easily recognized, weathered out against the limestone in the Mount Wilson area of Alberta. By the end of the Ordovician Period all the major groups of animals had come on the scene, and only the plants were lagging.

Dr. S. J. Nelson has pointed out that the fossils occurring in the Upper Ordovician rocks seem large and varied to such a degree that one suspects a tropical origin. If this is so, then the equator in those days, 400 million years ago, must have run through Alberta, or very near it, and Alberta must have been within the tropics.

It is difficult to determine whether the poles shifted and Earth spun on a different axis, or whether Alberta moved from its tropic position. The fit of the two sides of the Atlantic, if they were to be brought together, has been explained by continental drift. In fancy, one may see Alberta drifting on the sea of time past tropic latitudes with its course directed north and west for the last 400 million years.

The Silurian Period

It is assumed that the seas spread across southern Alberta at the end of the Ordovician Period and stayed there into Silurian time. The same warm seas carried the descendants of the Ordovician fossils and, though new models came in, the basic patterns remained, and so it is difficult in western Canada to distinguish between Late Ordovician and Early Silurian rock strata. Then, by Late Silurian time, Alberta was lifted up as dry land and most of her Late Ordovician-Silurian rocks disappeared through erosion.

Early Devonian time

The whole North American continent remained high in Early Devonian time. The high land provided freshwater habitats for fish, while the margins of lakes and rivers made possible the development of land plants, still with their stems safely in water. These first land plants were mainly stems, with leaves not much more than spikes or the simple, flattened ends of branches. From these humble beginnings the plants started to take over the land. Before the end of the Devonian Period, primitive conifers, ferns, clubmosses, and ancestral scouring rushes, such as the progenitor of the living horsetail rushes, came into being. The scorpions and insects followed the plants onto the land, and the early amphibians followed the food supply.

During this period western Alberta from Lethbridge to Peace River became a range of hills, now termed geologically the Western Alberta ridge. Another low range of hills, called the Peace River arch, ran from Dawson Creek in British Columbia over to the Lake Athabasca region, and a series of escarpment ridges faced northwest and stretched from north of Red Deer northeast into Saskatchewan. Just north of Alberta and southwest of Great Slave Lake, there was another low range of rolling hills, known as the Tathlina uplift.

Economic effects of Middle and Late Devonian times

The stage was set at the beginning of Middle Devonian time for the development of the economic fabric of Alberta. The Pacific Ocean could not enter Alberta across the Western Alberta ridge and had to find a way around it. The south end was blocked because Montana and Saskatchewan were high and dry. The sea therefore flooded in through northeastern British Columbia across a low barrier in the Fort Nelson area. This created a giant salt pan in northern Alberta, where the sea water evaporated for several million years. The salt accumulated in two thick beds centred around Cold Lake and around Fort Vermilion. The northern salt pan was separated from the southern by the Peace River arch. Then, as the sea washed over the Peace River arch, the underlying rock was smashed into a sand which is commonly called the Granite Wash by geologists. These Granite Wash sands were very porous and the Red Earth oil field is developed in them.

Non-porous rocks must lie above the oil accumulated in porous rocks within the earth. Since the sediments which are later to become rocks are laid down under water, at first water and the oil globules from rotting

Monograptus, a Silurian fossil.

Psilophyton, one of the most primitive land plants. A Devonian fossil.

29

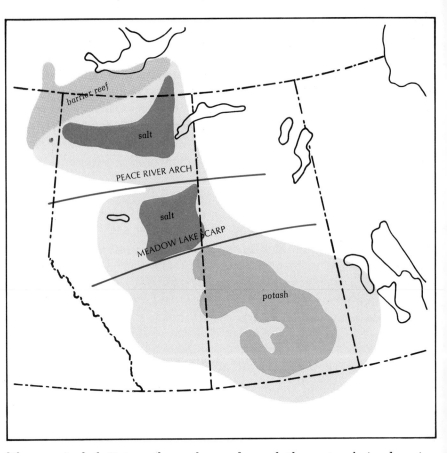

Elk Point basin with Middle Devonian salt and potash deposits.

life are mingled. But, as the rocks are formed, the water, being heavier, sinks and the oil floats up to the high points in porous rocks, making oil pools in sand bars and coral reefs. Coral reefs are usually composed of porous limestone and are generally shaped somewhat like a loaf of bread. The oil that is collected in the top of a coral-reef loaf is then trapped under the doming crest of a non-porous rock, such as shale. In the same way, oil in a sand bar collects at the high point of the bar and is kept from escaping by a layer of non-porous rock.

Over in northeastern British Columbia, at the mouth of the salt pan, coral reefs started growing. But, because a coral reef cannot grow in water which is much over a hundred feet deep, as the sea deepened, the coral reefs, to keep from drowning, had to grow higher or move in toward Alberta to find shallower water.

As the arm of the Pacific Ocean slowly flooded into Alberta, it left a series of coral reefs started wherever and whenever the water became about a hundred f   eep. Here is where the major oil wealth of Alberta developed. By late Middle Devonian time, this hundred-foot depth of water had entered the northwest corner of Alberta and left reefs, such as those now occupied by the Rainbow Lake oil field in Alberta, and the Pine Point lead and zinc deposit in the Northwest Territories just north of Alberta. By the end of Middle Devonian time, the hundred-foot depth line had reached the Peace River arch. The reefs on this arch produced the oil and gas fields of Worsley, Swan Hills, Kaybob, Judy Creek and Virginia Hills. By Late Devonian time, the hundred-foot depth line had penetrated to Edmonton on the east and also to the Western Alberta ridge. The reefs thus created are responsible for the oil and gas fields of Simonette, Berland River, Pine Creek and Windfall in the west, and in the east, those of Homeglen-Rimbey, Wizard Lake, Leduc-Woodbend and Golden Spike and, slightly later, the fields of Redwater, Malmo, New Norway, Clive, Fenn-Big Valley and Drumheller.

After these reefs were formed, the water deepened, killing the Alberta reefs, and the waters of the Pacific Ocean reached over into Saskatchewan and finally to Manitoba. But this arm of the sea seems to have run out of oil. Then it started to back out again and shallowed. Another series of hundred-foot depth marks had to be reached as the sea passed out over Alberta, leaving another set of attendant reefs and another group of potential oil fields, such as Obed and the upper parts (Nisku Formation) of the Joffre and Leduc-Woodbend fields. This time the sea retreated over the Western Alberta ridge so that only Alberta benefited by the second growth of coral reefs.

Late Devonian in Alberta

Suppose we take a look at Alberta in the early part of Late Devonian time. Most of it is under water. The west end of the Peace River arch is an island. A thin peninsula juts up from Montana along the site of what is now the Rocky Mountains to about Jasper National Park. Coral reefs are growing on the eastern, northern and southern margins of the Peace River island. The peninsula from Montana is being slowly chopped into islands, and the Peace River island grows smaller until in the later part of Devonian time all of Alberta is under water.

For the first time in Alberta's record, there are fish – armoured fish, jawless fish and primitive, shark-like fish. The earliest fish are believed to have developed in freshwater streams that flowed into the Ordovician seas, but by Devonian times a very respectable assemblage had taken to living in the ocean, Palaeontologists call them ostracoderms (covered by a single bony plate), placoderms (covered by many bony plates), and lung fish. Most of the fish were small, but some giant predator types, 20 to 30 feet long, were present, such as *Dinichthys*. Many of the fish lived in and around the coral reefs where there is a record of an abundance of life.

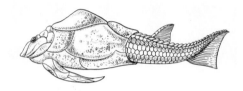

Devonian placoderm

In Alberta, during the Devonian period, the horn corals and the ordinary prismatic colonial corals were joined by an upward-growing, branching or staghorn type of coral known as *Cladopora*. This latter coral gave the reefs the vigorous upward growth that shaped the reefoid

C.H

Cladopora and Amphipora, the billion-dollar coralline twins of Alberta's oil industry.

31

LATE DEVONIAN SEAS AND CORAL REEFS IN ALBERTA

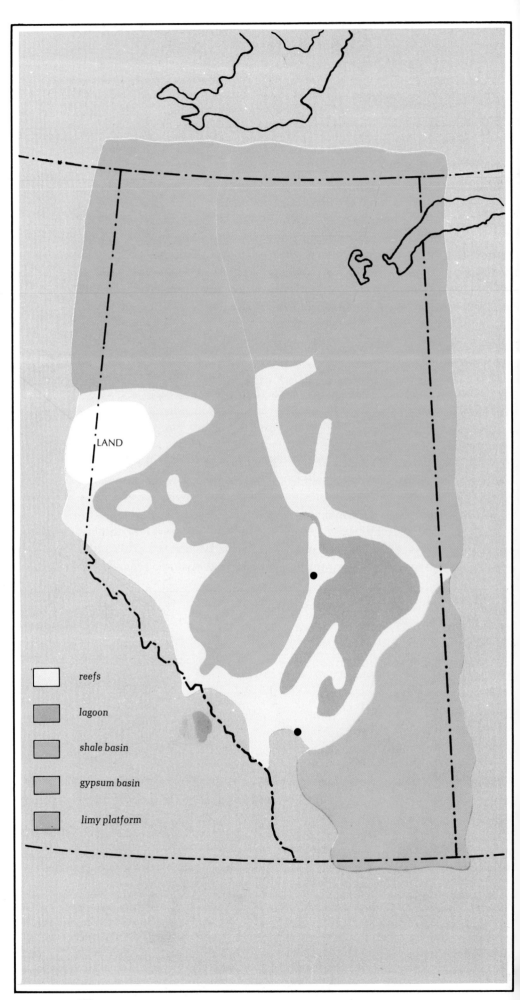

LAND

reefs

lagoon

shale basin

gypsum basin

limy platform

bodies into excellent oil traps. Along with *Cladopora* grew the ever-present stromatoporoids and calcareous algae, which added strength to the reefs and kept them from breaking up. In modern reefs, the algae are called nullipores (no pores) while the hydrocoralline millipores (thousands of pores) would correspond to the extinct stromatoporoids. One of the thin, pencil-shaped stromatoporoids was named *Amphipora* (pores all round). *Amphipora* and *Cladopora* are characteristic of all the oil-producing reefs of Alberta, and this pair can be considered the billion-dollar twins of the Alberta oil industry. It is strange that these humble animals, seldom individually greater than a millimeter in size, would ultimately mean so much to the surging economy of Alberta.

In and around the reefs and in the shallow waters behind them, bivalves and snails lived in profusion. Sea butterflies, nautiloids and their close relatives, the ammonites, swam in the upper waters along with the fish. Sea lilies, which are really animals, grew in gardens on the sea floor where the waters were quiet. The trilobites, however, had been reduced in number, since the fish could swallow them whole, armour and all.

A few dwarf plants were living on the peninsula on the west side of Alberta and, although very primitive, can be considered to be "land" plants, although they probably tolerated salt water and needed swampy conditions. These plants were plentiful enough in western Saskatchewan to leave thin coaly streaks in the beds above the previously deposited salt beds.

In the middle of the Late Devonian in Alberta, about the time the seas started to leave Saskatchewan, a fair amount of sand began to appear in the sediments. The areas behind the site of the recently dead coral reefs once again acted as salt pans and reddish beds appeared. The reddish beds of this period, which crop out at Vermilion Chutes on the Peace River, account for the name given to its rapids. Southern Alberta and eastern Alberta developed gypsum basins, and sandy islands appeared in the sea in the Jasper National Park area.

This sandy development marked the end of all corals in Alberta for the remainder of Devonian time. Distant events, perhaps, were shaping Alberta's pattern by upthrusting land masses athwart the warmer currents that nourished coral growth. Geologists have good evidence that there was a mountain range built or being built along the north coast, which contributed to the disappearance of the corals. But the water was not cold enough to stop the deposition of limestone, so that dark limestones were laid down under the sea in the Jasper to Banff area. The more porous fringes of these Late Devonian limestones contain the gas fields of Okotoks and Gold Creek. Small oil pools are located in these limestones over some of the various reef fields.

Early Carboniferous Period

Continents are not stable over long periods of geologic time but tend to tilt and warp as the materials under the crust adjust through slow flowage. The downwarping that started in northern Alberta and admitted the coral seas in Middle Devonian time continued to depress the west side of Alberta. By Early Carboniferous time, the Peace River island and the Western Alberta ridge had sunk beneath the waves. The Pacific Ocean again rolled across Alberta and extended as far as Manitoba. At first it was a muddy sea but it changed to a limy one, and corals, but not coral reefs, once more grew in the area that would become Alberta. It is not known whether there was any land in Alberta at this time, but it may be that the northeasternmost corner of the province formed part of the shore.

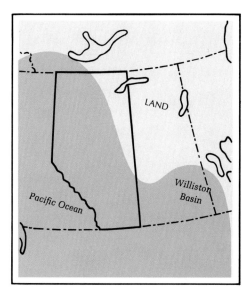

Early Carboniferous seas

Crinoid columnals. Broken-up stems of sea-lilies, each about the size of a pencil, form much of the Rundle Formation.

In the bottom of the shallow Early Carboniferous sea were tremendous banks of sea lilies. When the remains of these sea lilies are found today, stem-fragments are the main elements, since there were many fish that ate the heads. The crushing teeth of these fish can be seen in the rocks of Early Carboniferous age in Jasper and Banff National Parks. Mount Rundle is made up of rocks of this age, and occasional fish teeth have been found along with many brachiopods, bryozoans and large corals.

The limestone and dolomite beds of Early Carboniferous age within the Williston basin provide the oil wealth of southeast Saskatchewan and southwest Manitoba. The beds of this age in Alberta contain such classic oil and gas fields of the foothills as Pincher Creek, Waterton, Turner Valley and Jumping Pound, as well as the fields at Sundre and Edson and smaller fields in the Peace River country.

The Carboniferous Period gets its name from the fact that land plants were very abundant for the first time in the world's history so that, for example, coal seams were common in the eastern maritime provinces of Canada. Because Alberta was under water, the only trace of the land plants is the occasional log that floated out to sea, became waterlogged and sank. Occasionally the fossil trunks of giant clubmosses can be seen in the limestone of the mountains. There are good coal seams of Early Carboniferous age in the southeast corner of the Yukon, so that we know that the tree trunks could have floated in from the north.

Geologists like to name rocks after the first place they were observed. Consequently the rock at the top of Rundle Mountain is called Rundle Limestone (Early Carboniferous age); the recessive-weathering band of rock underneath its big cliffs is termed the Banff Shale (also Early Carboniferous age); and the heavy limestone beds along the base are known as the Minnewanka Limestone (of Devonian age). These rock formations may be traced from mountain to mountain and recognized in drill holes in the Alberta plains by their fossils and other characteristics.

If the Rundle, Banff and Minnewanka Formations are traced underneath the Alberta plains from drill hole to drill hole, the Rundle Formation on top disappears on a line running from about Calgary to Grande Prairie; the Banff Formation extends almost across the southwestern and southern part of Alberta; and only the Minnewanka Limestone or its equivalent is left in northeastern Alberta. This is the result of erosion after Carboniferous time.

The oil man is always interested in these lines of the disappearance of formations since they give rise to what is termed a pinch-out – in this case, an erosional pinch-out. As noted, the oil globules trapped with the water in the pores of the rock float up on the water to the highest point of the porous rock until they meet a barrier of non-porous rock. In Alberta, at a much later date, a relatively non-porous sequence was deposited on top of the erosional surface of the Carboniferous rock, and the oil floated up until it became trapped beneath the eroded surface. In this way, the old, buried erosional limestone escarpments provided for the potential Carboniferous oil traps such as Harmattan-Elkton and Sundre.

The Late Carboniferous and Permian Periods

The erosion in North America after Early Carboniferous time was caused by cold weather on other continents. In Early Carboniferous time, about 300 million years ago, there was a super-continent in the southern hemisphere which appears to have consisted of present-day South America, South Africa, India, Australia and Antarctica. This super-continent has been called Gondwanaland. As the ages rolled by, glaciation overtook

34

Gondwanaland and so much of the globe's water was tied up as ice that sea levels dropped all over the world. In Alberta the waters receded to about where the southern foothills rise today, while in the Peace River area the shoreline was over by Lesser Slave Lake. Rivers once more crossed the province from east to west, dumping sands into the new coastal waters. In the mountains of today, these sands are known as the Rocky Mountain Formation.

While the province was being eroded, just this side of what is now the Coast Range in today's British Columbia, a line of volcanic islands was thrown up from the ocean depths. No trace of the volcanic ash of that day is to be found in Alberta, either because the volcanoes were too far away, or because at that time the province may have been considerably farther south in the trade-wind belt so that the ash was blown west. Volcanic ash made the sea rich with certain mineral salts which were released to upwelling currents. As a result, in certain areas, chiefly in the United States, rich deposits of phosphates, used in modern times as fertilizers, were formed. Similarly formed but poorer deposits are known from the Rocky Mountains in Alberta.

The fossil record of the rocks laid down in Late Carboniferous and Permian times is sketchy in Alberta, and the only vertebrates known are

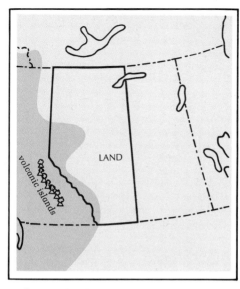

Early Permian seas

M.H.

Mount Rundle, an overthrust mountain. Mississippian rocks form the top strata and Devonian beds make up the lower cliffs.

35

fish and the big spiral tooth-battery of a shark known as *Helicoprion*. In the Rocky Mountain Formation, however, collectors occasionally find remains of a "large" one-celled creature, known as a fusulinid, about the size of a grain of wheat and with much the same shape but coiled. Inasmuch as these fusulinids occur all over the world, they give the palaeontologist a means of correlating events in Alberta with events in Texas, in the Arctic and on other continents. Brachiopods, clams, snails and scaphopods still lived in the shallows, but the Palaeozoic corals were gone from Alberta's shores and, along with the trilobites, the ancient lineages were doomed. At the end of the Palaeozoic Era, over the whole world almost all of the creatures that dwelt on the floor of the ocean were exterminated and left few or no descendants. Most of the swimming animals and the land animals and plants were little affected by this extermination so that when the term Palaeozoic, or "ancient life", is contrasted with the term Mesozoic, or "middle life", it only has real meaning with reference to bottom-dwelling marine life.

The Palaeozoic Era had endured for 375 million years. During this time, Alberta had alternated between dry land and sea, and life had evolved from simple plants and animals to vertebrates and dry-land vegetation. Still more important for Albertans, over the aeons the major foundations for the province's oil and gas industry had been created. No one can look backward through geologic time without a sense of awe.

The Mesozoic Era

When the Palaeozoic Era ended with the destruction of all or almost all bottom-dwelling marine life, the ensuing Mesozoic Era, which lasted from 225 to 70 million years ago, likewise subjected Alberta to alternation after alternation of upraisings of the land and infloodings of ocean waters. The Mesozoic is divided into three periods: the Triassic, Jurassic, and Cretaceous.

The Triassic Period

The opening of the Triassic Period saw a continuation of high and dry conditions in Alberta. In central British Columbia, explosive volcanoes belched molten rock. If molten rock is poured out from the bowels of the earth, the lava has to come from somewhere and must have been withdrawn in part from under eastern British Columbia and western Alberta. This caused a sinking of the western side of Alberta and the sea was again able to flood into the province. This Triassic seaway was restricted in southern Alberta to the foothills and mountains, but in the Peace River country the waters reached as far east as where the town of Peace River now stands.

Life in the Triassic

With the return of the seaway came a host of free-swimming animals, including ammonites and the swimming clams, which have relatives among the fossils on the far side of the Pacific Ocean and in the Alps. The ammonites and swimming clams trace their lineage back into the Permian Period. Sea-going reptiles, such as the ichthyosaurs, which were much the same shape as porpoises, apparently fed on the ammonites and on their relatives, the squid-like belemnites. The fish population during Triassic time is fairly well-known, since there was a sudden kill-off due to adverse conditions in the sea, near the end of the Early Triassic in the Rocky Mountain region. As a result, their fossil remains are common today along the front ranges and foothills. Most of the fossil fish found in Banff and Jasper National Parks have diamond-shaped scales similar to those on the garpike, a relative of the sturgeon.

Coelacanth fish are also preserved in the Triassic rocks of Alberta. These fish with lobed fins were thought to have died out in the Mesozoic

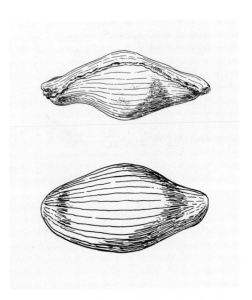

Fusulinids, fossil one-celled animals about the size of a grain of wheat.

Era, but recently an isolated relict colony of the group was found living in deep water off the coast of Madagascar. Today's coelacanths still look very much like their ancestors of 225 million years ago as preserved in the rocks at Banff and Jasper.

In the Triassic beds, the accumulation of fossil vertebrates is always at the same level, and so some strange upheaval or poisoning of the water must have caused the destruction. It seems apparent that in the region of the present Rocky Mountains there must have been a stagnant sea bottom which was poisonous to bottom-living forms, since only swimming forms are preserved as fossils. A sudden chilling of the surface water could have produced an overturn of surface and bottom water, bringing the poisonous waters up and killing the fish, or a severe rainstorm might well have resulted in their death. The reptiles do not seem to have been destroyed but occur as isolated skeletons throughout the Triassic sections.

The sediments laid down in Alberta in the Triassic Period were silts and sands with a high lime content and were regularly bedded so that they can be used today for building. Visitors can, for instance, see Triassic rocks in the building stone of the Banff Springs Hotel.

Middle and Late Triassic times

About Middle Triassic time, the southern end of the Triassic seaway was blocked off to some degree. The continent in the main was still hot and dry and presumably was within the trade-wind belt. The water became increasingly salty, and finally gypsum was deposited in the Triassic seaway from Banff to the Peace River country. Excellent deposits of gypsum of high quality are present in the mountains in the Mowitch Creek area north of Jasper. Late Triassic time saw a withdrawal of the waters from the southern Alberta end of the seaway so that the sea was almost entirely confined to the Peace River country. A new shoreline, however, developed within the northern part of the province as the Northwest Territories began to rise, together with the area now occupied by the Mackenzie Mountains. Finally the sea receded. In the Peace River country, we can see Middle Triassic beach sands together with limestones, which were porous accumulations of shell material known as coquinas. The farther eastward one travels in the Peace River region, the more numerous are the beach sands and coquinas. All these porous sands were truncated by Early Jurassic erosion and are eagerly sought as potential oil reservoirs of the shoestring (long and narrow) sand type.

The Jurassic Period

The complete withdrawal of the sea from Alberta at the end of the Triassic Period was geologically of short duration and the waters were back in early—though not earliest—Jurassic time. Some of the volcanic islands of British Columbia had foundered, sunk by their own weight. The Mackenzie Mountains area and northern Alberta probably remained dry land. Rivers flowed into Alberta from the north, east and south, bringing with them a pall of mud. This mud was to become the Fernie Shale of the foothills and mountain belt of Alberta.

The Jurassic sea, known as Logan's Sea, advanced across the southern half of the province and finally reached into Saskatchewan and down into the United States. A band of phosphate was deposited within the Fernie Shale, and this phosphate may prove to be very valuable. Phosphatic beds are often a good place to look for fossil bones and scales. In the main, the only bones found in the Fernie Shale are those of ichthyosaurs.

Other fossils are much more abundant, and true ammonites,

Ichthyosaurus, the reptile that went to sea and looked like a porpoise.

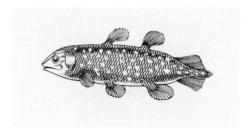

Triassic coelacanth fish

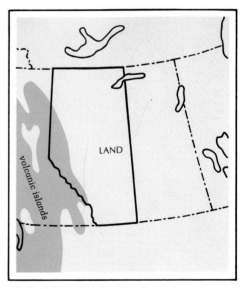

Late Triassic seas

37

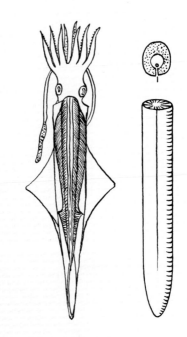

Belemnite, a primitive squid-like dweller in Mesozoic seas. Its fossil is on the right.

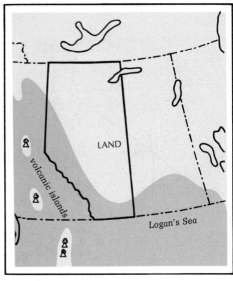

Late Middle Jurassic seas

descendants of a remnant group of the Triassic forms, are present. Tremendous accumulations of the skeletons of belemnites look like piles of petrified cigar-butts. Clams are abundant and, for the first time, oysters become plentiful. Only a few brachiopods remind us of the Palaeozoic.

At the start of Late Jurassic time a naturalist, orbiting high over northern Alberta, would have seen a broad arm of the Pacific Ocean stretching across southern Alberta and most of southern British Columbia, with possibly a large island out by Prince George and another one east of Vancouver. Toward the end of Jurassic time, the Black Hills of South Dakota started to rise and a swamp developed at the head of the embayment. This freshwater swamp became a breeding ground for large dinosaurs, like the 80-foot-long *Brontosaurus*. This huge beast is not known in Canada, although in Jurassic times individuals may have roamed northward and their bones may have been subsequently erased from the record.

Gradually, as the slow uplift of the Black Hills spread and became continental, Alberta and Saskatchewan rose from the waters to become: first, shoreline; then delta and swamp land; and, finally, river bottom. Coal deposits are found wherever the deltas were preserved as, for example, the Kootenay coal in the Crowsnest Pass and in Bow Valley.

The south end of the uplifted former Pacific embayment now became the valley of a large river system which drained the interior of the North American continent and flowed out through Alberta toward the Peace River area of British Columbia. This river system brought sand in such abundance that the deposits of the latest Jurassic time in the province are all sandstones. In the Peace River district, the Pacific embayment became smaller, with the southern shoreline apparently marked by a bed of oysters in the Kakwa River region, and the northern shore by the present valley of the Peace River. Finally, in the ensuing Cretaceous Period, about 120 million years ago, the Pacific Ocean was driven out of the Peace River area in both Alberta and British Columbia. Never again did the Pacific Ocean roll into what was to become Alberta.

Animal and plant life in the Late Jurassic

Dinosaurs roamed the headwaters of Alberta's river systems during Late Jurassic time, although their peak period was still to come. There were also oyster-like clams on the shallow shorelines and free-floating sea lilies and large ammonites in the deeper water.

The chief characteristic of the Late Jurassic in Alberta was a luxuriant plant growth on the deltas of its rivers. In Devonian times, primitive ferns and clubmosses had flourished. A naturalist, however, would have noted a few seed ferns which bore a resemblance to the possible ancestors of modern broad-leaved plants. Conifers were plentiful, and the progenitors of the maidenhair tree (Ginkgo) were becoming prominent. The abundance of vegetation meant that coal seams were laid down along the foothills region and over in the Fernie area of British Columbia. There were still volcanoes and volcanic islands out in what was to become British Columbia, but much of the region which was to become the present Omineca and Selkirk Mountains had already risen above the surface of the sea.

The Cretaceous Period

The next ten million years, a mere moment in geologic time, seem to be lacking in the record of Alberta's rocks, except for the Kakwa River area. Here a slow-moving river meandered across the landscape, probably finding its way out across British Columbia through canyons cut into the rising central portion – the Prince George or Quesnel region – to meet the ocean inlets somewhere east of today's Coast Range. The more the

38

land in British Columbia rose, the more difficult it was for the river to keep canyons cut deeply enough to allow access to the sea. Much of the load of gravel which should have been carried to the ocean was spread widely on gravel flats from Montana to the Peace River region, chiefly along the foothills area. When the river could no longer find its way out over the rising land of British Columbia, it had to turn and go north.

Similarly, in Middle Cretaceous time, the river systems of Alberta continued to drain northward to the Arctic Ocean, roughly along the line of the present Mackenzie River Valley. Then, 120 million years ago, a mountain range began to rear itself along the western margin of British Columbia so that, for the first time, that province became an integrated part of the North American continent. As this range was uplifted, rivers which had previously poured into the Pacific Ocean had to reverse their flow. These rivers, and the streams of central British Columbia, all turned north to join the river systems flowing to the Arctic Ocean.

The Arctic Ocean invasion

As the Coast Range rose, the support beneath Alberta and the Mackenzie River Valley was stolen by a flowage of material from under the Precambrian basement. Both areas sank, and the Arctic Ocean moved up an ancient Mackenzie River system until its waters reached the northern boundary of Alberta. Once the Arctic embayment crossed into Alberta, the northward-flowing rivers began to drop their loads of sediments into that embayment, and the sand along the shoreline became washed and clean. Hence came the McMurray Sands, famed for carrying, locked in them, an estimated 625 billion barrels of oil – heavy, tarry oil.

The McMurray Sands

The oil in the McMurray Sands probably came from two sources. As the streams of those days cut their way northward, they must have breached many a Palaeozoic coral-reef oil pool. The released oil could then accompany the water of the rivers until laid down in the loose sands along that ancient shoreline. Most of the heavy oil, however, probably came from the decomposing bodies of literally trillions of minute plants, which were deposited, along with muds, on top of the McMurray Sands as the ancient Arctic Ocean continued its relentless southward advance. Millions of years later, the tar from this rotting mess in the muds was squeezed out by earth pressures and seeped downward into the McMurray Sands.

The north-flowing rivers of Middle Cretaceous time developed levees and deposited bottom-channel gravels. Wells in these sands give us many of the heavy oil fields of south and central Alberta. As far as can be determined, the Arctic Ocean penetrated as far south as Turner Valley and the Drumheller region. As a result, oil fields of today are developed in the old shoreline and lagoonal sands all through central and southern Alberta, where they are known as Ostracode and Glauconite Sand pools. Except in the Peace River country, the Arctic Ocean did not flood much farther west than what is now the eastern edge of the foothills belt. Coal swamps came into being along the western margin of this arm of the Arctic Ocean. The tremendous reserves of coal in the Cadomin, Pocahontas, Smoky River, and the Peace River canyon areas belong to this ancient shoreline.

Gastroplites, a mid-Cretaceous ammonite.

The forests and coal beds of the Middle Cretaceous

The forests of Middle Cretaceous time differed little from those of the Late Jurassic. Conifers, cycads and ferns, ginkgos and seed ferns made up the forests that made the coal. Coal is formed by the accumulation of vegetation in swampy areas amid a preservation or pickling of some sort while the accumulation is going on. Stagnant waters can provide a pickling effect if enough humic acids – the brown-coloured acids present when vegetation rots in stagnant water – are available. When the pile of vegetation is thick and becomes buried, the moisture is squeezed out, the volatile fluids lost, and the carbon gradually concentrated. Over the ages, the colour slowly turns from brown to black. Most of the coal of Middle Cretaceous age had sufficient time to become bituminous and semi-bituminous coal.

While the coal swamps were developing along the edge of the land, brackish and freshwater lagoons and lakes were formed along the south end of the Arctic embayment. In these lagoons and lakes, continuous layers, composed of ostracodes – the small bivalved crustaceans already mentioned – were laid down and, in immediate succession, a sequence of greensands. The ostracode layer can be recognized in the subsurface over most of central Alberta, but in northern Alberta normal marine salinity prevailed and ostracodes are absent. The shallow mud-flats

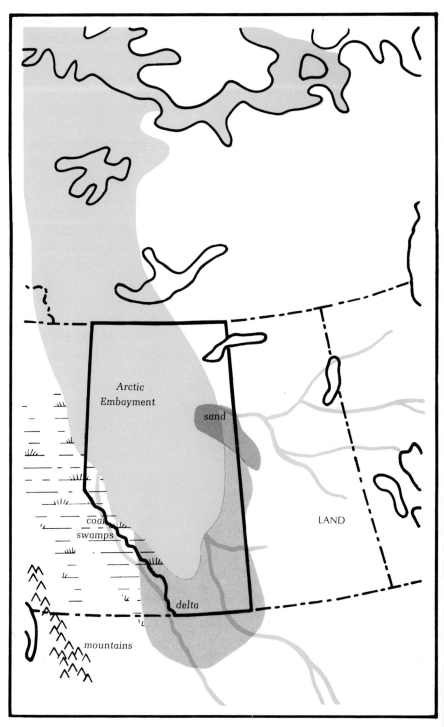

Arctic and McMurray seas of Early Cretaceous age. The Arctic ocean flooded into Alberta during the laying down of the McMurray tar-sands.

of central Alberta gradually filled with alternating fresh and marine sediments.

The whole of southern and eastern Alberta was finally uplifted sufficiently so that sands of freshwater origin, in part deltaic, covered the mud and built sandy beaches in the Peace River country. The cliffs bordering the river at Peace River town are carved from these old sandstones. The fauna – the animal life of a region or epoch – in this old arm of the Arctic Ocean is related to faunas found in England and along the Pacific Coast. This cold sea carried many clams and ammonites and a number of starfish. The ammonites had come over the polar route from Europe. In the bays of Alberta and northeastern British Columbia they developed a series of stout-ribbed forms called *Gastroplites*.

Then, when the Middle Cretaceous embayment in Alberta and northeastern British Columbia became land-locked by the rising Mackenzie Mountains, local forms of shell fish developed. The great majority of the Alberta fossils of late Middle Cretaceous age were of local origin and are unknown in the rest of the world. Most of the local varieties have been named for Canadian geologists, and the catalogue of the specific names of the fossils reads like a roster of the great geological explorers of Alberta. A. R. C. Selwyn, J. B. Tyrrell, D. B. Dowling, G. M. Dawson, R. G. McConnell, F. H. McLearn, P. S. Warren, R. L. Rutherford, G. S. Hume and J. A. Allan all provided patronyms.

Before the Middle Cretaceous embayment in Alberta became entirely land-locked, the waters were pushed out of northeastern British Columbia and out of the foothills region generally. This local regression of the sea allowed the waves to rework the sediments already laid down, and winnowed out the fine clay in certain areas, leaving bars and beaches over central and western Alberta south of Edmonton. Where these beaches and bars are clean sand they have become reservoirs for oil and gas, and the fields of Viking-Kinsella, Cessford, Joffre, Joarcam, Gilby, Ferrier, and a host of others attest to this temporary retreat of the sea. The sands of the winnowed beaches are usually termed Viking or Bow Island sands.

While the uplifting of the Mackenzie Mountains was cutting off the south end of the Arctic seaway and leaving it as an inland sea, the mountains to the west continued to rise. In the western United States, the Sierra Nevada was being built. In British Columbia, the Coast Range and the Selkirk Mountains were being formed. The deep crustal support for these mountains was once again drawn from the subcrust under west-central America, including Alberta and Saskatchewan. The inland sea spread into this sinking area and stretched, as the Mowry Sea, from about the northern edge of Alberta down to about the state of Colorado, with only narrow straits, if any, giving access to the large oceans.

The Late Cretaceous and the Mowry Sea

At the beginning of Late Cretaceous time, the Mowry Sea, somewhat like the Black Sea of today, was connected by narrow straits with the ocean; again, as in the Black Sea, the bottom was stagnant and no life flourished there. Swimming types of life, such as ammonites, fishes, and huge marine reptiles like the plesiosaurs were present. The fish were so abundant that in places the accumulated fish scales make rock ledges in outcrops. In oil-well records, these rock ledges are known as the "fish scale marker". The fish by this time were the modern bony fish. The ammonites were descendants of the land-locked Arctic stock.

This endemic (originating in a specific locality and not found elsewhere) fauna has one of the widest variabilities of form within a species

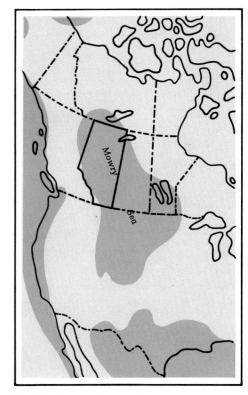

The Cretaceous Mowry Sea

41

Crowsnest volcanic boulders on the roadside near Coleman.

Fossil sycamore leaf

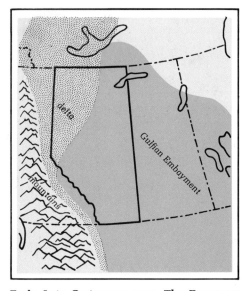

Early Late Cretaceous seas. The Dunvegan delta was built out into the head of a bay reaching in from the Gulf of Mexico.

of any identified fossil assemblage. The struggle for survival in a land-locked sea apparently demanded a plasticity of form that ordinary marine conditions would not have required. It is difficult to determine what the ammonites ate, but it may have been fish.

While the fish-scale beds were being laid down, the Crowsnest volcanic ash and lavas were being spewed out of a vent in the Crowsnest Pass region in southwestern Alberta. The thickest sequence of the volcanic rocks is somewhat north and west of Blairmore and can be seen in the road cuts just west of Coleman. The Rocky Mountains of Alberta carry only this one volcanic extrusion in all the eras since the Precambrian. The volcano stood on the shoreline of the Mowry Sea so that some of the dust from the vent fell out in the water and can be recognized in widespread thin beds. These thin bentonitic beds, formed from decayed volcanic ash, can be dated by radioactive methods, and so can the volcano. The absolute age when this volcano was active is given as 93 million years ago.

About the time the volcano was active, rivers had been bringing sand down to the land-locked sea, and many of these sands were later worked over by waves. The sands of the early Mowry Sea were followed by other sands of Late Cretaceous age.

During the millions of years the Mowry Sea lasted, the north end of the continent was slowly rising and the Gulf of Mexico end was slowly sinking. Within quite a short space of time, geologically speaking, the inland Mowry Sea was connected to the Gulf of Mexico. Northward up the long strait came near-tropical forms of life, such as oysters, large ammonites and an abundance of clams and snails. At the same time, the stagnant waters of the bottom of the Mowry Sea were stirred by circulation, and bottom-dwelling creatures reappeared.

Trees of the Cretaceous Period

By the end of Early Cretaceous time, forests of broad-leaved trees had taken over the shorelines. The ancestry of the broad-leaved trees, which we take for granted today, is difficult to trace, but the progenitors are thought to have been water-lily types that existed during the Jurassic Period. The broad-leaved forms, known as dicotyledons, developed originally in southeast Asia and then spread over the northern hemisphere.

The first dicotyledon to reach Alberta, just before the inland Mowry Sea had formed, was an ancestor of the Chinese lichinut tree, known as *Sapindopsis*. Then came magnolias and, by the time the Crowsnest volcano was belching its lava, sycamores and fig trees had reached the province. Some of the leaves of that far time may be seen trapped within the volcanic rocks of the Crowsnest Pass. Earlier forms of Mesozoic foliage, however, were still present.

Other evidence of the Cretaceous forests comes from the great delta built at this time from the Liard River gap into the head end of the bay which reached in from the Gulf of Mexico. Outcrops of the deltaic rocks from this formation, known as the Dunvegan Formation, are found along today's Peace River from the British Columbia border over to Watino on the Smoky River, and along the foothills southward from the Peace River to the Athabasca River; hence, the flora – the plants of a region or epoch – is well-known from its fossil remains. There were broad-leaved plants, and ferns, cycads, and conifers resembling modern species, but no ginkgos or seed-ferns. A naturalist, if transported to those days, would find his surroundings exciting, though not unfamiliar.

These same deltaic rocks present us with the first record of freshwater turtles in Alberta. Fish bones and the three-toed tracks of small dinosaurs are preserved in the rocks as well as tracks of small amphibians. The delta was apparently built out of the debris from erosion around the Omineca Mountains of British Columbia. Similar aprons of sand were spread through the Idaho and western Montana areas, where oil is produced from them.

The rising of the waters in the Late Cretaceous

Wherever the Dunvegan sands, or sands of similar type, are found, they are usually covered by a fairly thick sequence of fine clays which act as a cap-rock to seal the oil or gas below. These fine clays, which are now shale, were the result of deepening water all over North America, a deepening which came from a rise in the sea level all over the world.

The seas now poured across the Dunvegan delta and toward the Arctic along the line of the present Mackenzie Valley and spilled over into the Hudson Bay area. This seaway, joining the Arctic Ocean to the Gulf of Mexico and splitting North America into two segments, persisted for millions of years. In width, it stretched from the mountains in central British Columbia to low, rounded lands in eastern Manitoba and the Lake Superior region. Alberta itself, 85 million years ago, was entirely under water. Rivers from the elongate, mountainous country to the west flowed into the sea covering the province, and sand tongues were built into the Alberta part of the sea. One of these sand tongues, named the Cardium Sand from a little cockle shell found in it, forms the reservoir rock of the Pembina oil field west of Edmonton. This oil field, which covers some 350,000 acres, is one of the largest in area in the world. The sand body slopes toward the west under 5,000 feet of rock cover and pinches out to the east. The oil moved upward until it reached the eastern point of the disappearance of the sand. There it was trapped by deep-water clays laid down beneath and above the sand.

In latest Cretaceous time, in the chalky seas which give the period its name (Latin, *creta* – chalk; it being at this time that the chalk cliffs of

Cretaceous fossil figs C.H.

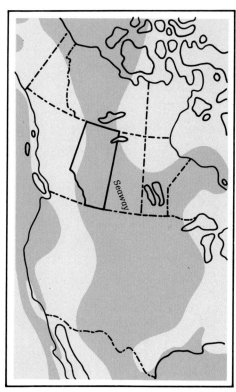

Arctic to Gulf of Mexico Seaway of Cretaceous times.

43

England were laid down), there were clams, oysters and ammonites in abundance. Although coiled forms of ammonites had been known for many millions of years, in this period some of them partially uncoiled, and others straightened out completely. The straight ammonites known as *Baculites*, with a sheen still on their mother-of-pearl shells, are often brought into the museum in the belief that they are fossil fish. From the Medicine Hat region come large, discus-shaped ammonites known as *Placenticeras*, which may be two to three feet in diameter.

The oysters of this period look very much like modern oysters. Their remains are so common in beds in the Drumheller area that today they are mined for chicken-feed supplement. Similarly, the clams and snails of that day anticipate modern forms. In those waters of 85 million years ago, there were also floating one-celled animals with limy skeletons, called *Globigerina*, which still live today, forming extensive deep-water deposits in our modern oceans. On land, dinosaurs made their habitat, but in Alberta their dominance was still in the future.

The dinosaurs and the Badlands

As the ages went by, the Arctic Ocean connection began to be disrupted until, finally, in the Great Slave Lake area, the elongate island to the west was reconnected with the heart of the continent. In British Columbia, the mountains were still rising and at long last the Rocky Mountains were beginning to stir.

The rising land in the west meant huge quantities of sand and mud for the rivers flowing eastward. Tremendous deltas were built all along the

C.H.

Scaphites, a Late Cretaceous ammonite that was beginning to uncoil.

Red Deer River Badlands near Rumsey, carved in dinosaur-bearing beds.

M.H

Tyrannosaurus – a Cretaceous dinosaur

western side of Alberta. On the lush, moist deltas, in among the swamps and among the luxuriant foliage, dwelt the dinosaurs which have made Alberta's Badlands known the world over.

The Badlands are developed in beds that have a considerable amount of decayed volcanic ash, or bentonite, in their make-up. The volcanoes from which the ash originated were apparently in the Yellowstone area and possibly in southern British Columbia. The ash blew over and settled in the lakes and on the marshes in Alberta. Bentonite seals off rock so that moisture cannot get in or out. As a result, instead of the rocks weathering in normal fashion with little ravines and low slopes, the hills remain steep and the rivulets form flutings.

The Red Deer Badlands extend from Atlee, near Steveville, to Nevis in the Stettler district of east-central Alberta. Their most spectacular development is in southern Alberta in the Dinosaur Provincial Park. Here, in comparatively recent times, the Red Deer River has carved a mile-wide valley to a depth of almost 400 feet through the multi-coloured beds laid down during and since Cretaceous time. Other streams have dug winding courses through the Badlands. The result is a striking panorama of steep bluffs and fluted gullies, featured by layers of coal, clay, ironstone, shale and sandstone in colours ranging from black through brown to gray and white. Here and there are gray-yellow cliffs. Still higher, up to the prairie level, sit yellow gravels, sands and silts, deposited in the Ice Age of the Pleistocene Epoch.

These Badlands are the main hunting-ground for the collecting of Alberta's dinosaur fossils. Many of these now reside, as reminders of a colourful part of our ancient past, in museums in Toronto, Ottawa and New York.

The dinosaurs of those days lived principally in two major deltas. The Belly River dinosaurs were there first and may be found in the Dinosaur Provincial Park. They included huge plant-eating hooded dinosaurs (hadrosaurs), horned dinosaurs, such as *Monoclonius*, and terrifying flesh-eating types, like *Gorgosaurus*. Smaller dinosaurs, such as *Stegoceras*, lurked in the swamps. The first traces of mammals in Alberta are also found in the Belly River beds.

The Edmonton delta, the rocks of which underlie much of central Alberta, was the last of those built out into the Gulf of Mexico embayment. Dinosaurs roamed this delta, too, and the swamps in which they flourished ranged from Lethbridge to Grande Prairie. Hence comes the coal of the Drumheller valley, of the Edmonton district and of the outer foothills belt. The plants from which the coal was made were subtropical species. They included sycamores, magnolias, fig trees, chestnut trees and the *Metasequoia*, the ancestor of the great redwoods of California.

As time passed, Alberta began to cool down from a subtropical

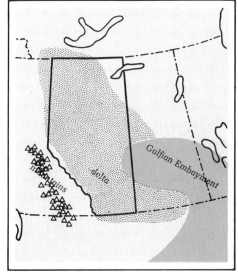

Cretaceous Belly River delta – the time of the dinosaurs.

45

Triceratops – the last of the dinosaurs

to a warm-temperate climate. Little furry mammals now appeared in abundance. The dinosaurs still dominated the scene. The huge flesh-eating dinosaurs, such as *Tyrannosaurus,* and his lesser-known cousin, *Gorgosaurus,* each of them 20 feet high with rows of jagged and serrated teeth edging gaping jaws, were the kings of the deltas. Hooded or duck-billed dinosaurs fed in the swamps, and crocodilian or turtle-like types lived alongside them. There were a number of varieties of horned dinosaurs, which were in body form something like a rhinoceros. One of these, *Triceratops,* which had three horns, survived to the end of the Mesozoic Era to become the last of the dinosaurs. Everywhere, the three-toed bird-like tracks stamped the "mark of the beast" into the soft mud of that day. When this mud became rock, the tracks were preserved. If we look at the fossils of the bigger dinosaurs, we wonder why these tremendous animals did not continue to tyrannize the world. Yet in a comparatively short period, geologically speaking, the dinosaurs became extinct.

What happened to destroy the dinosaurs? No one can answer the question definitely, although it is known that the uplifting of the swamps to form a high plains country turned much of Alberta into a drier and colder environment, and that the large dinosaurs could not adapt to the change. As the end of the Palaeozoic Era was signalled by the extinction of the bottom-dwelling species in the seas of that day, so the close of the Mesozoic Era and the beginning of the Cenozoic Era was marked by the extinction of the floating and swimming groups in the oceans, as well as by the destruction of land species such as the dinosaurs. The ammonites, for example, after hundreds of millions of years of existence, now disappeared. The bottom-dwelling creatures of the seas – along with plants, crocodiles, turtles and the burrow-dwelling mammals – survived.

The Cenozoic Era

The Cenozoic Era is divided into the Tertiary and Quaternary Periods and it extends from 70 million years ago to the present. The longer of the two Periods is the Tertiary, lasting for about 69 million years. It is sub-divided into the Paleocene, Eocene, Oligocene, Miocene and Pliocene Epochs. During this 69 million years, the Rocky Mountains were uplifted to above their present height and eroded down to about today's design. They are relatively recent mountains from a geological point of view.

The earliest Tertiary (Paleocene) beds were laid down in Alberta at a time when the sea from the Gulf of Mexico had been driven out of Canada and did not reach much farther north than North Dakota. These beds are called the Paskapoo Formation. The Porcupine Hills and the upper part of the Cypress Hills are mainly composed of these Early Tertiary rocks. In the centre of Alberta, in an area stretching from Calgary to beyond Whitecourt, the rocks of the Paskapoo Formation are also present. The debris which went to form the beds of the Paskapoo Formation was brought by the rivers from central British Columbia. But, as the

C.H.

Crowsnest Mountain – a "klippe". The cliffs are made of Mississippian and Devonian rocks thrust over Cretaceous sandstones.

Rocky Mountains kept on rising, this source was cut off and the next deposits in Alberta are coarse and seem to come from the mountains themselves.

In the Eocene Epoch, when the Rocky Mountains first were being built, the Great Plains were elevated along with them into a broad upland. The rivers spread gravels across this upland, later carved both valleys and benches in it, and then, in turn, covered the benches with gravel.

The eastward shift of Alberta's mountains

As the Rocky Mountains were being uplifted, their strata were subjected to tremendous pressure, particularly from the west. The general tendency was for the strata to fold and break. But then, in the Eocene Epoch, the present mountains of Waterton Lakes National Park began to slide from their original position in British Columbia into Alberta, on top of the Cretaceous rocks. Chief Mountain, the isolated peak on the southern border of Alberta, is an eroded Precambrian block separated from the Waterton sheet. Such a feature is known as a "klippe". So strong was the push from the west that, over a period of millions of years, the fore-shortening of the original strata in the Rocky Mountains amounted to about 50 miles. All the mountains west of Jasper and Banff, for instance, must have been brought from British Columbia by a tremendous over-thrust shove. The rocks of the mountains in Waterton Lakes National Park, originally laid down under water somewhere west of British Columbia's Flathead Valley, were uplifted and pushed over Alberta's foothills to their present site. If a motion picture of this tremendous shifting could have been filmed over the millions of years in which it took place and could then be speeded up, it would show us an awesome spectacle of massive mountains lurching ponderously eastward like inexorable, two-mile-high behemoths.

The maximum overthrusting and squeezing took place east of British Columbia's Nelson area. In this region, batholiths – huge bodies of molten rock which had been solidified deep under the crust – had, along with erosion and uplift, shouldered their way up among the existing rocks and had thus initiated much of the squeezing and thrusting. The severity of the overthrust in this area explains why Alberta's foothills are narrow in the Pincher Creek area, and why there are no true outer ranges of mountains until the north end of Waterton Lakes National Park is reached.

47

North of Jasper National Park, the foothills and the outer ranges have more breadth.

These outer ranges are in the main composed of Late Palaeozoic and Early Mesozoic limestones. They show high-angle overthrusts and repetitions and deformation of rock strata, as in Cascade Mountain. Hence comes the typical mountain scenery east of Banff and Jasper. Mount Rundle, The Three Sisters, Fiddle Range, Roche Miette, for instance, are all overthrust mountains.

The mountains along the Alberta-British Columbia border, however, such as Mount Robson, Mount Eisenhower and Mount Assiniboine, are known as "massifs". Mountains of this type, although they may have slid many miles from their original location, are primarily the result of uplift rather than overthrusting, and are built of Early Palaeozoic and Late Precambrian rocks. Massifs are usually big mountains with gently downwarped shape.

The foothills also felt the thrust. They show folding of their strata, which are, in general, made of Cretaceous rocks with a very occasional Palaeozoic limestone inset. Meanwhile, the plains of central Alberta were folded by pressure into a long, gentle downwarp, known as the Alberta syncline. This syncline preserved the Paskapoo Formation by pushing it below the average erosional level.

Other features of the Tertiary

The gravels laid down by the rivers of the Tertiary from the Eocene Epoch onward are occasionally recognized in Alberta. With the elevation of the Great Plains, the lush lowland vegetation of the dinosaur age gradually yielded to grassland, and a grassland fauna took over. The fossils of horses and camels are found in this period of Alberta's past.

The development of the horse from a five-toed animal, about the size of a fox-terrier, to a solid-hoofed courser of the plains can be traced in many of its stages in the Cypress Hills. So can that of the camel which, like the horse, was at first a mammal about the size of a jack rabbit. Both horses and camels spread into Asia over the Bering Strait land bridge and later on vanished from the North American scene. Horses returned to this continent in the 16th century A.D. with Cortez and his Spaniards, but camels are to be found in North America only in zoos and circuses. By the same Bering Strait land bridge elephants from Asia spread into Alberta.

Although the Tertiary was the Age of Mammals, the latest phases of the Mesozoic marked the beginning of most of the major groups, including primates. Mammals had been only small burrowing animals, smaller than a dog, but they now exploded into animals of many sizes and shapes. Two of the larger Tertiary mammals, of which fossils have been found in Saskatchewan on the eastern end of the Cypress Hills, were *Titano-*

Brontotherium — a large Tertiary mammal

Cross section from the granitic batholiths of British Columbia through the Rocky Mountains to the Alberta Plains. Note the position and attitude of the sedimentary rocks.

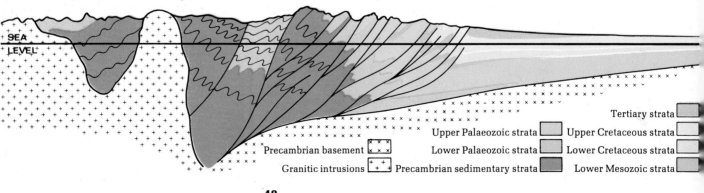

SEA LEVEL

Granitic intrusions | Precambrian sedimentary strata | Precambrian basement | Lower Palaeozoic strata | Upper Palaeozoic strata | Lower Mesozoic strata | Lower Cretaceous strata | Upper Cretaceous strata | Tertiary strata

therium and *Brontotherium*, four-footed animals, eight feet high at the shoulder and shaped somewhat like rhinoceroses.

Land pattern at the end of the Tertiary Period

By the end of the Tertiary Period, the province's basic framework was established. In the northeastern corner, erosion had once more exposed the low rounded hills of the Precambrian landscape. In general, the surface rocks on the eastern side of Alberta were tilted westward, and those on the western side eastward. The centre of the downfold between the two runs from about the Porcupine Hills through Calgary, and then curves gently to the west to cross the Peace River a few miles west of Hines Creek. Underneath the whole, Alberta's basement of Precambrian rocks slopes downward to the west and south. The strata of the plains were not without cross-warping. Several low upwarps (raised areas) corrugated their surface. Of these, the most important, the Sweetgrass arch, runs northward from the Sweetgrass Hills in Montana to pass between the Cypress and Porcupine Hills, and then swings east to cross the Alberta-Saskatchewan border east of Edmonton. A second upwarp trends from west to east along the Peace River until it fades out at about Peace River town.

Remnants of Late Tertiary plains may be seen today in the flat-topped Caribou Mountains, the Buffalo Head Hills, the Clear Hills, Nose Mountain (south of Grande Prairie), the Saddle Hills, House Mountain, the hills south of Whitecourt, the Hand Hills, the Wintering Hills, the

Folding Mountain. The mountains of the eastern ranges of the Rocky Mountains and of the foothills are carved from folded strata.

C.H.

49

Mammoth tooth. White circle indicates comparative size of a twenty-five cent piece.

Mammoth

Mastodon tooth. White circle indicates comparative size of a twenty-five cent piece.

Mastodon

Cypress Hills and, along the foothills front, in units such as the Porcupine Hills and the Crawford Plateau.

The foothills themselves were then, as now, in long ridges paralleling the mountains, the harder bands of rock forming the ridges and the softer rocks having been eroded into valleys. Behind the foothills, by Late Tertiary time, the Rocky Mountains, although they were to suffer further erosion by water and ice, had pretty well assumed their present positions and design. Most of the rivers of Alberta crossed the province from west to east.

In the Late Tertiary, however, all of Alberta's rivers, except for the Peace River, were beheaded. During the late Mesozoic and the Tertiary, the waters had flowed east from British Columbia into Alberta. But in Late Tertiary times, the central part of British Columbia was lowered relative to Alberta. British Columbia's streams now turned westward, and the headwaters of the rivers in the southern part of Alberta were restricted to within the Rocky Mountains.

The gravels laid down by Alberta's rivers during the period immediately preceding the advance of the ice are known as the Saskatchewan Gravels. From them comes the flour gold of the present Saskatchewan River. In these gravels are found the remains of horses, muskoxen, giant bison with huge horns, woolly mammoths (elephants) and bulky mastodons (cousins to elephants).

These last two species, like the earlier straight-tusked elephant, crossed from Asia to North America via the Bering Strait land bridge. Like the giant bison, they are now extinct, but frozen mammoths, with the hair and flesh intact, have been unearthed in Alaska and Siberia, and we know that mammoths were hunted by early man in Europe. The woolly mammoth is characteristic of cold climates, and the Bering Strait land bridge itself came into existence because glaciation in the northern hemisphere had locked up the water of the seas as ice, thus lowering the sea levels. By this time, then, North America had entered the Ice Age, and the Pleistocene Epoch of the Quaternary Period had begun.

The Quaternary Period and the Pleistocene Ice Age

No one knows why the Ice Age began. But, starting about one million years ago, huge ice-caps formed in the Arctic regions and began to flow southward over large areas of Eurasia and North America. Four times there were major advances of the ice and three times it retreated during what are known as interglacial periods.

On this continent, the centres of the vast accumulations of ice were around Hudson Bay whence it spread outward across western and eastern Canada and down into the United States as far as the junction of the Ohio and Missouri Rivers. On several occasions, including the first three major advances, the ice ground westward across Saskatchewan and may have reached or crossed Alberta's boundary. Alberta's climate was changed to Arctic or sub-Arctic, its flora and fauna were altered and the drainage of its rivers blocked, although in the interglacials, which tended to be warmer than now, the original types of animals and vegetation returned. But, even during the glaciations, Alberta remained as an ice-free corridor until about 35,000 years ago, while parts of Alaska and the Yukon Valley were never glaciated.

Finally, in the last great glaciation, termed the Wisconsin, slow-moving sheets of ice, up to 5,000 feet thick, partly from the east and partly from the north, began to grind ponderously over Alberta. At the same time, another sheet of ice massed in the Rocky Mountain region and flowed out to meet the ice moving down from the north. Then the two sheets of ice pushed slowly southward parallel to the mountains to meld with the ice sheet that had moved in across Saskatchewan. About 35,000 years ago, except for the high mountain peaks, the higher parts of the Cypress Hills, and patches of the Porcupine Hills, all of Alberta was a waste of ice.

The march of the ice was unrelenting and irresistible. As it advanced, it scoured the whole terrain. All vegetation was destroyed. The softer rocks were pulverized into clay and carried forward in the ice. Boulders bigger than houses were carried along, and the harder rocks were scratched and eroded. In the mountains, the rivers of ice carved the valley slopes into cliffs. The lower hills, such as Tunnel Mountain at Banff, were completely over-ridden and rounded off. The peaks of the higher ranges had hollows called cirques scooped out of their flanks by the heads of the glaciers. Everywhere the sea of ice left inescapable marks of its advance.

The last retreat of the ice, beginning about 12,000 years ago, also left enduring impressions on the landscape. As the ice melted, the wastage of rock and other material either incorporated in the ice sheet or borne upon its surface was dropped to lie where it fell. This debris became the parent material of today's Alberta soils. Wherever the ice withdrew rapidly, the glacial residue is thin. But, wherever the ice maintained a stationary front for a period of time, the load it had carried was deposited in great, elongate heaps, known as moraines; wherever the ice blocked the river drainage so that lakes were formed, lake clays were laid down.

The melt-water from the great ice sheet drained away in streams which left their patterns on the land. In southern Alberta, for example, where the ice pulled back earlier than in the north, the melt-waters at first flowed south through the Mississippi drainage system by a series of coulees parallel to the retreating ice-front. Then, as the ice receded farther, the rivers began to restore the eastward-flowing pattern and to cut new southeast-trending coulees. Later, when the ice had completely withdrawn, the rivers incised new channels down to the old drainage levels, sometimes following preglacial channels but sometimes carving arbitrary patterns across what had been inter-stream areas. The blocked drainages of the Canadian Shield resulted in thousands of tiny lakes nestled in Alberta's northeast corner. Similarly, many pothole lakes and sloughs were left on the plains; while in the mountains, valley moraines – acting as dams – begot chains of lakes. Tarns, such as Lake Louise, occupied abandoned cirques.

Although the essential design of the province's topography was established by Late Tertiary times, many of its features show the scars left by the advance of the ice and by its stubborn retreat. Today, a scattering of ice fields and glaciers along the continental divide remind us that the Ice Age is not too far in the past.

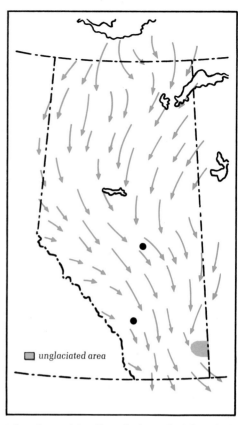

Directions of ice flow during Glacial Period

unglaciated area

H.R.

RICHMOND W. LONGLEY

CHAPTER THREE
Climate and Weather Patterns

AT ONE TIME ALBERTA sweltered in tropic climes and at another lay frozen under a sea of ice. Even after the retreat of the ice, there were major changes in its climate. In more recent times, shorter swings of climate's pendulum have brought cycles of drought or of increased precipitation and trends toward warmer or cooler weather.

Climate and weather are intertwined. Climate – the pattern over the years of temperature, wind, sunshine, cloudiness, and precipitation in a region – is a long-term phenomenon. Changes in it are likely to be slow-footed. But weather — the actual atmospheric conditions in any selected place at any given time – impinges on us every day. Day by day and season by season, it influences our bodily comfort and our psychological reactions. The wildlife, the products of the fields and the whole economy of the province are affected by its vagaries. Yet Alberta's weather is only the expression of its overall climate. That climate is determined largely by the province's geographical position.

The effects of latitude +

Alberta's climate is influenced primarily by its latitude, altitude, distance from the ocean and the direction of its prevailing winds. Its latitude, stretching between the 49th and 60th parallels, puts the province in the central belt of the northern cool temperate zone. The Rocky Mountains protect it somewhat from any extensive influence of the weather of the Pacific Ocean. Thus Alberta's climate is on the whole continental, and cold winters and short, cool summers are to be expected.

Alberta's winters are therefore considerably colder than those of British Columbia at the same latitudes. To the east, however, northern Manitoba and northwestern Ontario have a more severe year-round climate. If for purposes of contrast we examine the latitudinal band

Title picture – Rainstorm over Bow Lake

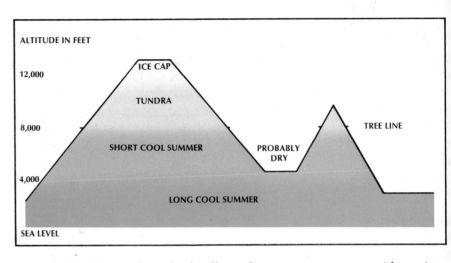

ALTITUDE IN FEET

12,000

ICE CAP

TUNDRA

8,000

TREE LINE

SHORT COOL SUMMER

PROBABLY DRY

4,000

LONG COOL SUMMER

SEA LEVEL

Relationship between altitude and climate

around the globe within which Alberta lies, we encounter a wide variety of climates: the damp cold of the coast of Labrador where the warmest month averages less than 50 degrees; the damp warmth of southwest Ireland where frosts are rare and tropical plants can survive in protected locations; the deserts of northern Mongolia where the annual rainfall is below ten inches; and the cold winters of some Siberian valleys where the January mean temperature is lower than 30 degrees below zero. Within Alberta itself, there are variations in temperature, particularly in winter, as one passes from the "banana-belt" around Medicine Hat and Lethbridge in the south through the area around Edmonton to the northern forests.

The effects of altitude

Latitude does not have as significant an effect on climate as might be expected. Other factors, such as altitude and the direction of the winds, are also important. The towering peaks of Alberta's Rocky Mountains, rising in places to 12,000 feet, are capped with year-round snow and the higher slopes are sub-polar in climate and vegetation. In the mountains, in summer, one can climb in a short distance from sun-warmed valleys through thick stands of timber to alpine tundra and glaciers or snow.

Insufficient temperature information is available to allow accurate identification of the climates high in the mountains. Attempts have been made to estimate them by allowing for a three degree decrease in temperature for each thousand feet of height, but neither this nor any other method of calculation has proved satisfactory. Winter temperatures at Banff and Jasper, however, are generally higher than elsewhere in Alberta because of climatic influences from the Pacific Ocean. On the Alberta plains which drop toward the northeast, the lower altitude cannot offset the effects of cold Arctic winds. In summer, however, the drop in altitude does have a definite influence on the climate, and temperatures recorded in the higher mountain valleys are lower than those on the plains.

Pacific and Arctic winds

Perhaps the most important factors in determining temperatures and precipitation in Alberta are the height and width of the Rocky Mountains and the direction of the prevailing winds. As part of the northern cool temperate zone, Alberta's prevailing winds are from the west, southwest and northwest. But winds shift in direction as storm centres and high and low pressure areas follow one another.

Changes in wind direction, particularly in winter, can cause the temperature to rise or fall as much as 40 degrees within 24 hours. The most rapid of these shifts in temperature come either from the Chinook winds named after an Indian tribe which lived in the Columbia River basin, or from the rush of Arctic air southward from the Mackenzie River basin

The "Chinook" is an Alberta winter phenomenon. It occurs most frequently in the Crowsnest Pass and in southern Alberta as far north as Calgary, although it has been known in central Alberta and the Peace River region. An arch of clouds in the western sky usually signals the coming of a Chinook – a mass of air from British Columbia, which, robbed of its moisture by the mountains, dips rapidly into Alberta and, heated by increasing pressure, descends upon the plains. A 40 degree rise in temperature within ten minutes is possible. A man at Peace River, in 1930, carried his skis up a snow-deep hill. By the time he reached the top, the slopes behind him were bare.

The opposite shift, when Arctic air massed in the Northwest Territories pours southward, can be just as dramatic. At Ralston, in southern Alberta, a woman went to the post office facing a 20 mile-an-hour south wind with the thermometer at 35 degrees. Ten minutes later, when she retraced her steps, she faced a bitter north wind and a temperature of five degrees.

Although Chinooks are most common in southern Alberta, a rise in temperature may occur as far north as Peace River or as far east as Winnipeg, if there is a long continued eastward flow of mild Pacific air. In 1930-31, the warmest winter on the prairies since records have been kept, the air-flow from the Pacific, which tends to follow the isobars (lines of equal pressure), continued with only short breaks. In contrast, in 1949-50, the coldest winter recorded, masses of cold air built up in the Yukon to sweep relentlessly over Alberta. That year, the mean tempera-

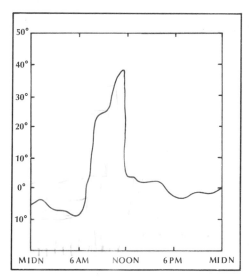

Thermograph trace during a rapid temperature change, Suffield, January 8, 1953.

Chinook arch near Edson.

Glacier lilies thrusting through snow in Highwood Pass.

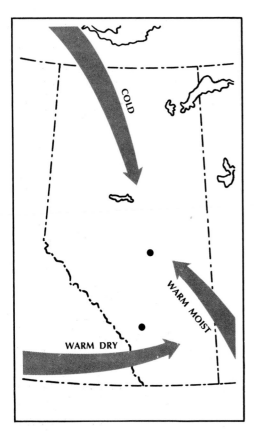

Winter air streams affecting Alberta weather

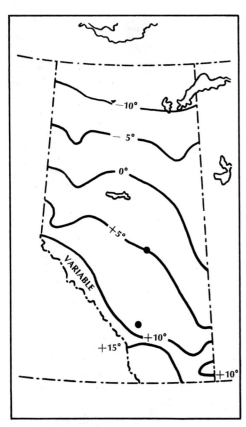

Mean January temperatures, 1931 - 1960.

ture – that is the average of the high and the low temperature calculated on a day-by-day basis – for January, the coldest month, was 27 degrees below normal.

The same sudden shifts in temperature, caused by a rapid change in the direction of the wind, can bring dismay in spring, summer and autumn. Snow has fallen on Alberta's plains and forests in every month of the year except July. Calgary, for example, has reported 4.1 inches of snow in August, and Edmonton has seen snowfalls in June. Yet grass may be green in February, and rain may fall in any month of the year.

Some local factors affecting temperatures

Local topography also affects temperatures. The tops of hills are likely to be colder than the plains around them. By an opposing phenomenon, there are frost hollows where, on a still night, cold air drains downward into valley bottoms. At the Three Hills weather station, northwest of Drumheller, which sits in a frost hollow, the mean January minimum temperature of 6.4 degrees below zero is lower than that of any other station in the vicinity. Similarly, in Edmonton on February 22nd, 1962, although the official temperature at the Municipal Airport was 22 degrees below zero, in the North Saskatchewan River valley a temperature of 35 degrees below zero was recorded. On the same night, in the centre of the city, which is on the same level as the airport, heat from the buildings – and the carbon dioxide cover – kept the temperature at only 10 degrees below zero. Thus in a three-mile zone there was a variation of 25 degrees in temperature.

Temperature inversion, in which a layer of warm air sits on top of a cold air mass, is another fairly frequent phenomenon. It is frustrating to hear in below zero weather that a half-mile or so above ground the temperature is higher than 32 degrees. Yet this situation is not uncommon.

Temperature Inversion and Air Pollution

Temperature inversions also contribute to air pollution. Air pollution is a product of civilized man's automobiles, trucks and industries, through which poisonous gases and small particles, such as those of unburned carbon, are emitted into the atmosphere. In the past, the amounts of pollutants passed into the atmosphere have been small, and any dangerous concentrations of them have been very much localized and quickly dispersed.

But, as Alberta's urban populations and concentrations of industry become greater, the rate of emission of pollutants will rise. At the same

c.h.

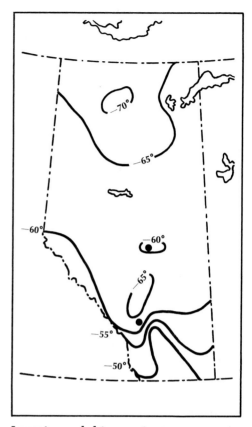

Lowest recorded temperatures

time, the common occurrence of temperature inversions in the winter months slows down the rate of dispersal of the pollutants. When the layers of air on the surface are warmer than the layers aloft, vertical currents carry the pollutants upward; but when, in a temperature inversion, the surface layers are colder than the air above them, the vertical currents are dampened down, and the poisonous gases can collect near the ground or move downwind without dispersing.

A study of air reports from Edmonton, for example, shows that in winter a temperature inversion is almost always present. If, for instance, a mass of cold Arctic air stagnates over the city, cooling by radiation causes the air near the ground to be colder than the air at 1,000 to 2,000 feet. If, instead, a ridge of cold air is located to the east of Edmonton, and warm air moves in above to form a lid over the cold air, once again a temperature inversion is formed. In both these situations, pollutants from automobiles, trucks and manufacturing industries become concentrated and can be dangerous.

This sort of temperature inversion is frequent in winter over most of the province. The danger of "smog" in Alberta may seem remote, but the meteorological situation to accentuate air pollution is already present.

Winter temperatures

December, January and February are the official winter months in the northern cool temperate zone. In Alberta, snow and cold often occur in the middle of November or even in late October. By contrast, there are years when mild weather will persist until Christmas or the New Year. At the other end of the official bracket, much of the province usually experiences wintry conditions until at least the middle of March and often there are outbursts of cold and snow in April and, occasionally, in the first week of May.

Although February is sometimes the coldest month, records show that, on the average, January is the most frigid, with its third week as the bitterest period. Temperatures, however, vary from the southern boundary through the central region to the northern forests. Carway, near the United States border, with a mean January temperature of 19.4 degrees, is the warmest spot in the province. Except for the mountain areas for which no reliable figures are available, the mean January temperature in the south and southwest of Alberta is ten degrees. This mean drops to five degrees and then to zero as one moves north to Lesser Slave Lake, and then to five and ten degrees below zero in the northern

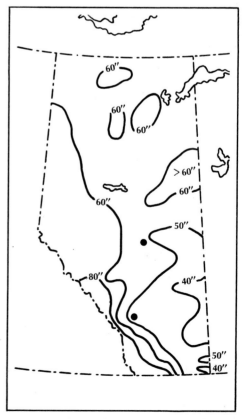

Mean annual snowfall, 1931 - 1960.

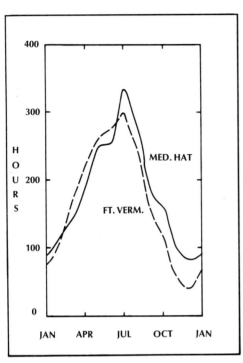

Graphs of mean hours of sunshine

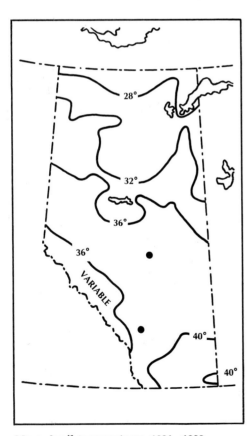

Mean April temperatures, 1931 - 1960.

part of the province. The coldest spot is Fort Smith just over the northern boundary with a mean temperature in January of 13.8 degrees below zero. Alberta's mean January temperatures are slightly lower than those for most other areas in comparable latitudes, but are higher than those in Manitoba and northwestern Ontario. Yet it should be noted that a temperature of 70 degrees below zero has been recorded in northern Alberta and that spells do occur of 30 to 40 degrees below zero in central Alberta, and 20 and 30 degrees below zero in the south. The northwest orientation of the isotherms (the lines which indicate places with the same temperature) comes from the influence of the air-flows from the Pacific Ocean. The Lake Athabasca region in northeast Alberta, like the Northwest Territories, is usually covered by Arctic air from whence, abruptly, it can sweep southward.

Winter snowfall, sunshine and winds

Snow and winter are almost synonymous in Alberta. While all of Alberta is normally blanketed by snow in winter, yet on the plains there is a variation from south to north. In the south, because of the Chinook winds, the ground is often laid bare so that stockmen as far north as Calgary can let their cattle graze all winter. The Chinooks therefore are of great benefit to the ranchers of southwestern Alberta. But in about one year in ten these winds fail them. Cold weather persists, snow piles deeper over the feeding areas, and feed must be supplied to the livestock. Even then the loss of stock may be heavy. In the rest of the province snow often covers the land from November to the end of March, and for longer than this in the northern forests. Most of the northern half of the province receives about five feet of snow each year, the minimum fall being along the Saskatchewan border between Lloydminster and Empress. In the valleys of the Rocky Mountains, the maximum is probably well over ten feet, and so skiing is a popular winter sport in Banff and Jasper National Parks.

Snowfall, cloudiness and sunshine are related. Alberta is noted for its sunshine, but in December and January, because of cloudiness, the sunshine is only 25 to 35 per cent of what is possible. From Calgary southward the percentage increases.

The winds of winter also vary. In the Crowsnest Pass, the Chinook wind speeds are extremely high, and at Pincher Creek the wind can be expected to reach 60 miles per hour at least once a month from November to February. Similarly, Lethbridge anticipates a 50 mile-an-hour wind and Calgary a 40 mile-an-hour wind once during each of these months. In the area around Lesser Slave Lake, the windiest months are also from November to February, apparently because the heat from the lake reduces the strength of the temperature inversion and thus brings down the stronger winds from aloft. When blizzards rage, winds of over 30 miles an hour whirl the falling and drifting snow so fiercely that landmarks are obliterated and visibility is reduced to a few yards. Temperatures below zero, intensified by wind chill (estimated at one and a half degrees lower for each mile of wind speed), have been known to freeze cattle and horses where they stood; and even in modern days people on foot have lost their way and have been frozen to death. A blizzard on the open prairie, or even in the more protected parkland, is all the more terrifying because of the wide expanse over which it swirls.

In the agricultural districts of Alberta, an average winter will see spells of severely cold weather relieved by interludes of mild air. Days of sunshine are frequent and the cold is usually a "dry" cold which does not bite into the marrow as in the damper climates of Canada's Atlantic provinces.

58

Spring temperatures

Officially, March, April and May are the spring months. Except for the southern section, winter in Alberta is likely to embrace March and to grasp at April. In the high mountains, snow may not melt until late May or in June, and on the plains, although the winter snow cover has gone by this time, there may be snowfalls in late April or in May. These late snowfalls are welcomed by farmers because the melting snow provides valuable spring moisture for their sprouting crops.

Two dates, however, are of prime importance to farmers and others with outdoor occupations and interests: the date when the mean temperature reaches freezing; and the date of the last spring frost. Once again, on the plains these dates vary from south to north. At some weather stations in the Crowsnest Pass, the mean temperature reaches the freezing point just before the end of February. By the end of March, the temperature in Calgary has not quite climbed to the 32 degree mark. During the first two weeks of April, however, a mean temperature at the freezing point is quickly in evidence in the north at Embarras on the Athabasca River and Fort Vermilion on the Peace River, although it is probable that the mean temperature on higher ground, such as the Birch Mountains, is still below freezing. The growing season commences when the mean temperature reaches 42 degrees, but if a late frost occurs the growth of tender plants will be checked. Furthermore, the first autumn frost essentially ends the growing season. These dates of the first and last frosts, which determine the length of the frost-free period, are of vital consequence to farmers and gardeners.

The period from 1951 to 1964 has been selected for a discussion of these two features of Alberta's climate partly because there were too few weather observing stations prior to 1951, and partly because of a trend in central and northern Alberta to warmer springs and autumns. For instance, in the area between Edmonton and Lloydminster the average frost-free period was nearly one month longer for the years from 1951 to 1964 than for the period of record to 1950. There is no assurance, of course, that there may not be a return to lower temperatures and a shorter frost-free span.

The average frost-free period begins before the middle of May at a few places south of the Oldman River. The Edmonton weather station, too, has an average frost-free period starting in early May but, being affected by the heat of the city, it does not represent the surrounding district. By the end of May the average date for the last spring frost is past for almost all the agricultural regions of the province as far north as Fort Vermilion. By the middle of June the risk of frost has dropped below 50 per cent except for locations among the foothills or in frost hollows, such as the one at Three Hills, where on two occasions between 1951 and 1964 frost occurred during the last week of June.

The late frosts, which come from strong influxes of Arctic air, bite savagely. Most weather stations with records dating back before 1951, including those as far south as the South Saskatchewan River basin, have experienced frosts after June 20th. Throughout the plains, however, just as frost or snowfall can occur as late as June, so flows of mild air from across the mountains or from the southeast can raise temperatures and start growth earlier than usual. Temperatures in the middle seventies have been recorded in the last week of April as far north as Fort McMurray.

Spring rainfall

Moisture is as essential as a long frost-free period for growing crops, but the total normal precipitation of rain and snow in Alberta, except for the

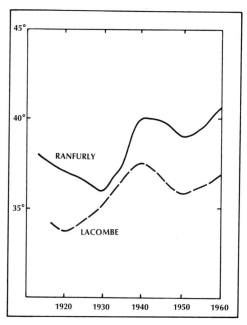

Mean minimum temperatures, showing trend to warmer autumns.

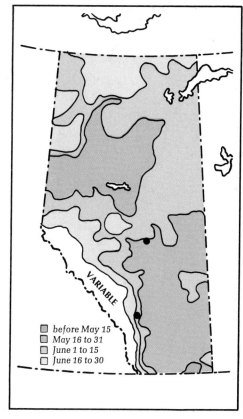

before May 15
May 16 to 31
June 1 to 15
June 16 to 30

Average date of last spring frost, 1951 - 1964.

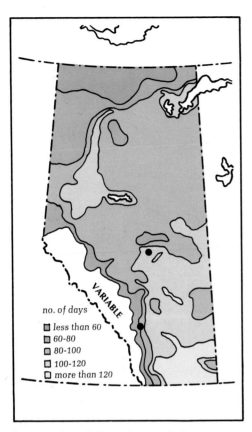

Average length frost-free period, 1951-1964.

no. of days
- ▣ less than 60
- ▣ 60-80
- ▣ 80-100
- ▣ 100-120
- ▣ more than 120

VARIABLE

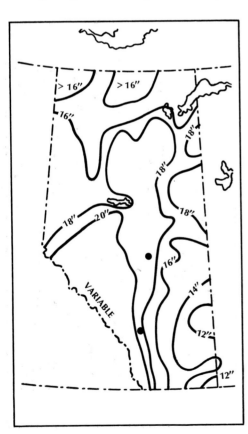

Total annual precipitation, 1951 - 1960.

mountain area, is light, being in fact somewhat less than half that of southern Ontario. A major cause for this dearth of rainfall is the mountains, which rob the rain-bearing winds of their moisture before they reach the plains. In the south, there is always a fear of drought, yet this theft of moisture produces the dry air of the province and a high incidence of sunshine.

The mean annual precipitation ranges from under 12 inches in some districts of southwestern Alberta to about 50 inches at Lake Louise. No part of the province in which agriculture is practised has more than 19 inches of precipitation. To make the situation more serious, there is usually little precipitation in the autumn months prior to the ground freezing. The soil therefore is often dry in spring, since much of the water from melting snow is lost as runoff. Fortunately, as with most northern continental climates, the maximum rainfall in the province occurs during the growing season. The only exception on record is at Lake Louise where the wettest month is December. It is probable that the mountain passes also have a maximum December precipitation.

Most of the general rains in the province are a result of storm centres which develop in or near Alberta along the boundary between Arctic air and Pacific air. During the winter these storms occur most frequently south of the United States border, although a few move into Alberta and along with them may come a flow of mild Chinook winds. As spring advances, these storm centres tend to occur more frequently within the province and to produce more rain since the warm air is then more moist. Mean rainfall therefore achieves its maximum in June in the south, and in July in the central and northern districts.

The total precipitation, snow and rain, for the spring months is normally over four inches west of a line parallel to the mountains through Lethbridge, Strathmore, Lacombe and Whitecourt, and thence westward to the Rocky Mountains. Within this area there are considerable variations. Along the Bow River, for example, the records read: Strathmore, 3.5 inches; Calgary, 4.4 inches; Kananaskis, 7.0 inches; Exshaw, 5.8 inches; Anthracite, 4.5 inches; and Banff, 4.1 inches. The wettest spot on record for this season is Waterton Lakes National Park Headquarters, where the normal rainfall is 11.7 inches, although at the townsite the total is only 7.4 inches. It appears that there is a line of maximum precipitation just to the east of the front ranges of the mountains and then as the clouds move farther eastward, the rainfall lessens. In the valleys within the mountains, precipitation is lighter. At Jasper, for example, the spring rainfall is only 2.7 inches, while Entrance, at the eastern end of the pass leading into Jasper, receives 4.3 inches. Apart from the districts already considered, the total spring precipitation averages between 2.8 and 4.0 inches, the lightest precipitation being in the east and the extreme north. Monthly precipitation in Alberta, however, is extremely variable.

May is the month which initiates the summer thunder and hail season although, quite rarely, there are thunderstorms during the winter. Frequently, by the last week of May several hail storms have hit some of the districts from Edmonton southward, but usually do not do as much damage as those later in the season, since the early crops can recover. The period of sunshine, too, increases rapidly from approximately 100 hours in January to between 240 to 280 hours in May. Banff, however, averages only 200 hours in that month, and the area between Calgary and Lacombe has sunshine for slightly less than 240 hours.

In the same month, low-hanging clouds tend to be replaced by high cumulus clouds, and the spring storms usually bring strong winds. In southern Alberta, except for the Crowsnest Pass, where the winds drop in velocity from the winter maximum, April is the windiest time of the year. At Calgary and Coronation, April and May are on equal terms in this respect. From Penhold northward, including the Peace River region, May is the windiest month.

Summer temperatures

The officially designated summer months are June, July and August. July is usually the hottest month. During the summer there is generally less temperature variation between the southern and northern parts of the province. The warmest region, around Medicine Hat, has a mean July temperature of 69 degrees, while at Fort Smith just across the northern boundary the mean is only eight degrees cooler. Mountainous areas are excepted from this general statement. Lake Louise, for example, has a July mean of 54 degrees, and mountain peaks and glaciers are much colder. Apart from these exceptions caused by altitude, Alberta's summer temperatures are similar to those for other continental regions at the same latitude, but are warmer than those in coastal regions.

Summer temperatures certainly disprove the popular conception that Alberta is a land of perpetual ice and cold. On hot days in this province, temperatures can rise to the eighties and nineties and on occasion to over one hundred degrees. The record maximum temperature for Alberta, 108 degrees, occurred at Medicine Hat in southern Alberta on July 12th, 1886. Temperatures in the eighties and above occur often in the dry southern district from the Cypress Hills north to Coronation and west to Brooks. In this region, almost every second summer day reaches a maximum of over 80 degrees. In the northern half of the province, temperatures reach the eighties, on the average, only 15 days each summer season. Except for mountain areas, the frequency of maximum temperatures above 80 degrees for the rest of the province varies between these two extremes.

High temperatures such as these can be extremely uncomfortable in eastern Canada, because they are usually accompanied by high humidity. In Alberta, as a rule, the heat is quite bearable because of the dryness of the atmosphere, which allows rapid evaporation from the body so that heat is quickly dissipated. Night-time cooling in Alberta is also greater than in a coastal climate because the clear skies and the low moisture content of the air permit a more rapid loss of heat from the surface of the earth to outer space. Consequently, even after a hot day, one usually needs a blanket for sleeping comfort.

During hot weather, the average daily temperature range, which is the difference between maximum and minimum temperatures, is much greater in Alberta than in eastern Canada or on the coast of British Columbia where the humidity is higher. On the plains in July, the range is between 25 and 30 degrees so that on a day with a maximum tempera-ture of 88 degrees a drop to 60 degrees may readily occur at night. Clear days with a bright sun have the greatest range. On rare occasions, between sunrise and noon, temperatures can climb from near freezing to over 80 degrees. Conversely, they may drop overnight from 90 degrees to the low forties. Furthermore, as in the other seasons, there can be invasions of cool air from the Arctic. Thus a period of 90-degree heat may be followed by one during which for several days the temperature does not rise above 60 or 65 degrees. Summer frosts in the frost hollows can occur at such times.

Summer rainfall

Summer is the season with the greatest precipitation. In southern Alberta, maximum rainfall occurs in early June and this peak rainfall

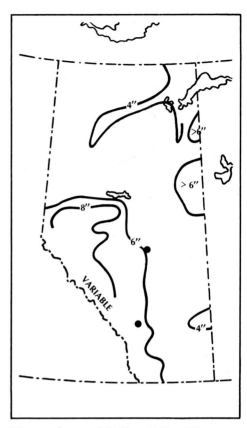

Mean spring precipitation, 1931 - 1960.

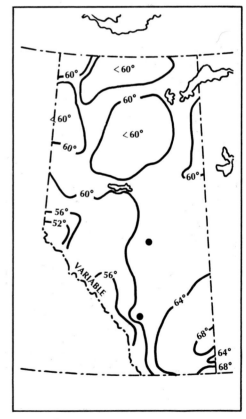

Mean July temperatures, 1931 - 1960.

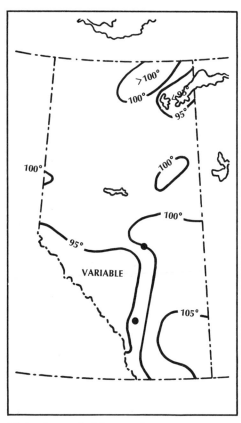

Highest recorded temperatures

Lake Louise in the rain.

period advances northward to Fort Smith by early August. The amount of summer rainfall varies considerably. South and east of Brooks the mean summer rainfall is less than six inches, and droughts are frequent. The mean rainfall is less than nine inches in the area east of a line drawn through Calgary, Edmonton and Athabasca. The farming area of the Peace River region likewise generally receives less than eight inches of summer rain. Summer rainfall is more than ten inches in the foothills north of High River. In northern Alberta, long-term records indicate under eight inches of summer precipitation, although information from recently established weather stations at forestry towers, usually placed at vantage points, shows that topography affects rainfall. Thus more than 12 inches falls on the hills between Fort McMurray and Lac La Biche. Similarly, farther north, the hilly country on both sides of the Peace and Athabasca Rivers receives more than eight inches of summer rain, compared with mean values of from five and a half to six and a half inches reported for several small towns on these rivers.

The summer rains usually fall as brief but, at times, heavy showers. Such showers are typical of Alberta. The extreme surface heating gives rise to cumulus clouds, which often tower like castles along the horizon or coalesce overhead into a storm. It is rare to have a day without a shower somewhere over the central and southern agricultural districts. A period of two or three days may occur with wide-spread showers or general rain, when a low-pressure area stagnates over the province. On the other hand, a drought will occur if, at upper levels, a high-pressure ridge stalls over Alberta. August, 1961, was one such period, and throughout most of the plains less than one inch of rainfall was recorded.

Summer is also thunderstorm time. Reports from 17 weather stations

M. H

over a 14-year period in which hourly observations were made indicate an average of eight hours of thunderstorm activity in June, 18 hours in July, and 12 hours in August. Lethbridge carries away the prize for June thunderstorms, with ten hours recorded. For July, Fort McMurray with 27 hours of thunderstorm activity is the unenvied victor. Other stations recording over 20 hours in July are Rocky Mountain House, Lac La Biche, Whitecourt and Calgary. It is lightning from these electrical storms that continually threatens the forested areas with fire.

The most severe thunderstorms, when clouds tower to six miles or more, are often accompanied by hail. Light falls of hail accompany many Alberta thunderstorms, but each summer, on the average, 10 to 15 severe hailstorms cut swaths of almost total destruction for 50 miles or more. These hailstorms are most frequent in the region between Drumheller and the Red Deer - Calgary highway but may occur anywhere in the province. They often begin in the foothills but reach their greatest intensity east of a line through Edmonton, Calgary and Lethbridge.

In this region of highest hail frequency, or in the foothills west of it, daytime heating causes vertical air currents which result in cumulus clouds, afternoon showers, and thunderstorms. Although these clouds do not usually grow high enough to produce much, if any, hail, when conditions for vigorous upward growth are right, the rising water vapour freezes in the colder upper atmosphere and hailstones are formed. These are carried upward in the vertical air currents, growing as they rise, until a point is reached at which they are heavy enough to fall to the ground against the force of the updraft. Hailstones as big as golf balls are common. After the onslaught of a severe hailstorm, all that remains of a field of wheat are broken stalks and heads. Usually the crop is too far

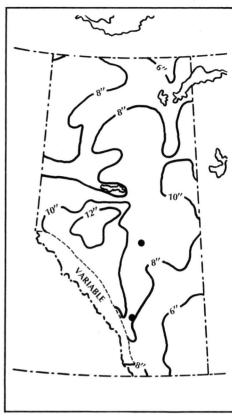

Mean summer rainfall, 1931 - 1960.

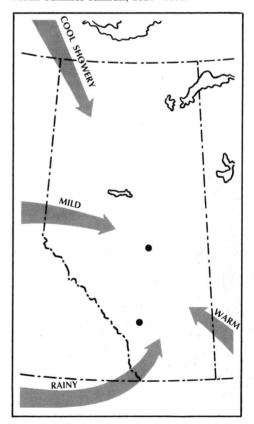

Summer air streams affecting Alberta weather.

Thunderhead over foothills

63

Hailstorm near Penhold, July 4, 1963, in which the hailstones exceeded the size of golfballs.

advanced at this time of the year for any possible recovery.

A few times each summer, a tornado accompanying one of the storms has a brief but violent life. A tornado is a relatively small vortex of very high winds that passes along the earth's surface. Its diameter is less than a quarter of a mile. In Alberta, tornadoes are not as frequent, as intense, or as long-lived, as those in the central United States, where they may have paths up to 50 miles long and winds in excess of 200 miles an hour. Alberta's tornadoes usually have paths less than one mile in length, although they can uproot trees and demolish farm buildings. Also, at times during the summer, there are cloudbursts, such as that of July 31st, 1953, which poured 4.5 inches of rain on Edmonton.

July and August are the least windy months of the year, and summer is the sunniest season, particularly because in northern latitudes the summer days are long, with up to 18 hours of daylight. Clear mornings are common, although there may be cloudiness and showers in the afternoons. By the middle of August, however, the height of summer is already past, and by Labour Day there is usually a chill to the air. Autumn has begun.

Autumn temperatures

During the autumn months of September to November, Alberta's continental position brings about a rapid drop in temperature from the preceding summer peak. For example, from April to July the average temperature at Lethbridge is one to three degrees higher than that at Halifax, Nova Scotia. By the middle of August, in Lethbridge it is 2.5 degrees lower, and by September the average thermometer reading is five degrees below that at Halifax. In the middle of November, the difference

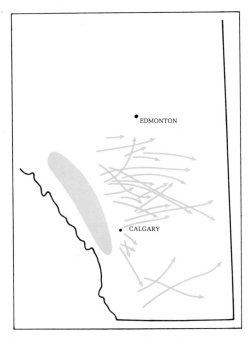

Hailstorm breeding grounds and main storm tracks for 1966.

C.H.

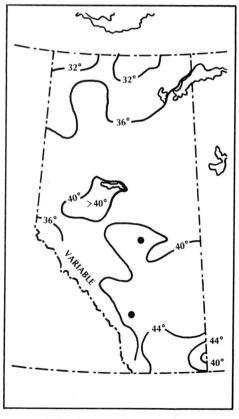

is ten degrees. By the end of September, the frost-free growing season is over for most of the province. At most mountain locations, in the far north, in frost pockets, and probably on top of some of the higher hills, the first autumn frost strikes before September 1st. By September 15th, the first frost of the winter has occurred over most of Alberta except in the area between the South Saskatchewan River and the United States border. By late September in most areas the low temperatures have brought growth almost to a standstill. From Medicine Hat to Fort MacLeod, however, the growing season lasts until the middle of October.

In general, the average frost-free period ranges from more than 120 days in the south to between 100 and 120 days for the northern agricultural regions. In marginal farming districts it varies from 80 to 100 days, and in the north from 60 to 80 days, dropping to less than 60 days in the extreme northern part of Alberta. It should be noted that, in this northern area, apart from the higher latitude which increases the number of hours of daylight during the summer, the relatively warm waters of the Peace and Athabasca Rivers prolong the growing season in the districts along their banks. Embarras, at the 58th parallel on the Athabasca River, has an average frost-free period of 100 days and Fort Vermilion on the Peace River has one almost as long. There is therefore time for modern strains of wheat to mature.

From year to year, variations in autumn temperatures can be extreme. During October, even in northern Alberta, the thermometer may reach the eighties, but there can also be sub-zero weather. Winter frequently sets in by the middle of November, although mild weather can last until well into December.

Prairie rainstorm at Nemiskam

Mean October temperatures, 1931 - 1960.

65

Tornado which occurred at Vulcan, in 1927.

G. F

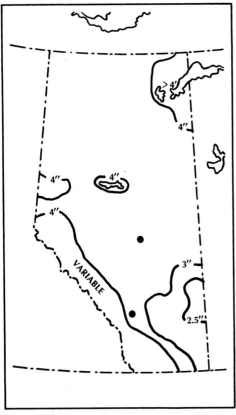

Mean autumn precipitation, 1931 - 1960.

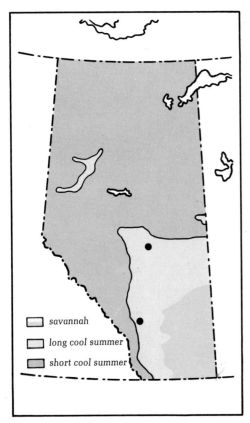

savannah

long cool summer

short cool summer

Climatic zones, according to Koeppen (data for 1931 - 1960).

Autumn rainfall

Over most of Alberta, mean monthly precipitation decreases rapidly from the summer maximum. By October, the total monthly precipitation averages about one inch and, in general, the total autumn precipitation lies between three and four inches. As a result, as mentioned, the soil in the agricultural areas holds little reserve of moisture for the spring. Always, however, there is year-to-year variability, and in some years in certain areas too much rain or snow makes harvesting difficult. Thus, in October, 1959, along the North Saskatchewan River and in the Peace River region, rain fell on 12 to 16 days instead of the normal nine to ten days, and wheat sprouted where it lay.

The number of hours of daylight decreases in autumn, and daytime cloudiness increases from five to ten per cent over the summer minimum, and the clouds are thicker and lower than those of summer. As the autumn months pass, the boundary between cold Arctic air and mild Pacific air lies with increasing frequency in Alberta. Strong winds there become common. As winter sets in, this boundary is generally either in

66

C.H.

southern Alberta or south of the United States border, and the wind speeds decrease, except in the Crowsnest Pass or around Wagner. By this time, the circle of the year is completed, and winter reigns once more.

Climatic zones of Alberta

According to the classification designed by the German scholar, W. Koeppen, most of Alberta lies in the cool temperate zone, although a polar climate prevails on some of the mountain peaks. The areas on the peaks permanently covered by snow belong to what is known as the ice-cap zone, and the remainder above the treeline to the tundra zone.

Alberta's cool temperate zone is divided into two sub-zones: one has a short cool summer; the other has a somewhat longer cool summer in which the period with a mean temperature over 50 degrees is four months long. If we use this distinction, most of the agricultural areas lie in the latter sub-zone. The boundary between the zones runs from Cold Lake to Lac La Biche, then westward until it almost reaches the McLeod River, and then southward to just west of a line through Calgary and Cardston. Data from a few weather stations near Grande Prairie also indicate the longer cool summer. Otherwise the areas north and west of the delineated frontier have a short, cool summer.

In parts of southeastern Alberta, rainfall is deficient. These districts, therefore, should be classified as possessing a grassland climate. Because the total annual precipitation is cyclic in nature, these regions vary in size from year to year, although the whole area south and east of Drumheller is close to being classified as belonging to the savannah climatic zone.

The climate and weather of Alberta have their own attractive and positive features. Though bitter temperatures may strike in winter, a bright sun in a blue sky compensates for the bite of the cold; and there is always the hope of warm winds from the Pacific Ocean. Spring may be late in coming, but when it arrives flowers burgeon and the pulse of life quickens. Summer passes all too swiftly but with autumn comes the reaping of the broad fields and the hunters' guns sounding through the crisp air. Indian summer may last for weeks or it may be gone in a few days. Year by year, season by season and day by day, Alberta's weather is never quite the same.

67

M.H.

CHAPTER FOUR
Mountains and Plains

ROBERT GREEN
ARLEIGH H. LAYCOCK

ALBERTA IS THE SCENE of spectacular triumphs and defeats of the forces of nature battling one against another in a never-ending struggle. In the west lie the massive ranges of the Rockies, thrust up from below sea level to heights of over 12,000 feet by uplift and mountain-building activity. Cut deeply into these are great valleys, to depths of up to 6,000 feet, demonstrating the abilities of the agents of erosion to keep pace. Eastward on the plains the struggle is fairly even, for although erosion by water, wind, frost and ice has levelled and relevelled the land surface for 60 million years, little change in overall appearance has taken place during that time. In Alberta's northeast corner, however, where the old Precambrian rocks stand out, erosion is nearer to victory, for these granites are the core or roots of ancient mountain ranges, now finally worn down and planed off. This much of a triumph has taken almost one billion years to achieve.

Everywhere in Alberta, one can see the effects of erosion and of the forces counteracting it. It is the interplay of these agents that has produced the main features of our landscape, and has given us our diversity of mountain, foothills, and plains scenery.

Major features of the landscape
Alberta is naturally divisible into four major regions, each distinctive in land forms and in geologic structure. In the northeast, the region east of the Slave and lower Athabasca Rivers is part of the hard, rugged, rolling surface of the Canadian Shield. Elsewhere, the younger and softer, flat-lying rocks covering the Precambrian basement form the extensive Plains region of Alberta. In western Alberta, from the international boundary to beyond Jasper, these Plains sandstones and shales are folded and tilted into a series of long ridges to form the foothills belt.

Title picture—Foothills and Rocky Mountains seen from the Porcupine Hills.

69

Hector Lake in a deep, glaciated valley, above which tower castellated cliffs. Glacial outwash debris is spreading an extensive delta into the lake.

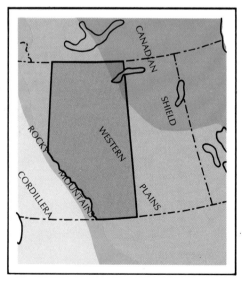

Physiographic regions. Alberta is the only Canadian province which includes parts of the Canadian Shield, the Prairies and the Cordillera.

Westward again, the eastern edge of the Rocky Mountains is marked by the first steep wall of steel-gray limestone dominating the foothills below.

Each of these regions illustrates the influence of the bedrock structure on the landscape. Each also bears the marks of erosional action. Predominant over all these are the legacies of the great Pleistocene ice sheets which left Alberta but ten thousand years ago. In that ten thousand years running water, wind, frost, ice and vegetation have worked to produce the landscape that we know today.

The Rocky Mountains

The western wall of this province consists of only a small part of a massive series of mountain ranges extending across the western United States northward through Canada and into Alaska, ranges so extensive that they appear on a map "like an army of caterpillars crawling northward out of Mexico". The Rocky Mountains are one of many distinct mountain groups, but are one of the most spectacular because of their particular makeup.

As one travels from Jasper Park gates to Jasper, or from Kananaskis to Banff, the front ranges are displayed in all their magnificence. As soon as one enters the mountains, massive gray ranges succeed one another row upon row, most of them with a steep eastern face and a gentler western slope. These are formed from once-continuous beds of hard Devonian and Mississippian limestones, now broken by faulting, and often folded and stacked in successive huge west-dipping slabs one on

70

C.H.

The massive Colin Range north of Jasper is formed by steeply tilted slabs of Devonian and Mississippian limestone.

another, somewhat like shingles on a roof. Between these ranges lie the deep valleys, cut by water and ice erosion along beds of softer Mesozoic rocks, or along the old fault lines with their shattered rock zones.

One great fault, known as the Lewis Fault or Castle Mountain Thrust, runs from Waterton northward to beyond Jasper. This is the demarcation line separating the complex folded and faulted limestone front ranges from the more simple and massive main ranges of the Rocky Mountain core. The fault crosses the Bow Valley just below the Sawback Range and lies about one mountain range east of the highway most of the way from Banff to Jasper. Main range mountains are for the most part made up of older strata of the Rockies – red, green, and gray Precambrian and Cambrian sandstones, shales and limestones, harder than the light gray limestones of the front ranges.

Erosion has sculptured the rocks into many forms, including several distinctive types of mountains. Mount Eisenhower and Crowsnest Mountain, both carved from flat-lying rocks into a series of steps, resemble ancient castles with high battlements. Such layer-cake mountains, with tall hard-rock cliffs alternating with sloping, soft-rock terraces also form, for example, the impressive Ramparts along the west side of Tonquin Valley near Jasper, and the mountains flanking Lake Louise and the Valley of the Ten Peaks.

In contrast, where a long hard-rock ridge has been tipped into a vertical position, erosion may act to cut into the joints and fractures and to produce a range looking like the teeth of a saw; the Sawback Range, obviously, is an example of this, as is the Colin Range north of Jasper.

Most common, however, are the scarp and dip type of mountains, formed from the tilted masses of sedimentary rocks. The smoother, dip

71

PREGLACIAL
RIVER VALLEYS
OF ALBERTA

Fort McMurray

Peace River

Jasper

Edmonton

Lloydminster

Red Deer

Banff

Calgary

Medicine Hat

Lethbridge

known course of preglacial river valley —————

approximate course of preglacial river valley — — — —

SOURCE OF INFORMATION:
RESEARCH COUNCIL
OF ALBERTA

slope often lies on one particular bed from crest to valley floor, while the steeper scarp face is jagged as it cuts across the upturned edges of successive rock layers to form impregnable faces like that of Mount Rundle.

Southward from Banff, the number of front ranges decreases where the mountains have not been uplifted so high; on the Highwood Pass no more than two ranges remain, and farther south the Oldman River, rising on the Continental Divide, cuts through only the Livingstone Range before entering the foothills. Even these mountains have plunged beneath the surface before the massive cliffs of the main ranges at Waterton have been reached.

Between the mountain ranges lie the valleys, most of which run from northwest to southeast. Only a few – the Kananaskis, Bow, North Saskatchewan, Athabasca, and Smoky – slash through the mountain ranges to drain away melt-waters from the snowfields and from the icefields along Alberta's western boundary. These are the valleys wherein erosion by water kept pace with mountain uplift, maintaining narrow gorges across the uprising ranges in Tertiary time. Since then glaciation has affected the region in Pleistocene time, sculpturing the mountains, rounding off protruding ridges and smoothing, widening, and deepening the river valleys.

The ice-caps and snowfields that we see today are but puny representatives of the great glaciers that were carving through the Rocky Mountains only ten thousand years ago. Some impression of their extent can be gained from the presence of foreign rock fragments near the crest of

Glaciated U-shaped valley near Highwood Pass in southern Alberta.

A.H.

Sulphur Mountain at Banff. These were carried there and deposited by a huge river of ice that filled the whole Bow Valley, overtopping and rounding the protruding knob of Tunnel Mountain in the process.

A river first cuts a steep-sided valley that looks like a letter V in cross section, while a glacier carves a valley with a U shape – a flat floor and almost vertical sides. Most of the mountain valleys show signs of such glacial action. The main valleys all carried large powerful glaciers which eroded the valley floors to lower levels, leaving the smaller tributary valleys hanging high up on the new side walls. Here then we have some indication of the amount of ice erosion that has taken place in the mountains. This erosion cut the Bow Valley floor down from the level of Lake Louise or from the top of Johnson's Canyon, and carved the Athabasca Valley floor down to the level of Jasper from that of the Maligne Canyon teahouse.

A river tries to carve a valley in a smooth gradient from headwaters to mouth, while a glacial valley has a steep head wall and often descends in a series of steps. Behind such steps, or behind piles of rock debris (moraines), dropped by the melting ice, are formed many of our most beautiful lakes – Waterton, Crowsnest, Spray, Minnewanka, Egypt, Louise, Peyto, Bow and Maligne, to mention but a few. In these glacial valleys today we can see the streams and rivers at work, removing silt, sand, gravel, and boulders and carving falls and gorges, all part of the process of smoothing out the valleys once more.

In the process of levelling irregularities along main valley floors, run-

Sunwapta Falls, where the Sunwapta River pours over a cliff of Cambrian sandstone. The rounded mountain "massif" in the background consists of Precambrian rocks.

M.H.

Clouds over Turtle Mountain from which fell the Frank Slide, seen in the foreground.

ning water in no more than eight thousand years has trenched the gorges below the Snake Indian, Sunwapta and Athabasca Falls. More common are the gorges and falls where the tributary streams are using their powers to lower the hanging valleys down to main valley level. This phase of erosion gives us Maligne, Mistaya and Johnson's Canyons, the deep Cline River gorge west of Nordegg, as well as the beautiful Bridal Veil Falls near Sunwapta Pass.

The mountain rivers are also at work on the immense volumes of broken rock material left by the melting of the glaciers. Much of this has already been smoothed into immense gravel blankets, such as those in the upper reaches of the North Saskatchewan and Sunwapta River valleys, in the Athabasca Valley around Jasper and in the Oldman Valley above The Gap. This loose rock, in all sizes and shapes, is continually being carried or rolled downstream by moving water, to build deltas that fan out into mountain lakes, and to fill low areas in the river valleys.

The glaciers are not alone in contributing rock fragments for the rivers to carry away. Everywhere are signs of avalanches and landslides that carry rock masses from the peaks down to the valley floors, and of frost action that widens cracks and pries boulders loose on the slopes. Along the highways the warning signs and the litter of pebbles and rocks attest that erosion is still active. One great avalanche of limestone blocking the Maligne Valley has formed Medicine Lake; another mass of rock fell from the south to dam Moraine Lake in the Valley of the Ten Peaks; a third sprawls across the Sunwapta Valley near Jonas Creek. Most spectacular is the 50-foot blanket of white limestone boulders covering a square mile of the floor of the Crowsnest Pass near Blairmore. This mass of rock, perhaps 100 million tons in all, fell from the steep east face of Turtle Mountain in April, 1903, killing 66 people in the town of Frank. Such was the momentum of the slide that the rocks climbed as much as 500 feet up the opposite side of the valley.

Glacial outwash gravel and sand flats deposited by the Clearwater River.

Huge cracks and fissures still exist on that mountain top today. More common on the mountain crests, however, wherever the slopes are not steep, are extensive jumbled masses of boulders, pried loose from the bedrock by water freezing and thawing in cracks and joints year after year. Between and on these rock blankets the alpine vegetation retains its precarious hold. Loose rock piles (screes) also flank the sides of most of the mountains, and rain and snow help to add more rock debris to these piles. Anyone who walks across or climbs these unstable slopes sends loose boulders tumbling and bounding down toward the valleys a few hundred years sooner than would natural erosion processes. Nevertheless, it will still be several centuries more before such boulders or their fragments will pass through the foothills on their long water-borne journey eastward.

The foothills

Flanking the Rocky Mountains to the east lies a belt of lower but still rugged hill country. Characteristically, these foothills consist of long northwesterly trending ridges with steep-sided valleys between, the product of the erosion of folded and faulted Mesozoic sandstones and shales. The massive gray limestones of the Rocky Mountains are absent except for a few conspicuous mountain outliers – Moose Mountain south of Morley, the Brazeau Range near Nordegg, and one or two more. East ward the sandstone ridges and the valleys between them become lower and less distinct and finally grade into the high plains.

The foothills possess their own unique character, being chiefly a ridged, heavily forested country with scattered grasslands in the broader valleys and sparse trees along the highest crests. Hard sandstones show through along the scarp ridge tops and loose rock debris litters some of the slopes below. The small streams in the valleys cut down into the dark Cretaceous shales or meander indistinctly over peaty and muskeg covered flats. Here once more we have the detritus of glaciation, the boulder-laden mixed clays and sands left by the ice-melt, clogging the valley floors and blanketing the more gentle slopes. Limestone and hard white or red sandstone boulders may be found along the highest ridges, showing that mountain ice once covered the whole region. In the foothills, however, it seems that the basic pattern of ridges and valleys was little changed by glaciation, and so much of the drainage retains its original Tertiary pattern.

Many of the rivers carrying waters from the mountains now pass through the foothills in valleys widened and deepened by glaciers. Today these valleys are filled with sand and gravel. The broad flats of the Bow River valley around Morley and of the Red Deer River valley near Sundre are classic examples. In other instances the debris left by stagnating ice completely blocked the old valleys, causing the mountain rivers to slice new courses through the tilted foothill rocks, as did both the Athabasca River in its gorge at Entrance and the Smoky River which used to flow due east into today's Little Smoky valley. Other changes have led rivers such as the Ram, the southern Sheep, Muskeg and many others to cut deep canyons into the black Cretaceous shales, thus producing another characteristic feature of the foothills region. Where hard sandstone ribs cross such valleys beautiful falls may result, as are found on the Ram River and on the northern Sheep River. Some three dozen rivers bearing mountain detritus pass through the foothills, and increase in size as many small tributaries contribute both water and sediment for the benefit of the plains.

The plains

Alberta's plains cover over three-quarters of the province and contain practically all of the province's arable soils and much of its natural resources. These plains are underlain by soft, flat-lying rocks, easily eroded by any process, and so bear many marks of a long and destructive history. As in the mountains, the major topographic features were formed in the last 60 million years, and, as in the mountains, these carry everywhere the signs of glacial action. Yet all these features are in some way unique to the plains region.

Many are the names that have been given to Alberta's plain lands. The uplands in the west, reaching up to 4,500 feet above sea level, are called the "high plains", while the northeastern flatlands along the lower Peace and Athabasca Rivers have been included in the "Mackenzie lowlands". From Manitoba the plains rise westward in several steps, so that much of Alberta forms part of the "third prairie level". Yet our plains are not simple in form, for a number of diverse processes have contributed to their makeup, and it is from this aspect that the best understanding of them can be obtained. The plain lands contain flat-topped high hill regions, rolling upland areas, both undulating and flat lowland surfaces, and marshy, swamp-covered regions studded with shallow lakes.

Hill lands within the plains

Within the plains region are extensive hilly areas that may stand more than 2,000 feet above the prairie level. Most of these were present long before the Ice Age. From the mammal bones and teeth found in the hilltop gravel caps, we have learned that these are remnants of older plains. The oldest, the Cypress Hills, dates back to perhaps 50 million years ago.

All regions, except the Cypress Hills and the southern end of the Porcupine Hills, were over-ridden by the continental ice sheet that ground its way into Alberta from the northeast. The ice smoothed and rounded the hill forms. In many places, on melting it left unsorted deposits of mixed clay, sand and boulders, called till, veneering the summits and

C.H.

The Porcupine Hills, a hill remnant along the western edge of the plains region.

plastering the flanks. In a few places, the ice sheet pushed up and folded great masses of bedrock to form new highlands, such as the Neutral Hills east of Coronation. The hill regions all have somewhat higher rainfall than the surrounding lower plains, and thus the steep flanks are today extensively cut into and gullied by many closely spaced streams.

In southern Alberta, the Cypress Hills rise 1,800 feet above the neighbouring plains. Westward is the Milk River Ridge with 900 feet of relief. Farther north the bare Wintering and Hand Hills, flanking the Red Deer Valley, rise about 600 feet above the plains. The 700-foot-high Nose Hill, near Calgary, is virtually an eastward-protruding foothills ridge. To the south the Porcupine Hills with their scattered parkland and thin spruce-fir forest remnants, rising some 1,500 feet above the plains to the east, also resemble the foothills in many respects.

To the north beyond the Athabasca River lie the most extensive upland regions, the first being the rolling mass of the Swan Hills, capped by a gravel of hard quartzite boulders. This cover causes so much trouble to oil-well rigs that drillers prefer to scrape the 15 or 20 feet of gravel away with bulldozers rather than drill down through it. From the shores of Lesser Slave Lake, the Swan Hills appear like a mountain range to the south, rising 2,500 feet from lake level. Thus its main prominences carry names – Wallace and House Mountains in the west and Deer Mountain in the east.

Northeastward across the broad Lesser Slave River valley rises another highland, the forest-clad Pelican Mountains. The boreal forest region of northern Alberta contains many such hill remnants; around Fort McMurray, Stony Mountain lies to the south and Muskeg Mountain to the northeast. Westward the Thickwood Hills form the southern limit of the Birch Mountains that flank the Athabasca valley northward for 100 miles, culminating in a rugged scarp overlooking Lake Claire and the adjacent lowlands. Between the Wabiskaw and Peace Rivers lie the Buffalo Head Hills. Northward from its crest can be seen the long gray ridge

C.H.

Huge glacial erratics were carried by ice from the mountains near Jasper southward to be left near Okotoks.

of the Caribou Mountains, rising 2,400 feet from the Peace River valley. In northwestern Alberta, the scarp face of the Clear Hills marks the northwestern limit of the aspen parkland of the Peace River country, and a long highland tongue pushes northward to form the Chinchaga, Hawk and Naylor Hills.

All of the northern hills are cut from dark gray Cretaceous shales, often with a sandstone cap. Very susceptible to water erosion, these shales are easily and deeply cut into by streams, thus forming valleys with steep unstable flanks. Down the valley sides creep and slide water-saturated and frost-loosened shale masses that quickly disintegrate into mud. The forest cover on these slumped masses is often turned into a near-impenetrable tangle of trees, criss-crossing at all angles.

The rolling upland surfaces, however, carry only sparse forest cover in the far north, for permanently frozen ground limits tree growth. Lower shrub and dwarfed tree growth is more typical around the large lakes scattered across these old plain remnants – Margaret, Eva and Pit-chimi on the Caribou Mountains, Eaglenest, Legend and the clear-water Namur on the Birch Mountains, and Wadlin Lake, a retreat of the white pelican, on the Buffalo Head Hills. These lakes feed slow, clear streams that meander across the gently rolling uplands before sweeping swiftly down the slopes to the more recently developed plains below.

Till plains

The melting and disintegration of the great Pleistocene ice sheets left a till or moraine blanket over Alberta, a blanket of only a few inches on much of the higher ground, but many hundreds of feet thick in some old river valleys. In northern Alberta as much as half of this surface has been covered with other later materials, but till plains become succes-sively more wide-spread as we travel southward. Two types of till plains are recognized.

The ground moraine plains have a gently undulating surface with what is termed a swell and swale topography. Many of the numerous

79

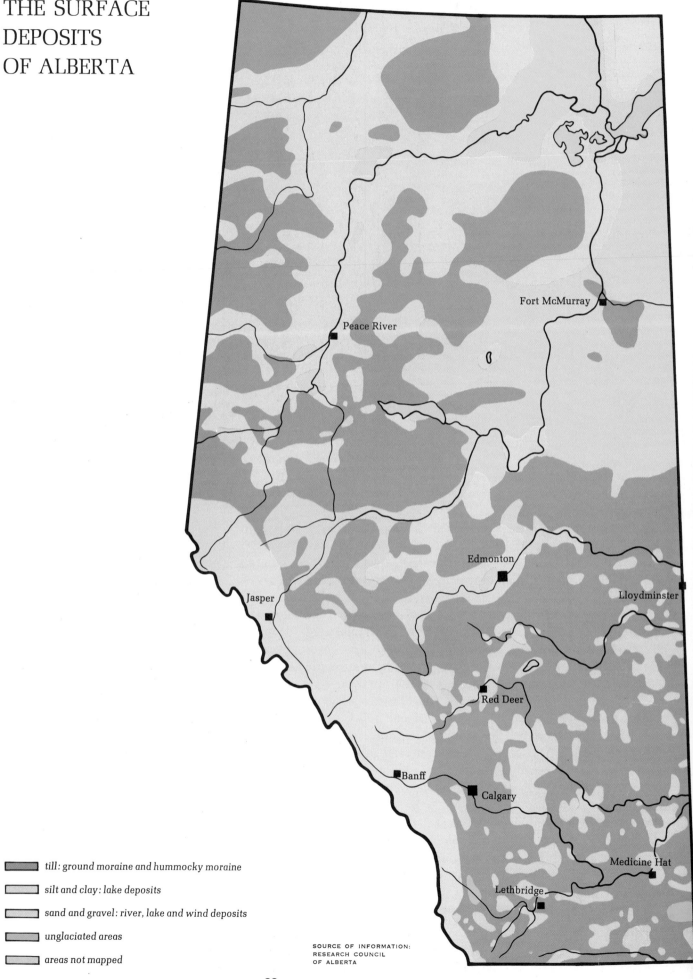

THE SURFACE
DEPOSITS
OF ALBERTA

Fort McMurray

Peace River

Edmonton

Lloydminster

Jasper

Red Deer

Banff

Calgary

Medicine Hat

Lethbridge

till: ground moraine and hummocky moraine

silt and clay: lake deposits

sand and gravel: river, lake and wind deposits

unglaciated areas

areas not mapped

SOURCE OF INFORMATION:
RESEARCH COUNCIL
OF ALBERTA

Flat lake plain, extensively gullied by the South Saskatchewan River and tributary streams, around Rapid Narrows, north of Medicine Hat, where the river has cut a 500-foot valley deep into the bedrock.

depressions, or swales, are occupied by permanent or seasonal lakes and sloughs. Local relief is low, the drainage pattern is not well developed and, especially in the south, many streams drain into local depressions where water evaporates from them in the summer. Many other depressions are fed largely by ground-water and they serve as local evaporation basins, the water becoming successively more saline year by year. Boulders left by the melting ice are numerous but usually not so abundant that cultivation is greatly hindered.

The gently undulating surfaces grade into terrain that is more rolling and rougher. These are the hummocky moraine plains, such as those around Red Deer, east from Lethbridge to Conrad and beyond, and in the area from Elk Island Park southward to beyond Cooking Lake. Drainage is very poorly developed and much of the water flows away as ground-water. Potholes, sloughs, marshes and small lakes occupy the depressions, collect some of the surface run-off, and also serve as evaporation basins for ground-water flow.

Cutting through the till plains are long, steep-sided, flat-floored valleys that carried away the huge volumes of melt-water from the ice. In many places these exist in parallel series, marking retreat stages of the glaciers ten thousand years ago. Today these valleys are dry or are occupied by streams much too small to have cut the channels. On the southern prairies Verdigris, Etzikom, Chin and Forty Mile Coulees are part of one series of melt-water channels. Others cross Highway 2 south of Olds. The Battle River flows in segments of such channels through most of its length, channels that carried eastward the melt-water from proglacial Lake Edmonton.

Lake plains

As the continental ice front retreated downslope northeastward from the western Alberta high plains, melt-waters gathered and formed lakes along and against the ice margin. Water flowed southward from one lake to another through melt-water channels, eroding and sorting the vast quantities of rock debris. Numerous sandy deltas or fans were formed where these streams entered lakes, and the finer silts and clays settled on the lake floors, often covering previously formed moraines. On the further retreat of the glaciers the lakes were drained, leaving the widespread lake plains, particularly in northern Alberta. Few of these plains are absolutely flat because the original lake floor usually was not even, and the thin lake clays still show shallow depressions above the swales of the underlying till surface. Where the lake sediments are thick, the surface is level. The relatively flat terrain and fine surface materials, which retain moisture well, make these plains excellent for cultivated crop production. The rolling wheatlands around Drumheller and southward to beyond Gleichen lie on lake plains, as does much of the irrigated country around Lethbridge, Taber and Bow Island. Edmonton stands on a lake plain that extends west at least as far as Entwistle and south to beyond Drayton Valley. Almost all of northern Alberta except the uplands is covered with a layer of lake silts and clays, which result in the good agricultural soils of the Peace River country, but which also aided development of the extensive muskegs farther north and east.

Where the lake sediments are sandy in character, as north of the Peace River in Wood Buffalo Park, wind has worked on these deposits to produce the dunes of yet another plains type.

Aeolian plains

Wind in Alberta today is a relatively slow and ineffective agent of erosion, except where the soils of cultivated land are exposed under drought

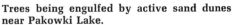

Trees being engulfed by active sand dunes near Pakowki Lake.

conditions. During part of postglacial time, however, when the climate was drier than that of today, northwest winds formed large sand dunes in many parts of the province. Large dune areas lie south of Grande Prairie, north of Devon and near Morningside; the military reserve at Wainwright encompasses a dune plain, and the desolate Middle Sand Hills between Medicine Hat and Empress encompass another. Dunes several miles long and fifty feet high are scattered through Wood Buffalo Park and southeast of it. South of Lake Athabasca, large areas of dune sands are still moving eastward, burying jackpine forests in the process. In most parts of Alberta the dunes have now been stabilized by vegetation, and in the forests they carry jackpine, juniper and blueberries on the sand ridges, but marshes lie in the depressions between.

Alluvial plains

Glacial materials were worked over not only by wind but also by water. During the ice retreat, water was sorting the debris and depositing it in fans or deltas on the margins of glacial lakes. This process continues today, thus extending slowly and continuously the stream-deposited plains.

In northeastern Alberta, where the Peace and Athabasca Rivers jointly deposit their loads of debris into Lake Athabasca, a huge stream-laid plain has been formed during the last 10,000 years. This plain, covering over 3,500 square miles, consists of huge mudflats and muskegs and areas of shallow lakes. Trees grow only along narrow levees of drier ground bordering the innumerable meandering river and stream channels. Hundreds of square miles become a single sheet of water when lake levels are high, and an impassable expanse of soft mud when the water levels fall. Similar but smaller plains exist in Hay Lake in northwest Alberta, and on the margins of Lesser Slave Lake at the mouths of the Heart, Prairie, Driftpile and Swan Rivers. More rare in Alberta are the alluvial plains not connected with lakes and formed by river flooding alone, as near Barrhead along the Paddle and Pembina Rivers.

The Canadian Shield

East of the lower Athabasca and Slave Rivers is a region composed of extremely hard erosion-resistant rocks which represent the roots of ancient mountains, worn down through aeons of time to a relatively level plain-like surface. This is only a fragment of the Canadian Shield, composed of Precambrian rocks, which extends eastward to Labrador and north to the Arctic Ocean. Over this surface advanced the Pleistocene ice sheet which polished, abraded, plucked and scoured the surface, removing the crystalline rock debris and scattering it over Alberta as the identifying mark of the continental glacier. As a result, this Shield region is now characterized by numerous rounded and bare knobs of hard Precambrian rocks, abundant angular lakes and marshy depressions, and a highly disorganized drainage system. It is of almost no value for agriculture because, apart from climatic limitations, much of the land is steeply sloping, is excessively or inadequately drained, and lacks fine-grained surface materials. A sparse vegetation is rooted in cracks in the rocks, and only in a few sandy areas does jackpine exist in any abundance.

Alberta's rivers

Across the Alberta plains flow a few large rivers, carrying water to the Arctic Ocean, Hudson Bay, and the Gulf of Mexico. Over half of the province is drained to the Arctic Ocean, whereas only a small fragment in the south is drained by the Milk River into the Missouri River system and onward to the Gulf of Mexico.

M. H.
Vast low-lying alluvial plain west of Lake Claire. Note old channel of the Peace River outlined by willows.

The majestic Peace River, rising in the interior of British Columbia, has carved a huge valley up to 900 feet deep and over a mile across through the fertile Peace River country of Alberta. Northward from Peace River town, the valley gradually broadens and becomes shallower, until in Wood Buffalo Park the river flows through the flat delta filling the west end of Lake Athabasca. The plains around Fairview and Grimshaw carry an extensive buried blanket of river gravels – a source of water supply and road materials – that marks an ancient terrace level of the river. Thus the whole plains region of the Peace River country was cut by this river in preglacial time.

The Peace River is joined by many tributaries draining the relatively moist northern plains. From the south enters the Smoky River which gathers the run-off waters from the northern part of the Alberta Rocky Mountains. From the west, the Whitemud, Notikewin, Hotchkiss and Meikle Rivers slice deep-cut valleys as they drop down from the Clear and Chinchaga Hills. The central interior of northern Alberta is drained by the Wabiskaw River, and from the opposite side of the Peace many small streams rush southward down the slope of the Caribou Mountains.

The turbid Athabasca, with its source in the Columbia Icefields, carries a load of glacial detritus, much of which is deposited in Jasper and Brulé Lakes, and will eventually fill them up. Passing through its ice-widened gorge around Hinton, the Athabasca enters a broad valley extending from Whitecourt to Smith, and then carves a narrow V-shaped valley for 200 miles to Fort McMurray. On the sandy muskeg-covered plain north of Athabasca town, this valley is invisible until one reaches

Bow River, south of Calgary, is deeply incised into a low-relief till plain. Westward rise the Porcupine Hills, and beyond them the Rocky Mountain foothills.

its very edge. In places the banks are precipitous with sandstone cliffs; in other parts, the black and gray shales have slumped and slid to such an extent that David Thompson, the first white man to traverse this part of the river, in 1799 recorded in his diary: "the Banks are in a ruinous State".

A number of streams join the Athabasca River around Fort Mc-Murray. The largest, entering from the east, is named the "Clearwater" because of the contrast its waters make with the muddy browns and greens of the main river. Farther north, in the delta where the Athabasca works over and deposits its sediment load, the main channels must be checked continually to prevent tugs and barges running aground on the moving sand bars.

Central and southern Alberta are drained mainly by the Saskatchewan system, the major supplier of surface waters to the Canadian prairies. Between seven- and nine-tenths of the water of these rivers, the North Saskatchewan, Red Deer, Bow and South Saskatchewan, originates in the mountains and foothills, and only in spring or in times of particularly heavy rainfall do the plains contribute significantly to river flow. Each of these rivers has a valley in which broad flat or rolling floors alternate with sections sliced narrowly into bedrock. Contrast, for instance, the North Saskatchewan gorge from Devon downstream with the open valley from Edmonton to beyond Fort Saskatchewan, the Bow Valley above and below Bassano, and the broad Red Deer and narrow South Saskatchewan valleys at Empress. The narrow gorges mark post-glacial, ten-thousand-year-old valleys, while the broader stretches indicate where the rivers flow in re-excavated preglacial valleys.

Greenish milky waters, such as those of the North Saskatchewan River west from Nordegg and of the upper parts of the Bow River, indicate that these rivers are fed by melt-waters of the high glaciers. In contrast, the clear waters of the Red Deer, McLeod, Clearwater, James, and other streams tells us that the water supply comes mainly from melting snow or from rain. The clear darker brown of some northern plains streams indicates drainage of organic materials from muskegs, while the muddy browns and greens are most common at times of high water when abundant suspended sediment is present in the waters. Streams draining agricultural land may be black with topsoil during flood periods.

Streamflow

The patterns of flow of Alberta's rivers reflect local water situations fairly closely. The Slave River, receiving all of the huge Peace River and Athabasca River drainage, has by far the largest flow and relatively small annual and seasonal variations. Other rivers drain proportionately much smaller basins and most of their flow is obtained from the mountains and foothills. Rivers and streams that rise within the southern plains are small, they have highly variable flows, and the size of their drainage basins varies greatly from year to year.

Many of the mountain rivers rise in glaciers and snowfields in the main ranges of the Rocky Mountains. The flow from the glaciers is light in spring, heavy in the early and middle summer, and lighter in late summer and autumn. In contrast, that from snowfields tends to be heavy in the spring but by the middle of summer it generally becomes light because only rapidly dwindling remnants of the snowfields remain.

The largest portion of the flow of streams which rise in the front ranges or foothills is derived from melting snow, although summer precipitation is still important. These streams have an earlier peak flow than those rising from glaciers, yields are more variable and by mid-summer in more arid years the river channels are relatively dry. Streams with

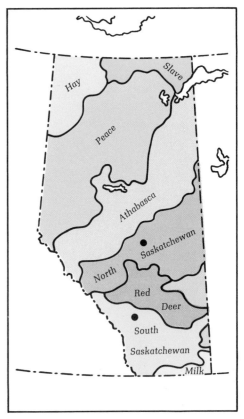

Major drainage basins

Runoff from heavy storms causing soil erosion near Cowley.

85

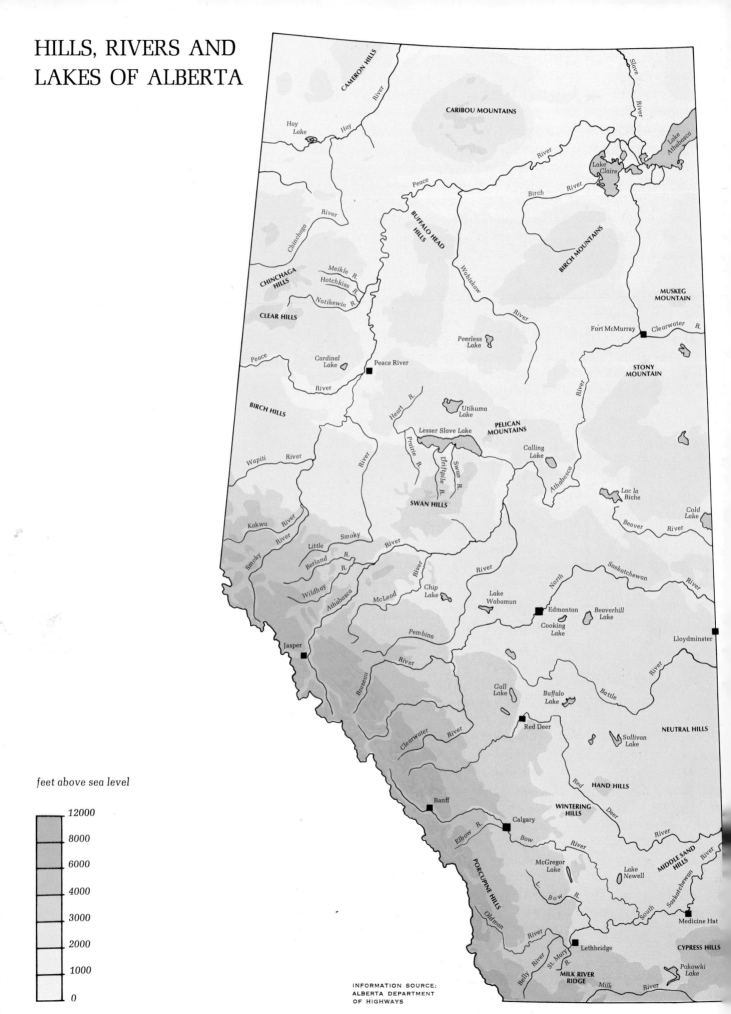

HILLS, RIVERS AND LAKES OF ALBERTA

CAMERON HILLS

CARIBOU MOUNTAINS

Hay Lake

Hay River

Slave River

Lake Athabasca

Peace River

Lake Claire

Birch River

BUFFALO HEAD HILLS

CHINCHAGA HILLS

Chinchaga River

Meikle R.

Hotchkiss R.

Notikewin R.

CLEAR HILLS

BIRCH MOUNTAINS

MUSKEG MOUNTAIN

Wabiskaw

River

Peerless Lake

Fort McMurray

Clearwater R.

Peace River

Cardinal Lake

Peace River

STONY MOUNTAIN

BIRCH HILLS

Wapiti River

River

Heart R.

Utikuma Lake

Lesser Slave Lake

Prairie R.

Driftpile R.

Swan R.

PELICAN MOUNTAINS

Calling Lake

Athabasca

River

SWAN HILLS

Lac la Biche

Cold Lake

Kokwa River

Smoky River

Little Smoky

River

Berland R.

Wildhay R.

Athabasca

McLeod

Chip Lake

Lake Wabamun

River

North Saskatchewan River

River

Beaver River

Jasper

Brazeau

Pembina

River

Edmonton

Beaverhill Lake

Cooking Lake

Lloydminster

Gull Lake

Buffalo Lake

Battle River

NEUTRAL HILLS

Clearwater River

Red Deer

Sullivan Lake

Banff

Red Deer River

HAND HILLS

WINTERING HILLS

Elbow R.

Calgary

Bow

River

MIDDLE SAND HILLS

River

PORCUPINE HILLS

McGregor Lake

Lake Newell

Saskatchewan River

L.

Bow R.

South Saskatchewan

Medicine Hat

Oldman River

Belly River

St. Mary R.

Lethbridge

CYPRESS HILLS

MILK RIVER RIDGE

Milk River

Pakowki Lake

feet above sea level

	12000
	8000
	6000
	4000
	3000
	2000
	1000
	0

INFORMATION SOURCE:
ALBERTA DEPARTMENT
OF HIGHWAYS

their origins in the foothills are much smaller than those rising in the front ranges of the mountains, have greater variation in flow from one year to the next, and have greater tendencies to flood. Most of the flood water is derived from intense rains in late spring or early summer.

In the more humid plains, largely in west-central and northern Alberta, the streams flow strongest in the spring when the snows are melting, but spring and summer rains and the discharge of ground-water through springs and seepages provide some flow at other seasons. Erosion and flooding occur during very heavy rains in spring and summer in some years, particularly where soils have been widely exposed by clearing or cultivation. Flood problems are most acute on streams that have steep gradients in their upper courses and shallow gradients in floodplains and deltas in their middle and lower courses. The Pembina and Paddle Rivers are prime examples of this. Most major streams have deeply cut channels and so flood problems are not extensive, although gully erosion is a major concern in some areas.

In the drier plains, water yields are generally small and flow is concentrated in a brief early period when the snow is melting. Exceptionally heavy rains may result in some addition to flow in spring and summer but most streams dry up in the summer season. Streamflow is extremely variable from one year to the next, and these dry plains cannot be considered to be dependable sources of water. Indeed, most of the dependable flow for the plains region comes from mountain and foothill sources.

Development of Alberta's soils

The kind of soil that develops in any one place is a result of a combination of factors, particularly those of moisture, temperature and biological activity acting on glacial deposits or bedrock over a long period of time. Wherever conditions, such as slope, drainage, climate and vegetation, are the same, similar soils will develop.

Soils are classified by their physical and chemical properties. Over 1,500 individual soils have been described so far in Canada, and these may be grouped together into a few "great soil groups", most of which have representatives in Alberta. Four of these groups – the Brown, Dark Brown, Thin Black, and Black – belong to the Chernozems, the agriculturally important soils of the grassland regions. The largest proportion of Alberta soils, however, has developed under forest cover where leaf litter accumulates on the surface. These are known as the Podzolic soils, to which belong the Dark Gray, Dark Gray Wooded, and Gray Wooded soils of the province. Podzolic soils are characterized by an impoverished leached layer close to the surface, and a deeper layer enriched with clay and organic materials.

Using the major soil groups as a basis, Canada has been divided into a number of major soil zones, which roughly coincide with the major climatic and vegetation regions. Six, or possibly seven of these zones are present in Alberta.

Brown soils are found in the plains of the southeastern corner of the province where the climate is semi-arid and characterized by an average annual precipitation of 11 to 13 inches. Drought, high evaporation, and hot dry winds are frequent. Vegetation is limited to short grass, on a soil about five inches deep and brown in colour. Lack of moisture is the principal limiting factor in the fertility of the area. These soils are also low in nitrogen and phosphorus, but under irrigation or in a wet year will respond to fertilizers supplying these elements. Ranching is the most suitable land use and only the most favourable soil types can be considered arable. Where farming takes place, wheat is the principal crop

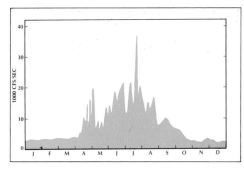

Hydrograph showing flow, in thousands of cubic feet per second, of the North Saskatchewan River at Edmonton.

87

to be grown. Development of irrigation in the zone is assisted by the comparatively long frost-free period.

The Dark Brown soil zone extends in an arc, 40 to 50 miles in width, from south of Lethbridge to the Saskatchewan border beyond Provost. In this zone the precipitation increases to from 13 to 15 inches and, though high evaporation and hot dry winds persist, droughts are less frequent. Grass is still the predominant vegetative cover, but is denser and taller. The soil, a darker brown in colour, has a depth of seven inches. Fertility is still subject to the same limiting factors as in the Brown soil zone, but the moisture deficiency and low level in nitrogen and phos-

THE MAJOR SOIL ZONES OF ALBERTA

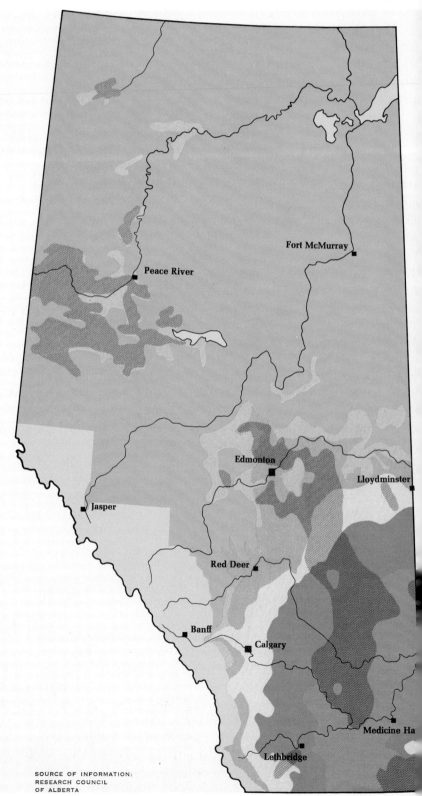

■ brown soils

■ dark brown soils

□ thin black soils

▨ black soils

▨ dark gray and dark gray wooded soils

▨ gray wooded soils

▨ saline soil areas

□ areas not mapped by soil survey

□ lakes

SOURCE OF INFORMATION:
RESEARCH COUNCIL
OF ALBERTA

phorus are slightly less pronounced. Only the better soils may be considered arable, the remainder providing good pasture land.

Extending along the edge of the Dark Brown zone in a second narrower arc, is the area of the Thin Black soil. Again the level of fertility moves slightly but definitely upwards. Precipitation increases to an average of from 14 to 17 inches and droughts occur only occasionally. The soil averages ten inches in depth, of which the upper three to six inches are black, the remainder dark brown. Nitrogen and organic matter are now fairly well supplied but there is a continuing deficiency in phosphorus. A greater relative area may now be considered arable, and most non-arable land provides very good pasture.

The Black soil region, roughly triangular in shape, with its base along the Thin Black arc, its apex at a point some 60 miles northwest of Edmonton, is the most fertile in Alberta. Precipitation averages between 17 and 19 inches and severe droughts are rare. Evaporation is lower than in the southern soil zones and hot winds less frequent. This is the more humid parkland area, where grassland has been partially invaded by woodlands, mainly of deciduous trees. The soil – black to very dark brown in colour, with an average depth of from 12 to 14 inches – contains three to four times as much nitrogen and organic matter as the average Brown or Gray Wooded variety. A high percentage of the zone is arable.

The more humid plains, stretching from the Black zone northward, are largely forested, the cover varying from open woodland to dense and mature coniferous forests. Scattered grasslands occur and soil patterns are irregular. Podzolic soils predominate, although the organic soils of the peat bogs and muskegs are extensive in some northern areas.

Dark Gray and Dark Gray Wooded soils occur in a discontinuous band bordering and within the Black soil zone and in parts of the Peace River region. Average annual precipitation varies from 12 inches in the northern section to about 20 inches in the southern. Evaporation is lower than in the other soil zones. The soil, underneath a thin surface layer of semi-decomposed leaf litter which may be absent in burnt-over areas, is black, gray black, or dark brown to a depth of from ten to 12 inches. These soils are usually not as rich as those of the Black zone. Leaching of the surface horizons has resulted in the loss of some plant nutrients, and nitrogen, phosphorus, and sometimes sulphur may be deficient. A system of mixed farming that includes legumes and grasses in rotation is best suited for this zone.

Apart from areas, mostly mountainous, not yet explored by soil surveyors, the remainder of the province is known to belong in the Gray Wooded zone. The climate is characterized by cooler temperatures, lower evaporation, and a shorter growing season. Average annual precipitation again varies from 12 inches in the north to 20 inches in the south. Vegetation consists of a mixed deciduous and evergreen woodland in which muskegs and sedge bogs frequently occur. Soils in this zone have developed under humid soil conditions. Again semi-decomposed leaf litter may be present at the surface. Beneath is a six- to eight-inch thick, severely leached layer, gray black, brown, or gray brown in colour. Because of leaching, soils in the zone are relatively less fertile, and are usually deficient in nitrogen, phosphorus, organic matter, and sometimes sulphur. Again mixed farming, with legumes, hays, and coarse grains, is the most desirable land use.

These, then, along with the muskegs and saline areas, are the soils developed in Alberta during the one hundred centuries since the disappearance of the ice sheets. On these soils grows the vegetation cover which adds to the variety of the landscape.

M.H.
Parkland zone gray wooded soil near Clover Bar.

C.H.
Huge lateral moraine of rock debris flanking the Athabasca Glacier.

M.H.
End moraine and outwash fan of the Peyto Glacier.

PART II / FLORA AND FAUNA

FLORA AND FAUNA

CLIMATE, TERRAIN AND GEOLOGIC HISTORY affect the types of plant and animal life that dwell in Alberta. On the southern prairie a tendency to aridity nurtures sturdy mid-grasses and a wildlife suited to the environment, although in the extreme southeast the Cypress Hills harbour their own special forms of natural life. In central Alberta, the parkland presents distinctive mosaics of flora and fauna, while from the boreal forest, covering most of the northern half of the province, comes an absorbing story of a vegetative and animal life adapted to its soils and to the rigours of a sub-Arctic climate. Still another and even more intriguing world of nature is to be found in the foothills and the mountains.

To describe the diversity of this flora and fauna, the method followed is to examine separately the particular features of each region. In each chapter emphasis has been placed on the ecology of the area, that is, upon the interrelationships of the plant and animal life with their environment and with each other.

What exists on land is not the whole picture. In the standing and running waters of the province is an aquatic universe of plants, invertebrates and fish — and this world is described in a separate chapter. To a non-specialist, the chain of articles in this division of the book makes clear how little most of us know about the complexities and interrelationships of a natural world that lies just beyond our doorsteps.

Title Picture Part II — Geese over the Bow River, Calgary — by C. Hampson.

C.H.

CHAPTER FIVE

The Prairie World

GRASSLANDS ARE THE HEART-BLOOD of human existence. Where the plough has furrowed them, they fill the granaries of the world. Elsewhere, they are mantled with millions of grazing livestock. Alberta's grasslands are part of the Great Plains which stretch from the Gulf of Mexico into Canada's prairie provinces. The Great Plains are among the largest expanses of the gently rolling grasslands which exist in the interior of all continents except Antarctica. Wherever rainfall is enough to prevent desert but not enough to produce forests, there grasses grow.

Like Caesar's Gaul, grasslands are divided into three types – plains or steppes, prairies and savannahs. Plains or steppes are lands of short grasses, where yearly precipitation varies between 10 and 30 inches and dust storms darken the sky. The soils beneath the grass are poor in quality. The southeastern extremity of Alberta belongs in this category.

Prairies are wide stretches of medium and tall grasses in temperate climates with an annual precipitation of from 20 to 40 inches. If left to themselves, the grasses will reach to a height of five to eight feet, like a forest in miniature, with a root system anchored six feet deep. Beneath these grasses is soil rich in humus. With the southeastern corner of Alberta placed in a separate category, the rest of southern Alberta is not true prairie. In its natural state it produces only medium grasses and its precipitation is less than the low end of the scale for prairie country. It is therefore called mixed prairie.

Where tall grasses thrive amid scattered clumps of trees and high rainfall is interrupted each year by a dry, hot season, savannahs flourish, as in Africa, Australia and South America. In some respects, Alberta's aspen parkland resembles this type of grassland but this parkland is not true savannah.

ROBERT WEBB
ALEXANDER JOHNSTON
J. DEWEY SOPER

Title picture – Prairie in bloom

PLACE NAMES
OF ALBERTA

Fort Fitzgerald

WOOD   BUFFALO

NATIONAL

PARK

Fort
Chipewyan

• High Level

Fort Vermilion   • Red River

• Keg River

Fort MacKay •

• Manning

Fort McMurray •

• Worsley
• Grimshaw
Peace River •   • Pelican Portage
• Fairview

Spirit River •
• Wanham   • Watino   • McLennan
Hythe •
Beaverlodge •
Grande Prairie •   • High Prairie
Slave Lake •   Lac La Biche •
• Valleyview   • Smith
                                                    • Athabasca
• Little Smoky   Cold Lake •
• Swan Hills
Fox Creek •   • Judy Creek   • Fort   Glendon •   • Bonnyville
                   Assiniboine
                                          Smoky Lake •   • St. Paul   • Elk Point
Windfall • Whitecourt Barrhead • • Clyde
              • Westlock   Redwater •   • Bruderheim   • Two Hills   Derwent •
                          Onoway •   St. Albert • Fort   Vegreville •   Vermilion •
• Obed   • Edson   Evansburg •   Saskatchewan • Mannville   Lloydminster •
• Hinton   □ EDMONTON
                      Drayton Valley •   Leduc • Cooking Lake •
Jasper •   • Warburg   • Viking
JASPER   Camrose □   • Killam   • Wainwright
NATIONAL • Cadomin   Battle Lake • Wetaskiwin
PARK   Rimbey •   Ponoka •   Hardisty •
                   • Nordegg   Gilby •   • Bashaw   • Forestburg
                          Rocky Mountain Lacombe •   • Alliance   Provost •
                          House   Joffre •
                   Caroline • Penhold • RED DEER • Stettler Castor •
BANFF   • Delburne   Coronation •   • Consort
NATIONAL   Sundre • Innisfail •   Big Valley •
PARK   • Olds   Trochu •
• Lake Louise   Elkton •   Three Hills • • Morrin   Hanna •   • Youngstown
                Crossfield • Beiseker •   Drumheller •   Cereal •
Banff •   Rockyford •   • Dorothy
Kananaskis •   Strathmore •   • Cessford   Empress •
          □ CALGARY   • Gleichen
Turner Valley •   • Okotoks • Cluny Bassano •   DINOSAUR
          • High River   Brooks •   PROVINCIAL PARK
Nanton •   • Vulcan   Bow City •
     Carmangay •   Bow City   Suffield •
Claresholm •   Vauxhall •
                                          MEDICINE HAT
Blairmore •   Chin • Taber   Bow Island •
  Frank • Fort   LETHBRIDGE   Skiff •
Pincher Creek • Macleod • Raymond   Etzikom •   Manyberries •
     • Waterton • Cardston   • Milk River

94

A.J.

Hay land near Pincher Creek

All grasslands are cousins. Droughts plague them, and the shifts in temperature are savage. Strong winds sweep across them. The plant cover and the animal life peculiar to any one type of grassland are relatively uniform, and the ocean-like expanse allows a wide and easy dispersion of species. In North America it took a long chain of events to bring them into being.

The origin and development of North American grasslands

Some 60 million years ago, by the beginning of the Eocene Epoch of the Tertiary Period, continental uplifts aided in establishing a continental climate in North America. Perhaps, too, the newborn Rocky Mountains were intercepting the moisture-laden winds from the Pacific.

These factors created the first tentative grasslands. For about 20 million years, amid favouring climates, grasses and grass-like plants were sheltered under subtropical forests. In response, grass-eating animals, the distant ancestors of our present-day herbivores, evolved. During the same epoch the number of species of rodents expanded, primates for some inexplicable reason vanished from this continent, and birds and mammals, including the herbivores, became locked in a struggle for supremacy.

With the coming of the next epoch, the Oligocene, North America's inland areas grew cooler and drier. The forests were forced southward. Sod-forming grasses and flowering species evolved in specialized ways. Similarly, the grass-eating mammals adapted themselves to an environment that was uniform, lacking in tree-cover and semi-arid. So did the carnivores or flesh-eaters which preyed on them. Hoofed animals or ungulates of two types, odd-toed and even-toed, including ancestral horses, pigs, deer and camels, began to roam the newly formed grasslands. So did dog and cat types. Rabbits flourished, and beavers, gophers, rats and mice were added to the order of rodents. In the skies and on the ground, a multitude of birds flew and nested.

But it was in the following epoch, the Miocene, as further continental uplift and continued rising of the Rocky Mountains made the climate still cooler and drier, that grasses marched across the land to become the dominant vegetation. Eventually a sea of waving grass stretched for league on league from the highlands of Mexico through the United States to northern Canada, and from the eastern deciduous woodlands to the pine-clad foothills of the Rocky Mountains. In this way, swiftly in terms of geologic time, the vast grasslands of NorthAmerica were created.

Rough fescue grass

95

Blue grama grass

Little bluestem

On their broad expanses both branches of ungulates prospered. The Miocene horse, *Merychippus*, emerged, fully adapted for the plains, with smaller hooves, more graceful proportions, greater intelligence and better sensory organs than its ancestors; with its grinding teeth, the horse was especially adapted for chewing grasses. The progenitors of deer-like animals, camels and pronghorns came into being. Among the carnivores, weasels were diversified into a number of types. Raccoons, skunks and bears ambled across the plains and birds multiplied. By the end of the Miocene Epoch, the Great Plains teemed with a more luxuriant wildlife than ever before or since.

During the following epoch, the Pliocene, there was a continuous cooling, which culminated in the Ice Age of the Pleistocene Epoch. Even though Alberta was not glaciated until the fourth advance of the ice sheet, it shared in the changes of climate on the Great Plains. As the ice advanced, there were the same successive zones of vegetation in front of it as there are today – Arctic tundra, coniferous forest, mixed willow and aspen parkland, and finally grassland – yet these zones were compressed and thrust southward. During the interglacial periods, when the ice retreated, the zones pressed north again. Hence plant life migrated to and fro. So did the animals.

The result for both plants and animals was a vast intermingling of species and an intense evolution. Some species flourished while others could not adapt to the changes and vanished. In the animal world, giganticism was the vogue and massive bears, wolves and tigers snarled defiance at immigrants from Siberia, huge mastodons and woolly mammoths. Bison and even beavers grew to sizes unknown today.

When the disappearance of the ice began about 12,000 years ago, for some unknown reason most of the beasts that had developed giganticism, along with mastodons and mammoths, vanished from prehistory. Horses and camels had already disappeared from North America. Bison, deer and late-comers from Siberia – moose and elk – dominated the grasslands, and upon them leapt the Great Plains wolves and the Great Plains grizzlies. Comparatively modern times had begun.

It is an axiom in evolution that the last important change in environment determines much of the ensuing character of plant and animal life in a country, as well as the physical shape of its landforms. Just as glaciation and deglaciation modified the physical design inherited by Alberta from the Tertiary Period, so shifts in postglacial climate left their mark on the migrations and the evolution of plant and animal life initiated by the advance and retreat of the ice sheet.

At first the postglacial climate of the grasslands was warm and dry. Then, excluding minor variations, it shifted to cool-moist; next, between 8,000 and 4,000 years ago, to a still warmer and drier phase, known as the Altithermal; and, presently, back to its cool-moist stage. These climatic variations – and in particular the Altithermal phase – have stamped an impress on Alberta's plant and animal life of today. The Peace River prairie, for example, is a relict of a time when grassland reached unbroken from the south to far north of its present frontier. Rough fescue, the dominant natural vegetation of bunchgrass prairie, illustrates how plant life migrated to and fro.

Rough fescue sprouted first in the northwest. During the last advance of the ice, it was pushed far to the south. Then, as the weather grew warmer and drier, it crept eastward over a wide range, maintaining its gains during the first cool-moist period. In the Altithermal it raided deep into northern Canada. Elsewhere in North America today, rough fescue

(a)

C.H.

(a) Garter snakes
(b) Richardson's ground squirrel
(c) Thirteen-lined ground squirrel
(d) Porcupine

(c)

C.H.

(b)

.H.

(d)

C.H.

Wheat grass

Spear grass

inhabits a wide territory. But in Alberta, except for its beleaguered outpost in the Peace River area, rough fescue has retreated to the aspen parkland.

Similar migrations brought to the province blue grama grass from the Mexican highlands, bluestem grass, often found in sandy soils, from far to the south and east in the Kansas-Missouri region, and wheat grasses, needle grasses and June grass from the Washington-Oregon area. Vegetation species not only evolve like animal species but migrate back and forth. Thus, in semi-arid southeastern Alberta, hoary sage and buckbrush thrive. Among them, as relics of the Altithermal, dwell the so-called horned toad, really a lizard, and, possibly, the kangaroo rat.

While plant and animal life had been developing and migrating, after primates had been absent for some 60 million years, the most adaptable primate, man, appeared on the American scene. In the millennia before the arrival of the Europeans, he did little to disturb the animal and plant life of the grasslands. But after the white man settled, man's economic needs radically changed the countryside.

Although such animal species as the bison and the Great Plains grizzly had to yield to the new pressures, the grasses, to survive heavy grazing – by bison in particular – had already developed a tough resistance. At the base of the leaf there is a growth zone, known as the apical meristem. A cow or horse can bite off most of the leaf above the apical meristem, and the leaf grows again. Even if the apical meristem and part of the stem is cropped, the grass regrows from buds at the base of the stem. Grasses can only be killed through grazing when animals continually crop the leaves, the food-manufacturing part of the grass, until the plant is forced to grow itself to death through the exhaustion of its root food. Hence comes the axiom of modern grassland management: if you keep down the shoot, you will kill the root. Grasslands, given a chance survive.

Alberta's prairie

Alberta's true grassland country of some 30 million acres stretches from the southern edge of the parkland, at about the latitude of Olds, to the international boundary and from the foothills to the Saskatchewan boundary. In the southeast of this area, covering about 12 million acres are the Shortgrass Plains where sagebrush, buckbrush and other semi-arid plants, together with the white-gleaming, alkaline shores of lakes add a desert touch to the landscape. Arching out from these Plains to the north, west and south, as if shrinking from droughts and duststorms are some 18 million acres of what is often termed "mixed prairie". Much of all this region is now, of course, either ranchland or under cultivation But, throughout the whole expanse, few trees grow, except for planted windbreaks and those species which find a home on the bottom lands along some of the streams and in coulees.

Except for the Cypress Hills and for areas of human occupancy, to the casual observer the impression is of a vast and monotonous land lying vacant under a wide-reaching sky. To the perceptive mind there is history and infinite variety. Everywhere are the marks left by the massive advance of the ice and its reluctant retreat. There are sands and gravels and moraines, uplifted above the plain as hills or reduced to gently rolling knobs and depressions. Glacial lakes, dried up or left as mere remnants of themselves, as at Many Islands Lake, may be recognized in fine textured lacustrine plains. Ridges of sand dunes, sometimes miles in extent, mark where wide waters once gleamed in the sun, as at Pakowki Lake or near Hilda and Schuler. Similarly, many postglacial river channels, modified by erosion to rounded and broad valleys, curve through level or undulating prairie. Over much of the landscape fine wind-blown deposits, called loess, have softened the outlines.

Features like these give variety to the terrain, and so do the rivers. The Milk River flows through the extreme southern part of the province before it turns south into the United States to lose itself in the Missouri River. The Bow and Oldman Rivers meander east and southeast through deep-cut valleys to join the northeastward-travelling South Saskatchewan River. Among the other streams, the most spectacular is the Red Deer River which gouges its way through fine clays before it, too, joins the South Saskatchewan River, just beyond the Saskatchewan border. Fluted pinnacles and gullies mark its course, particularly in the Badlands, the hunting ground for the collectors of fossils of prehistoric oysters, turtles and dinosaurs. In other river reaches, there are steep-walled canyons or broad valleys into which run deep coulees and ravines that often furrow backward for miles. If one adds trees along valley bottoms and the changing lights and shadows under a sky that seems to stretch to infinity, the varying aspects of the prairie are kaleidoscopic.

The prairie climate

The prairie is a land of violent extremes. At Medicine Hat, for example, meteorological records show a range in temperature from 51 degrees below zero in January to 108 degrees in July, and in annual precipitation from six inches in 1910 to 28 inches in 1927. The average annual precipitation in the brown soil of the Shortgrass Plains is from 11 to 14 inches, with a frost-free period of from 100 to 140 days, while in the dark brown soil zone the limits are from 14 to 18 inches, but frost-free days are reduced to between 80 and 100. Heat, drought, frost and snow plague the prairie.

Although the ground is frozen for most of each winter and often covered with snow, the famed Chinook winds can brush away the snow

June grass

Brilliant autumn colours in coulee near Trochu.

.H.

99

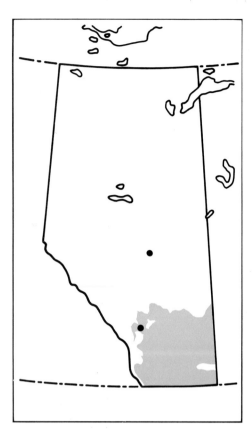

Outline map of prairie zone

Prairie esker near Balzac.

C.H.

as if by magic and send temperatures soaring. While the Chinooks mean better survival chances for some animals, such as the pronghorn, if the mercury then drops rapidly to zero or below, exposed plants may be killed.

Drought hampers vegetation, but prairie cover often survives by effective use of scanty rainfall. Forbs—broad-leaved annuals—intermingled with dense grasses break the impact of raindrops, prevent puddling of the soil surface and assure the maximum absorption and use of water. If enough spring rainfall comes, early growing and cool-season species such as spear grass, produce seed in profusion. If rainfall is later in the summer, sickle-shaped heads of blue grama grass, a late-growing and warm season type, will nod across the prairie. If rains fail to come, prairie grasses may remain dormant. Thus, if the rainfall stops in early summer, the grasses aestivate or, as it were, sleep through the summer to avoid the effects of drought. Certain other species, especially annuals, defeat drought by compressing their life cycle and survive as seeds. In these different ways grasses and forbs defy drought.

All species produce less top growth in dry years but grow well when the welcome moisture returns. Experiments at the Manyberries Experimental Range Station in the southeast of the province demonstrate this variation dramatically. Here the lowest yield of forage from native prairie in 1961, a dry year, was 84 pounds per acre; the highest, in the wet season of 1942, 825 pounds per acre. The long-term average yield in the area is 332 pounds per acre. Prairie cover huddles into itself in dry weather, but expands with open arms when the rains come.

Climax cover

Before settlement by Europeans wide-ranging fires, crackling unhindered across the prairie, terrorized beast and man and destroyed woodland, thus extending the grasslands. Today, with prairie fires controlled, the aspen parkland is moving southward.

Besides climate and fire, grazing has helped maintain the Shortgrass Plains of the southeast. Here the dominant grass is the Mexico-derived, short-growing, curly blue grama. Yet given the opportunity, the taller spear and wheat grasses grow just as well; so it is now recognized that the Shortgrass Plains have been kept in short grasses, or in what is known as disclimax cover, by grazing, at first by bison, and now by cattle.

Disclimax is a pulling away from climax cover. Climax cover means the kind of grass and plant community which would last indefinitely in an area, such as the Shortgrass Plains, if the climate and the soils did not

Dust storm over Pearce, April, 1942.

C.G.

change, and if men or animals, wild or domestic, did not interfere.

Climax cover, then, is the best native cover for an area in terms of drought, rainfall and resistance to erosion. If any disturbance, such as mankind's activities or a variation in climate, lasts long enough, bare ground will replace grass. Climax cover is the hub of nature's wheel; the rim is bare ground. If bare ground is left alone, nature will finally put back a climax cover, that is, the kind of vegetation that was there in the first place.

Prairie soils and grasses

Just as climate finally determines the types of vegetation on the prairie, so it helps determine the kinds of soils beneath that vegetation. A semi-arid climate aided in developing the brown soils of the Shortgrass Plains where cactus, low-growing fringe sage and hoary sage mingle with the blue grama grassland. Brown soil mixtures reveal themselves in growths of rose plants, sedges and a number of forbs.

A greater yearly precipitation helped form the dark brown and shallow black soils of the mixed prairie. Here, wherever moisture is more abundant, medium grasses are dominant and the sod is thick; but in drier areas short grasses grow among widely spaced middle grasses. There are often two layers of grass: the first is three to four inches high and consists of blue grama grass, June grass and Sandberg's blue grass; the second is composed of spear and wheat grasses. Any of these grasses can dominate in a limited area in response to soil types and growing conditions.

Prairie fire at night near Medicine Hat

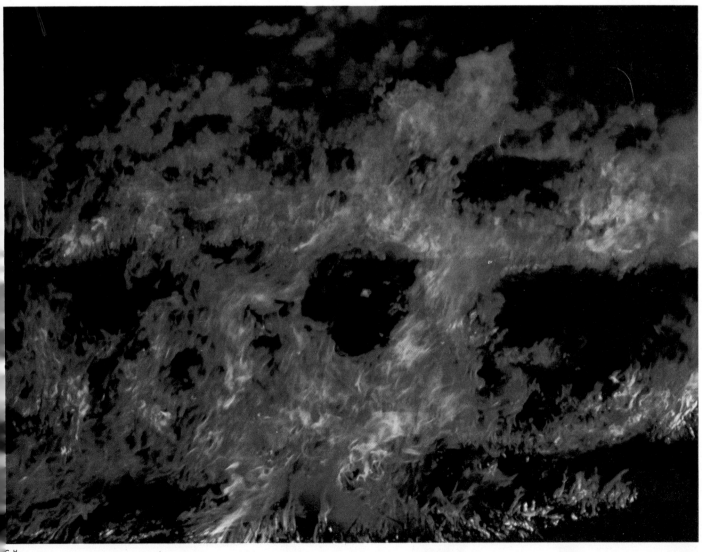

C.H.

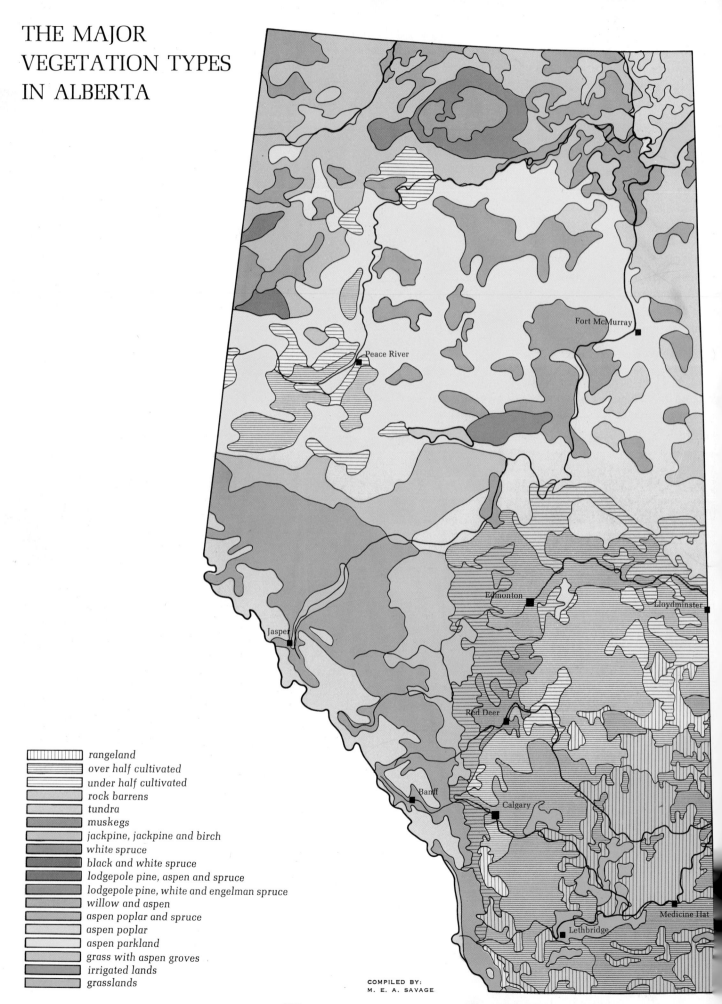

THE MAJOR VEGETATION TYPES IN ALBERTA

Fort McMurray

Peace River

Edmonton

Lloydminster

Jasper

Red Deer

Banff

Calgary

Medicine Hat

Lethbridge

Legend:
- rangeland
- over half cultivated
- under half cultivated
- rock barrens
- tundra
- muskegs
- jackpine, jackpine and birch
- white spruce
- black and white spruce
- lodgepole pine, aspen and spruce
- lodgepole pine, white and engelman spruce
- willow and aspen
- aspen poplar and spruce
- aspen poplar
- aspen parkland
- grass with aspen groves
- irrigated lands
- grasslands

COMPILED BY:
M. E. A. SAVAGE

For those interested in vegetation, the mixed prairie and the Short-grass Plains offer five more or less stable combinations of grasses as climax cover, with a sixth on eroded areas as a subclimax. The spear grass and blue grama marriage, for example, is the most extensive. It flourishes on medium-textured soils upon glacial till deposits in the drier areas of the dark brown soil zone and the wetter parts of the brown soils. Dark brown soils, with more moisture, welcome the spear grass-wheat grasses grouping. Wheat grasses and June grass co-exist successfully on clay lacustrine plains. On the Shortgrass Plains, on clay loam saline soils, known as solonetzic soils, and on eroded patches, called burnouts, in the arid southeast, the blue grama-wheat grasses association finds a footing. There are also mat-forming species, including everlasting and little club moss, lichens and true mosses. Among non-grass plants are shrubs with woody stems branching from ground level, which furnish food for wild animals during drought and heavy snow cover.

Overgrazing of the mixed prairie begins when, year after year, more than one-half of the annual growth is bitten off. One result is that un-grazed weedy plants shoulder out middle grasses until they are replaced by blue grama grass and such plants as broomweed, crocus, moss phlox and hoary sage. To the discerning eye the vegetation of any area reveals not only the climate and soils which created it, but also the use or misuse man has made of the natural cover. The plant species of the prairie are in their own way as specialized as the animals that roam the plains and the birds that nest upon them or wing through the air.

The extinction and near-extinction of species

Before the white man entered Alberta plants and animals on its grass-land had reached a sort of dynamic equilibrium. There was change, but it was a long-term variation based on built-in checks and balances. Herbivores, dependent for their welfare upon various stages of grass succession, were utilized and in a way controlled by carnivores. These in turn varied numerically according to the available number of herbivores.

Today, still not a century since the onset of agricultural settlement, every prairie community of plant and animal life has felt the impact of the white man. Just as vegetation has experienced the plough and the irrigation ditch – at times to its benefit, but often to its harm – so wildlife has been affected by the spread of human occupancy. New species have been introduced and some native species have expanded in numbers and range, while other species have been extinguished or forced to migrate.

Until the fur trader and the huntsman came, the bison, an undulating carpet of shaggy brown, blanketed the grasslands on both sides of the international boundary and ranged north into the aspen parkland. At first the fur traders made little impact on their multitudes. Then, with settlement along Manitoba's Red River, great annual hunts for pelts and the making of pemmican were organized. As early as 1859, the Stoney Indians told Dr. James Hector, the geologist of the Palliser expedition, that "the buffalo could not be depended upon as before".

Since the bison knew no frontier, the cataclysmic disaster for them was the American migration into the Great Plains, a migration which in the late 1860s spilled over into Canada to fur-trading centres such as Fort Whoop-Up. In the United States farmers destroyed bison when they invaded their grazing lands; sportsmen came out to shoot "buffalo"; and to add to the destruction, a market was created in the United States for "buffalo" hides for leather belting, for "buffalo" robes and coats, such as our policemen still wear, and for salted "buffalo" tongues.

The slaughter was for profit and sport. The Americans sold repeating rifles to the Indians and joined with them in a gargantuan massacre. For

Sage brush flats

about a quarter of a century some 100,000 bison hides were floated down the Missouri River annually, while the meat, except for the tongues, was left stinking on the plains. Within a few short years the seemingly inexhaustible herds had practically vanished. In Canada, in 1879, the Blackfoot Indians recorded in their winter count: *"Itsistsitsis awenimiopi"* – when first no more buffalo. South of the border, in the region between the Missouri and the Judith Rivers, the last herd was imprisoned for the final kill. In 1883, 150,000 robes were sold in St. Louis. The next year there were only 300 robes, and in 1888 the United States Game Report announced that only six "buffalo" were left.

The story has a hopeful ending. Although bison no longer thunder over the grasslands, careful conservation maintains a herd in Elk Island Park near Edmonton, and a much larger herd, mingled with wood bison – some 12,000 in all – in Wood Buffalo National Park in northern Alberta.

The graceful pronghorns, which today range Alberta's Shortgrass Plains, almost shared the fate of the bison. Pronghorns are not antelope but belong to a unique American family with but one species. They were also uniquely fitted for co-existence with the bison. The bison's principal food is grass, while pronghorns munch such broad-leaved perennials as cacti, rose and sage, but rarely grass.

Pronghorns are also superbly specialized for life in a wide and open countryside which is subject to extremes of heat and cold. Their telescopic eyesight spots movement a mile away. Hollow hairs insulate them against the cold. An open-mouthed panting system of heat dissipation makes endurable hot summer days on the prairie and, combined with an oversized windpipe, makes possible tremendous and continuous outbursts of energy. When startled, their slender, well muscled limbs carry them in fifteen-foot leaps at speeds of up to sixty miles an hour. To watch pronghorns dash under a two-strand, barbed-wire fence without any perceptible break in stride is to marvel at their grace and adaptability.

As if these attributes were not enough, pronghorns are blessed with a silent alarm device. Pronghorns sport a large patch of white on their rumps. When alerted, each pronghorn erects the hairs of its white patch to semaphore danger to its comrades. At one instant a herd may be feeding peacefully; in the next the landscape is dotted with brilliant white flashes dancing swiftly up the nearest slope to vanish over its crest.

All these sophisticated refinements for prairie life do not protect pronghorns against long-enduring, deep-crusted snow. For some reason

Pronghorn fawn

C.H.

(a)

C.H.

PRAIRIE FLOWERS

(a) **Prickly pear cactus**
(b) **Pincushion cactus**
(c) **Narrow-leaved stonecrop**
(d) **Scarlet mallow**
(e) **Sand dock**
(f) **Prairie purple clover**

(d)

W.J.H.

(b)

R.N.S.

(e)

C.H.

(c)

I.R.H.

(f)

M.H.

105

White-tailed deer

C.H.

they feed by sight and will not paw through the snow to invisible forage. Instead they must migrate to a range where plants or browse are in sight. In the winter of 1964-65 some herds, failing to find food, starved to death.

The near destruction of the pronghorns began when the bison vanished and the Indians turned to them and other animals for food. In addition, ranching and settlement reduced their range; winter conditions and hunting, their numbers. By 1890 the herds were shrinking and the severe winter of 1906-07 reduced them to fewer than 2,000, ranging near Brooks and Nemiskam. By 1915 the pronghorns faced extinction. At this crisis the Federal Government set up Nemiskam National Park with a nucleus of 42 pronghorns. By 1947 the battle for their preservation was won and the park was abolished. Today between 15,000 and 20,000 pronghorns range freely over southern Alberta, and the control of hunting through permits ensures their survival.

Although the pronghorn and bison escaped extinction, the Great Plains grizzly has joined the host of vanished animals. The Great Plains wolf, though more tenacious, disappeared before 1920, and along with it went the charming kit fox. It is possible, too, that, although environmental factors were involved, ranching, settlement and hunting were chiefly

106

responsible for the demise of elk herds on the plains, and the near-extinction of mule and white-tailed deer during the period from 1875 to 1900. Moose and black bears disappeared from the prairies around 1900. Among birds, the magnificent whooping crane and the beautiful trumpeter swan nest no more on the prairie. Hunting in early days and settlement, then, have destroyed or forced into migration some of the former inhabitants of the grasslands. Those that remain have had to adjust to human occupancy. Even so, the prairie boasts a surprising variety of living things.

Prairie animals

Much of the prairie's wildlife is shared with the rest of Alberta. Yet among the mammals, some, like the beaver or the pallid vole, display a pale colouration as an adaptation to the arid or semi-arid landscape of the south. A number of species, too, such as the prairie rattlesnake or the sage grouse, are found nowhere else in the province. Still other species select the habitat which suits them, whether it be wetlands or semi-desert plain or the Badlands, and sometimes vary their dwelling-place to suit the seasons. Prairie rattlesnakes infest the arid southeast. In winter, together with bull snakes and garter snakes, they huddle in holes and crevices in the clay hills of the Badlands. Besides snakes, the Badlands host both summer and winter visitors. Here in summer, keen-eyed prairie falcons stoop, and ferruginous rough-legged hawks soar on broad wings, searching for prey. The golden eagle, every line and pose an expression of untamed freedom, perches on pinnacles and nests on cliffs and hillsides or along water courses.

Prairie falcon   C. H.

In this same area, in winter, mule deer and pronghorns often shelter, browsing along water courses and among sandhills and in the Badlands on saskatoon and rose bushes and on big sage and juniper. White-tailed deer feed along water reaches on dense thickets of thorn-apple, willow, buffalo-berry, box elder and cottonwoods. All three species spill out over the plains when summer comes.

In the extreme southeast of the province, among the sagebrush and the gleaming white stretches of alkali, dwells the sage grouse, a year-round inhabitant with a colouration adapted to its surroundings. This bird is never numerous on the Alberta plains, since it is dependent on dense stands of sagebrush for its existence. The sharp-tailed grouse, however, can tolerate other types of vegetation, and so is more numerous and widespread. But this grouse does need a certain amount of shrub or tree cover to survive. Consequently it is most often found in sandhill regions, along sparsely treed water courses, and on mixed prairie that grows extensive stands of snowberry, rose, small clumps of aspen and silverberry.

Horned "toad"—in actuality a lizard   C. H.

In the southeast corner dwells a unique lizard, often called the horned toad, together with the grasshopper mouse, the Maximilian pocket mouse, and Anderson's pocket gopher, paler in colour than its cousins elsewhere. Gophers, because of the mounds of earth they leave, are often mistaken for moles, although moles are not found in Alberta. There is a possibility that another inhabitant of the arid southeast may be the kangaroo rat, that curious rodent which, like a kangaroo, jumps on long hind legs and can live for extended periods of time without water.

Elsewhere on the grasslands white-footed and deer mice roam, and so do meadow voles. Voles, which are sometimes mistaken for mice, are chunky, short-legged little animals with short tails and rounded heads. Whereas voles usually travel in runways between their various retreats and feeding places, the comparatively long-legged, long-tailed and pointed-faced mice scamper about at random.

107

Barred bobcat

Mouse

Vole

R.MC.

Of the other voles found in the south, the red-backed vole, with its distinctive red dorsal stripe, is paler in colour than its relatives to the north and west. The most numerous vole is the Badland's vole, often called the bean mouse. Early explorers told of it storing wild beans, hog peanuts, tubers of wild sunflower, and bulbs of Cree turnips in little cellars about six inches below ground and holding as much as several pints. In early autumn the Indians used to rob these storerooms.

Besides the Missouri beaver, other rodents on the prairie include the muskrat and the California porcupine. Everywhere, too, is the droll buff-yellow clown of the prairie, Richardson's ground squirrel, usually, but erroneously, called a gopher. Anyone who has travelled the prairies has heard its piping whistle and seen it standing on its hind legs, as if motivated by an insatiable curiosity.

Families of Richardson's ground squirrels live in loosely associated colonies of underground homes, in which they hibernate during the winter. Their numbers are greater wherever there are light, sandy soils and whenever drought or over-grazing gives them more favourable conditions. They form a large part of the summer diet of coyotes, badgers, golden eagles and large, broad-winged hawks. Thus Richardson's ground squirrel is an important inhabitant, ecologically, of the prairies.

Only one other squirrel, the pale striped ground squirrel, is found in the south. Though rare and shy, its bubbling trills sometimes betray it. Its burrows, hidden in rank grass and shrubbery, are hard to find, because in many instances no mound of excavated earth is left at the den opening.

Many rodents, like the Richardson's ground squirrel, hibernate in the winter. The smaller types, too, are prey for birds or flesh-eaters.

In today's world the lynx and the Rocky Mountain cougar sometimes visit the prairies, the lynx often in large numbers for short periods of a year or two, as from 1962 to 1965. The barred bobcat still spits and snarls in dry, rocky and Badlands' habitats, but has recently extended its range

108

the pale, big-eared bat and Say masked bat, are habitual summer residents of southern Alberta, and the little brown bat may be their companion. Two other species, the red bat and hoary bat, sometimes pass through on migrations. During the day these tiny furred mammals with parchment wings and needle-sharp teeth roost in clusters or singly in hollow trees, rock crevices, abandoned buildings or elsewhere. Late at night, looking like flying mice, they swoop out for insects, avoiding obstacles by a built-in sonar system. Some Alberta bats hibernate in winter but most seek warmer weather in the far south.

Scarcely anyone can travel the prairies without seeing the white-tailed prairie hare, erroneously called the jack rabbit, which has been clocked at speeds up to 35 miles an hour. Hares are larger than rabbits and turn white in winter, whereas rabbits remain in dark fur throughout the year. Young hares are active at birth, but rabbits are born naked, with eyes closed, in underground burrows. The only true rabbit on the prairies is the Black Hills cottontail. At first limited to the Cypress Hills, and to creek and river bottom lands in southeastern Alberta, its bobbing powder-puff of a tail can now be seen as far north as Steveville and Delburne.

The mammals of the prairies, then, are reasonably numerous and varied. Of amphibians, which in ancient geologic time flourished in what was to be southern Alberta, only three species exist today – one type of toad, one kind of frog and the tiger salamander. But the grasslands abound in insects. In wet years, mosquitoes are a pest. In periods of drought, as in the 1930's, grasshoppers devastate vegetation. In all seasons myriads of insects are food for many birds, mammals and amphibians.

Prairie birds

Amphibians and prairie mammals are, except for bats and occasional immigrants, tied to the land. Birds, with the freedom of the skies as nature's gift, are usually spring or summer visitors, like the golden eagle, or migrants using the plains as staging areas.

Each spring brings to the grasslands flocks of insect – or seed-eating birds, most of them belonging to the sparrow family. Many species are restricted to the shortgrass area in southeast Alberta but some range over the mixed prairie. Almost overnight, after the silent snows of winter, the land is filled with a host of brightly singing, inconspicuously coloured bundles of energy. Horned larks, McCown's and chestnut-collared longspurs, lark buntings, vesper sparrows and meadow larks, all carol their songs. On and along every pond and pothole, ducks and shorebirds wade, swim and nest. If we look up, we see the pintail duck in its courting flight, a series of aerial acrobatics culminating in a screaming dive from as high as a thousand feet to ground level.

If we gaze at the shorebirds, among the long-billed curlews, marbled godwits, upland plover and western willets, we are likely to pick out the colourful avocet, a bird that favours the margins of alkaline sloughs. Standing 15 inches high on slender, sky-blue legs, its contrasting jet-black and snow-white plumage set off by a rich reddish-chestnut neck and head, the avocet is one of the most striking of the shorebirds. When it feeds, it runs forward in the water, sweeping its head from side to side to scoop up aquatic life with its upcurved beak of polished ebony. Avocets often nest in groups along the shore, placing large blotched eggs in ill-constructed nests of coarse grass and reeds. Two females will frequently lay eggs in the same nest and share incubation. Bold and aggressive, the avocets accompany their flashing flight with yelping screams, as if defiant of the world.

Cottontail rabbit

Tiger salamander

Long-billed curlew

Marbled godwit

Marshes and lakes, more permanent than potholes, are the summer homes of gulls, red-winged and yellow-headed blackbirds, rails, coots, diving ducks, marsh wrens and the continent-famed Canada geese. Here, too, a few colonies of pelicans raise their young, while in spring and autumn clouds of Canada geese, white-fronted geese, snow geese, Ross's geese, whistling swans and sandhill cranes drop down on their way to and from their nesting grounds in the North to cover the waters and shorelines.

The prairie, then, is not an empty land. Its plants and wildlife are not as teeming or as exotic as the lush growth, the brightly plumaged birds and multifarious animals of the tropics. But, everywhere, if one looks and understands, its sturdy species suit the environment.

The preservation of the prairies

Apart from the fur traders and the North-West Mounted Police, who rode into southern Alberta in 1874, the first settlers on the province's prairies were ranchers. They developed ranches, first along the bunchgrass areas of the foothills, and then on the plains, believing that cattle could thrive where bison had fed. But then in 1885, when the Canadian Pacific Railway thrust its shining rails through to the British Columbia coast, homesteaders debouched onto the grasslands to invade the ranges the ranchers had thought would be theirs.

Both ranchers and farmers were deluded by abnormally wet years in the late 1870's and early 1880's which produced tall and dense grasses on the prairie never before seen, and likely never to be seen again. Even arid stretches in the Shortgrass Plains pushed up vegetation resembling healthy stands of mid-grasses. Over the whole area there were no longer millions of bison to graze the grasses. This period of abnormal growth and non-use of the grasses caused ranchers to extend their ranges, and led settlers to plough land which should never have been cultivated.

This same period of wet years, non-use and heavy growth may have played an important rôle in the history of the long-grass grouse known as the prairie chicken. The prairie chicken was not found in Alberta before 1880. No reference, for instance, is made to the prairie chicken by the early explorers, naturalists and fur traders who visited the province. Yet by 1890 it was a regular Alberta resident, and by 1920 its sudden, darting flight along roadsides or in wheatfields or amid the grass was seen everywhere. For its habitat this bird needs large tracts of tall or at least midgrass prairies in good condition, along with a minimum acreage of cereal grains for autumn and winter food. It cannot, however, live successfully amid short grasses or when there is drought, overgrazing or intensive agriculture. The period from 1900 to 1920 met its ecological requirements, and so it invaded Alberta and prospered temporarily. It has now disappeared from this province because of drought, overstocked ranges and the extension of cultivation. Any attempt to reintroduce the prairie chicken into Alberta, unless the environment changes, would probably be a failure.

Somewhat the same history applies to the first ranchers and farmers in some parts of southern Alberta. Although ranches still exist, the doom of the early cattlemen was spelled out by drought, falling prices and the competition of homesteaders. The final blow was the severe winter of 1906-07, when shortage of feed and very low temperatures destroyed thousands of cattle. The farmers lasted longer, but the drought of the thirties was a scarcely survived disaster. Many farms were abandoned. Gradually, out of the debris, was evolved the tillage of today. Shallow cultivation with blade implements on a stubble-covered surface has replaced the deep bite of the plough. Strip-farming, contour tillage, a grain-summerfallow rotation to conserve moisture, and larger holdings now maintain agriculture. Commercial fertilizers enrich the soil, and field and farmstead shelter-belts of trees dot the once open prairie. Irrigation, especially in the three-million-acre cultivated zone of brown soils, makes possible specialized crops such as sugar-beets. In farming in the south, there has been a quiet revolution.

The impact of settlement on plant, animal, bird and insect life continues. Natural plant cover has been, and will be, either eradicated or

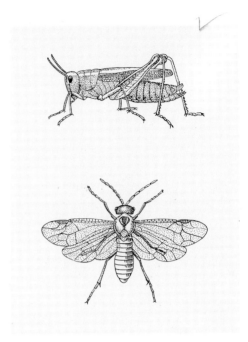

Migratory grasshopper
Wheat-stem sawfly

Hungarian partridge

H.

113

Female ring-necked pheasant

C. H

disturbed. Insect explosions, such as those of the wheat stem sawfly grasshoppers and the beet webworm, have been combatted by a deluge of poisonous chemicals. Only recently have the possible harmful effects of this deluge on fish and wildlife been considered.

More dramatic has been the impact of settlement on wildlife. In addi tion to reducing or changing the environment for animals and birds, man either accidentally or purposefully, has introduced new species. Star lings, pigeons and sparrows, imported from Europe, often crowd ou native birds. House mice and Norway rats are pests which came of thei own accord, although the Provincial Government has so far, in general maintained the frontier against the rats. Other pests from abroad, such as the face fly and the potato beetle, are harder to eradicate.

Some comparatively recent importations, however, have blended wel into the natural wildlife of southern Alberta. The Hungarian partridge and the ring-necked pheasant were both introduced around 1909. The first of these found a suitable habitat in grain fields abutting on grassland and weedy headlands. It spread throughout the prairies and reached it peak number in the 1930's. The pheasant achieved its greatest numbers i the 1940's, although in many regions its peak occurrence was in the earl 1960's. This bird thrives best in irrigation districts, while the Hungaria partridge prospers in dryland regions. Thus the two species fill slightl different ecological niches, neither of which existed in pre-settlemen days. There is some overlap of the two, however, and probably a certai degree of competition for space and food. Initially, also, there was som displacement of sharp-tailed grouse. But these two imports are beautifu birds and an annual lure for thousands of resident and non-residen hunters. Each year over half a million are shot, and hunters spend mil lions of dollars in the pursuit of them. Because of these imports, an because of wise conservation measures, more upland game birds exist o the prairies today than 100 years ago. This fact represents an economi as well as an aesthetic improvement.

Two other birds have settled of their own accord in the province One, the night heron, first appeared in the south about 1950, but now it long legs and flapping flight are seen as far north as Edmonton. The othe the cattle egret, is a snow-white, medium-sized bird which seems to hav appeared recently in the province. The egret was first seen in 1964 near Iron Springs, and a second sighting was made in 1965 near Strathmore. It is too soon to know whether this attractive newcomer will establish itself in Alberta. If it does, it will be a welcome immigrant.

Changes in agriculture, along with the 40-year trend to warmer weather on the prairies, particularly in winter, seem also to have contributed to the increase and spread of some species of native wildlife. The badger, for example, which had become rare in southern Alberta, has responded to protection and to the rise in numbers of one of its principal sources of food, Richardson's ground squirrel. Another predator, the red fox, during the last 15 years has established itself firmly in the southernmost sections of the plains. Prairie hares, too, are reaching greater numbers because of partial assistance from agricultural products for food. Similarly, cottontail rabbits have now been found in older, well-established irrigation districts, a new habitat for them.

One of the most striking responses to game protection, good management practices, climatic changes and shifts in the use of land has been that of mule and white-tailed deer. Although close to extinction on the prairies by about 1900, they have now increased greatly and, during the last 40 years, have invaded new ranges. Today they exist at capacity in all areas open to them, and are extremely important as game animals. In 1963, the last year for which figures are available, 15,000 resident sportsmen hunted on the prairie from Red Deer south, and killed approximately 3,000 deer. Once again careful conservation policies, which give due consideration to the needs of agriculture and ranching, have led to the preservation and increase of two important big game animals.

A number of other birds and animals have found settlement and a changed environment to their liking. Red-winged, yellow-headed and Brewer's blackbirds now nest in thousands around water impoundments, spill areas, canals and in coniferous shelter-belts in the irrigated areas. Bronzed grackles, magpies, barn and cliff swallows, martins, Canada geese, coyotes, weasels, skunks and a host of small birds and mammals have likewise found habitat niches in both irrigated and dryland farming areas. Settlement today has two sides to its coin, one harmful to wildlife, the other beneficial.

In the future of the prairie there is a two-fold challenge. As human populations explode, crop efficiency is a necessity that brooks no retardation. But wildlife, too, must be considered, not only to control pests or to add to human enjoyment, but above all to preserve the species.

This, then, is the prairie world: a land of bitter extremes in climate, but one of infinite natural variety, and fortunate in its sturdy and surprisingly diversified plant and animal life. Without the vast stretches of grasslands, Alberta would lack one of its most fascinating features.

N.

CHAPTER SIX

The Cypress Hills

**CHARLES D. BIRD
IAN A. R. HALLADAY**

N THE SOUTHEASTERN CORNER of Alberta, 30 miles north of the international boundary, the treeless plain is interrupted by the intriuing Cypress Hills which straddle the Alberta-Saskatchewan border.

As the traveller approaches the Hills from the south, he becomes ware that the plains over which he is travelling rise gently and become olling. Suddenly he sees in front of him masses of dark trees, outlined gainst the horizon. A mile or two more, and he is out of the sun-baked rairie and in an elevated sanctuary of forests, lakes, rolling hills, treams and rich pastures.

The Cypress Hills, called on occasion "the hills that shouldn't be", vere known to the Blackfoot as *"Katewius Netumoo"*, the Pine Hills. ut the French-Canadian explorers, who mistakenly thought the lodge- ole pine of these hills to be their "cyprès"– the jackpine of eastern anada – named the area *Montagne de Cyprès*. In the English translation, his misnomer became the Cypress Hills.

The Cypress Hills are a flat-topped plateau of about a thousand quare miles, one-third of which lies within Alberta. Its varying widths re up to 25 miles; its length, depending on where one feels that the rising lain becomes the Hills, is 85 to 100 miles. From 4,810 feet above sea evel at its western end, 22 miles northeast of Manyberries, Alberta, the evel of the plateau drops gently east and south until, at its eastern end, ear Eastend, Saskatchewan, it is only 3,500 feet above sea level. In two reas, the plateau is slashed into or right through by many short and arrow north-south valleys, so that on the Saskatchewan side – or in the ast block, as it is called – a series of individual hills climb back up to he average elevation of the plateau, which is about 1,500 feet above the lains. Both the elevation and the surface gradient of the Cypress Hills

Title picture – Cypress Hills as seen from the northwest.

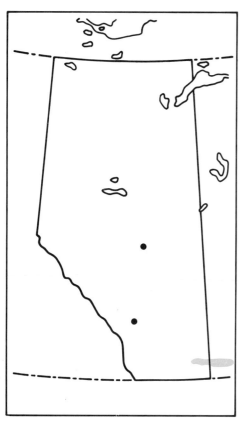

Location of the Cypress Hills

Outline map of the Cypress Hills, showing hill scarps and elevations.

are determined by the Cypress Hills conglomerate that forms the hill capping. Therefore, since this boulder gravel cap on the Hills rises in elevation westward, the Alberta end of the Hills stands 2,500 feet above the surrounding plains.

At its perimeter, this prairie table-top breaks off precipitately on the north and west sides into steep slopes or nearly vertical cliffs, formed in part by ice-marginal, melt-water flow at the end of the Pleistocene glaciation. On the south side, however, the plateau merges gradually into the plain. The coniferous forest gives way to deciduous forest which, in turn, gives way to the prairie. This change is not sharply delineated because from east to west the relief is strong. You tend to go from one gully across a ridge, and into another gully. On the ridges you are on prairie; in the gullies you are among the trees. The gullies come out of the Cypress Hills and the woods follow the moister gullies out onto the plain. This interfingering of forests and highlands, carrying out to the plains, gives the contrast that makes the area a fascinating one.

The scenery of the Cypress Hills – in fact, their very existence – has long stirred the imagination of travellers. Captain John Palliser, heading the first official exploratory and scientific group to enter the Cypress Hills, wrote in his journal on July 28th, 1859: "The Cypress Mountains formed indeed a great contrast to the level country through which we have been travelling. They are covered with timber, much of which is very valuable for building purposes. The soil is rich, and the supply of water abundant. These hills are a perfect oasis in the desert we have travelled".

The Cypress Hills form an oasis because – while they lie near the centre of the base of a triangular area of very low precipitation, delineated by John Palliser and now known as "Palliser's Triangle" – their higher elevation results in higher precipitation and lower temperature than in the area surrounding the hills. Palliser had regarded the area surrounding the Cypress Hills as part of an interior North American desert. Later exploration, however, proved it to be not desert land but a short grass, treeless country, subject to cycles of severe drought in which no standing water remained, yet favoured in other years by cooler summer and heavier rainfall.

The summit of the Cypress Hills, which is known as the "Head of the Mountain", is at its western extremity, and reaches a maximum elevation

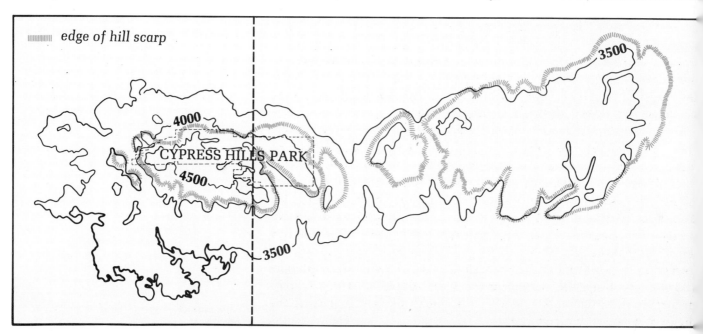

edge of hill scarp

4000

CYPRESS HILLS PARK

4500

3500

3500

.G.

Part of the north-facing slope, illustrating prairie interfingering with aspen, lodgepole pine and white spruce.

f 4,810 feet, the highest Canadian elevation between Labrador and the Rocky Mountains. This height, which commands a 60-mile sweep of prairie scenery, shares with one other small area on the Canadian prairies the distinction of never having been submerged by any of the great ice-sheets which flowed down from the Rocky Mountains or advanced from the Hudson Bay and Keewatin area.

The Cypress Hills Formation which caps the hills is a conglomerate composed of rounded pebbles and cobbles carried eastward by stream action from the Rocky Mountains during Oligocene time. In layman's language, the present level top of the Cypress Hills was once the bed of a broad stream bringing quartz pebbles and boulders eastward over the plains. The conglomerate is underlain by sandstone and shale of the Ravenscrag Formation of Paleocene age. These two Tertiary strata, which are up to 775 feet thick, rest conformably upon the Frenchman, Battle, Whitemud and Eastend Formations, all of Late Cretaceous age. These beds, in turn, rest upon the shales of the Bearpaw Formation which outcrop over much of the country north and south of the Hills.

During the time of Pleistocene glaciation, the south-bound ice-sheets thinned and split as they reached the 4,500-foot level of the plateau. The 310-foot summit above this level remained unglaciated, standing out through the ice as a nunatak of approximately 80 square miles. Today a deposit of wind-blown material – referred to by geologists as loess – is present up to eight feet in thickness on the higher parts of the plateau where it covers the rocks of the Cypress Hills Formation. This indicates the existence of arid, windy conditions around the hills at the time of the retreat of the continental glacier.

119

I.R. F

Cypress Hills Formation, which is covered by a thin layer of loess.

It is this glacial phenomenon which has endowed the Cypress Hill with the sensationalism which presupposes that, because the plateau wa not glaciated, a "tropical" flora and fauna survived there as relics of th distant past – "a glimpse of how it was before the Ice Age". Thus on reads of the "geological practical joke" by which mountain plant flourish on slopes 150 miles from the Rocky Mountains and "fragile fern and wild orchids thrive in moist shady nooks while in the neighbourin foothills horned toads and scorpions, a thousand miles from their kind scramble through semi-tropical Yucca grass".

The scorpions and horned toads are there, admittedly, along with such other desert-loving species as McCown's longspur, the sage grouse the kangaroo rat, the sagebrush vole and the hog-nosed snake. But thes animals are not in the moist forests of the Cypress Hills: they are in th cactus and sagebrush of the semi-arid, heat-baked regions nearby. An they would still be there even if the Hills were not.

An examination of all the "southern" forms of vertebrates that ar found here reveals that they are living in an environment similar to tha of their southern area. Their interest to the biologist and naturalis therefore lies in the fact that they represent a fauna which has its centr of distribution far south of the 49th Parallel and of which the member have reached the northern fringe of their range in the Cypress Hills area and that here these plants and animals, so characteristic of the semi-ari central desert, are found immediately adjacent to and interrelated wit those of the coniferous forests which are characteristic of much of th northern part of Canada.

Contrasting remarkably with the "southern" flora and fauna is a biot – a community of living things – which one would expect to find in th Rocky Mountains, for it is only rarely that one finds members of between the Rocky Mountains and the Cypress Hills. The presence c this biota in the ecologically isolated Cypress Hills suggests therefor

(a)

(a) Mourning dove
(b) Wilson's snipe
(c) White-crowned sparrow
(d) Long-eared owl
(e) Brown thrasher

(c)

C.H.

(d)

C.H.

(b)

(e)

C.H.

121

that a forest connection between the mountains and the Cypress Hills existed in early postglacial times.

Early exploration

As far back as the 1850's, scientists have been intrigued by the climate the geography and the geology of the Cypress Hills area. The young geologist-physician, James Hector, who accompanied Palliser throughout his surveys of the West and provided a notable record of the geology and origin of the Cypress Hills country, is reported to have left the Hills with much regret, as he felt it promised to be one of the most interesting areas in the country for studying certain geological problems.

The second geologist to explore the area, George Mercer Dawson visited the Cypress Hills in 1873-74, when he was connected with the British North American Boundary Commission. His subsequent writings are considered to be classics of exploration geology. Of Dawson and his remarkable achievement, F. J. Alcock, former Curator of the National Museum of Canada, wrote: "One of the greatest scientists that Canada has produced, he carried out extensive work in the Great Plains belt, and more particularly in the Cordilleran country to the west, that laid the foundation of much of our knowledge of these regions".

The third geologist, R. G. McConnell, who was Dawson's one-time assistant, visited southeastern Alberta in 1883 and 1884. He discovered the Oligocene gravels of the Cypress Hills and the mammal bones from which the age of the Cypress Hills was determined, and he published a full and fundamental account of the geology of the area.

In imagination we glimpse those years in which this wild and hitherto unsurveyed country was first seen by scientists like Dawson and McConnell as they travelled by horseback and Red River cart. Their guides were from the tribes of the Plains Indians; their food was the game they shot and the fish they caught in little streams; at night they pitched their tent in some pretty valley shared with the Indians and with the birds and animals.

The Cypress Hills had changed in the latter half of the 19th century from a "no-man's-land" between the Blackfoot and Assiniboines to an excellent hunting ground. Out on the prairie settlement was beginning and more and more animals moved into the Hills, which were abundant in water, nutritious grasses, herbs and mosses. The Indians – Blackfoot Assiniboine and Cree – followed. The mischievous kit fox, the size of a well-fed house cat, still searched for mice and voles around the settlements but in a few short decades was to vanish from the scene. The Great Plains grizzly, feared and hunted, prowled in the Hills which may have been second to the Swan Hills as his last retreat. He wintered in cave or jumble of boulders or, perhaps, in a hole or hollow in evergreen timber, and he moved with the bison, the deer and the pronghorn. With him on the outskirts of the great feeding herds – himself already doomed to extinction – lurked the Great Plains or "Lobo" wolf, picking off the calves and yearlings, the wounded and the aged.

The spectacular white bird, the trumpeter swan, still nested in the Cypress Hills. On some elevated spot near shallow water from which the adults pulled up vegetation with their long black bills, they constructed an enormous nest of grass and stalks, feathers and down. But time and man's greed brought near-extinction to this beautiful species. The young were caught or shot before they could fly, and the magnificent adults were added to the traffic in swans' down. Soon the trumpeter swan became one of the rarest of waterfowl. Thirty-five years ago only about 200 of them were known to exist. As a result of strict protective measures since that time, the swan has increased in numbers to several

Male trumpeter swan or cob

Trumpeter swan cygnets in nest

(a)

D.B.

FLOWERS OF THE CYPRESS HILLS

(a) Pincherry
(b) Bunchberry
(c) Shooting star
(d) Gaillardia
(e) Coral root
(f) Juniper

(c)

C.H.

(d)

C.H.

(b)

H.

(e)

R.D.B.

(f)

C.D.B.

123

hundreds. For the last 15 years at least one pair has nested in the Cypress Hills and has successfully raised their young there.

The decades following the turn of the century have brought other changes within the Cypress Hills. Surface exploration continued under geologists such as M. Y. Williams, W. S. Dyer, L. S. Russell, and R. W. Landes. The southern part of Alberta and the southwest corner of Saskatchewan were mapped by M. Y. Williams and W. S. Dyer from 1923 to 1926. In the years from 1931 to 1937, L. S. Russell and R. W. Landes remapped the areas in the southeast corner of Alberta, and in 1940 and 1941, G. M. Furnival remapped in greater detail the Saskatchewan side of the Cypress Hills.

John Macoun, pioneer Canadian botanist, visited the Cypress Hills in 1880, 1894 and 1895 and collected large numbers of mosses and higher plants. Although most of Macoun's work was concerned with the Saskatchewan side of the hills, in his book *Manitoba and the Great North West,* he gives historically important information on the flora and fauna of the Hills as a whole.

In 1945, R. G. H. Cormack of the University of Alberta investigated the forest ecology of the area. As a result of this work, he prepared a report and produced a paper on the orchids of the hills. He made a special point of collecting sedges, grasses, and orchids, and many of his records appeared later in Breitung's catalogue.

A. J. Breitung botanized in the area in July and August of 1947, and later compiled his records with those he could find elsewhere to produce the first catalogue and description of the vascular vegetation of the region. A total of 241 species was recorded from the Alberta side of the Hills, to which a further 112 species have been added as the result of recent studies by B. de Vries and C. D. Bird.

Soils and climate

The distribution of soil types is closely associated with vegetation. The black soil found on the top of the plateau is especially associated with fescue prairie and aspen groves. Gray wooded soil on the northern exposures and at higher elevations is correlated with the distribution of white spruce and lodgepole pine. On the dark brown soil of moister grassland areas grows the wheat grass - needle and thread climax. On brown soil, found on south-facing hillsides at lower elevations, occurs the blue grama - needle and thread climax. The depth of the soil and the darkness of the surface horizon both increase from east to west in the Cypress Hills, along with parallel increases in elevation and precipitation.

The low precipitation and the high rate of evaporation are the main reasons why the plains surrounding the Cypress Hills are treeless. But in the Cypress Hills the evaporation rate is lower since it depends upon wind velocity, relative humidity and temperature, and this allows forest cover to develop. This is particularly true on the more shaded north facing slopes, where there is less evaporation and consequently more moisture.

Long term weather data is not available for the Alberta portion of the Cypress Hills, and only incomplete information has been accumulated on the Saskatchewan side. It is certain, however, that due to higher elevation the Hills are cooler and moister than the surrounding prairie. The yearly average precipitation is probably 17 to 20 inches in contrast to 13.3 inches for Medicine Hat, 14.9 for Swift Current, Saskatchewan, and little over 10 inches south of the Hills along the Montana border. In the Hills, the mean annual temperature is close to 36 degrees, while it is 41 degrees at Medicine Hat and 39 degrees at Swift Current. The daily mean

Audubon's warbler (male)

124

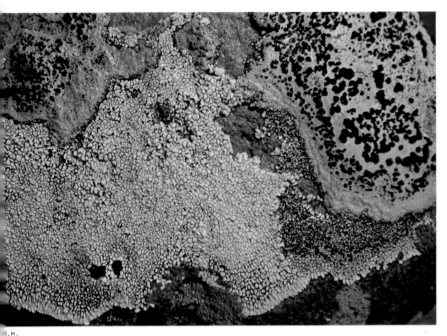

.H.

Common rock lichens. The gray lichen with black fringing areas is Lecidea, the dark red lichen is Caloplaca.

temperature in the Hills is at its highest in July, at which time it is about 10 degrees lower than that of the surrounding scorching prairies.

The prevailing wind is from the southwest. During the winter Chinook winds frequently blow. The combination of high wind velocity, warm temperature and low humidity associated with these winds results in rapid melting of the snow cover, and often causes permanent damage to trees and shrubs due to excessive dehydration of conifer needles and bark cambium on the windward side.

Vegetation and associated fauna

On the Cypress Hills plateau, two major types of vegetation occur. These are the forests at higher elevations, along stream valleys, and on more northerly exposed slopes, and grasslands which occur at the lower elevations of the plateau and on the more southerly exposed slopes.

In general, plant species are restricted in occurrence to either grassland or forest or to a subtype of either. However, a number of plants can tolerate wide-ranging environmental conditions and may be found throughout the region. Plants which especially show this feature are such introduced weeds as quack grass, awnless brome, common knotweed, many mustards, the alsike, red and white clovers, the ox-eye daisy and the dandelion.

While most species of the local fauna are capable of free movement throughout the plant communities that exist in the area, they tend to have preferences for particular habitats. This is particularly true in the choice of habitat used for nesting purposes. For example, Audubon's warbler may be found hunting for food in the aspen groves, but it nests in the lodgepole pine forest. Similarly, while the raccoon, though very rare in the Cypress Hills, may wander into the lodgepole pine forest or into the grasslands, it usually has its den in a hollow tree in an aspen grove.

The grasslands

Due to greater precipitation, the prairie on the Alberta side of the Hills is noticeably more luxuriant than that on the Saskatchewan side, and differs in floristic composition. Most of the Cypress Hills plateau is covered with grasslands. These vary from extensive areas, especially on south-facing exposures, to small open spaces in the conifer regions and between aspen groves. In general, the grasslands may be divided into fescue prairie, which occupies most of the area on top of the plateau, and mixed-grass prairie at lower elevations and on south-facing slopes.

R.D.B.

A club moss associated with feather mosses, bunchberry and wintergreens.

C. H

Bull snake

White camas

Rough fescue or bunch grass is the leading species of this grassland and with it grow timber oat grass, bluebunch fescue, bluegrass and bearded wheat grass. Also common are moss phlox, white camas, death camas and shrubby cinquefoil. This type of prairie is especially attractive, as it has a flower garden appearance throughout the growing period of the year. In the spring the blossoms of such plants as the early cinquefoil, puccoon, golden bean and shooting star are especially noticeable while in the late summer and autumn their place is taken by red paintbrush, bluebells, yarrow, gaillardia, showy everlasting and goldenrod.

Mosses, though inconspicuous because of their small size, are abundant and characteristic components of both fescue and mixed-grass prairie. They grow nearly everywhere as long as there is some moisture and a little space not occupied by taller and stronger-growing forms of vegetation. Mosses are usually bright green though some are red, yellow, brown, or even black. As a rule lichens are gray, yellow, or brown, and are small and tend to be hidden by the larger grasses. Mosses and lichens have a very real value to mankind. They rapidly colonize new areas and tend to form a carpet over the ground which, along with soil algae, resembles a crust. This cover acts in two ways. It retains water and thus tends to keep the soil moist; and it acts as a blanket to prevent soil erosion by runoff of rainfall and by strong winds.

Major grasses of the mixed-grass prairie are northern wheat grass, needle and thread, and blue grama. Associated with these are a number of other grasses including western wheat grass, bearded wheat grass, fescue and june grass. Two sedges, the little club moss, and two low shrubs – the ground juniper and the creeping juniper – are often encountered.

Most of this prairie is found on relatively dry south-facing slopes. Typical and attractive plants of this habitat are the prairie onion, yellow umbrella plant, bladder pod, the succulent stonecrop, cushion milk vetch, and the mat-forming moss phlox and pussy-toes.

Fauna of the grasslands

In the grassland areas on the Cypress Hills the bird population includes both the eastern and western kingbird, Brewer's blackbird, brown-headed cowbird and the western meadowlark whose rollicking song is a familiar sound in the grasslands of the West. The horned lark, along with the savannah, vesper and clay-coloured sparrows, gather here and are more often recognized by their songs than by sight. The common night-hawk nests here and is seen regularly at dusk, hunting for insects high over the hills. Game birds present are the sharp-tailed grouse, ring-neck-ed pheasant and the gray or Hungarian partridge, the latter two species having been introduced.

Mammals include many species that are found in other habitats as well. Some tend to prefer the open areas, however, and these include the white-tailed prairie hare or jack rabbit, Richardson's ground squirrel and the little striped or 13-lined ground squirrel. Usually found near the borders of the grasslands are the cottontail rabbit, pocket gopher and skunk. Two weasels, the long-tailed and the short-tailed, can fluctuate greatly in number from year to year. The red fox and the coyote are often seen on the grasslands, and the pronghorn, more commonly known as the antelope, occasionally leaves the surrounding plains to visit the higher parts of the Hills.

The number of amphibians and reptiles is not large, but the western plains garter snake is often seen on the grasslands as is the bull snake, usually observed along the roadsides. Boreal chorus frogs and leopard frogs breed in wetlands and spend a great amount of time in the grass-land areas feeding on insects.

The forest

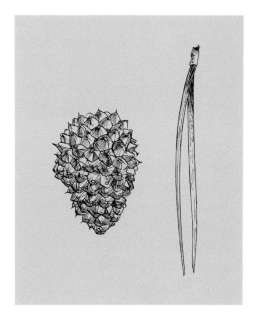

Four tree species occur in the Alberta Cypress Hills. These are lodgepole pine, white spruce, aspen poplar and balsam poplar. Often each will form pure stands, and each has a different ecological distribution. Due to fires and logging, mixed forests of all four trees occur, depending on the area and the stage of succession involved. A large number of other species of vascular plants grow in these mixed stands, and many with wide toler-ances grow in all types of forest. These include a number of shrubs, such as wild black currant, common wild rose, wolf willow, Canadian buffalo berry and low bush cranberry. Other frequently encountered plants are false Solomon's seal, baneberry, trailing purple clematis, meadow rue, wintergreen and showy aster.

Lodegpole pine – cone and needles

Pure stands of lodgepole pine tend to occupy dryer parts of the coniferous forest. Little ground cover is found under dense stands, due to heavy shade, and most associated species are confined to open stands and around margins, especially along roadsides or clearings. Some of the many species more or less restricted to the lodgepole pine forest are ground cedar, spike trisetum, sedge, Venus'-slipper, dwarf mistletoe, which is a parasite on pine trunks and branches, Prince's pine, one-flowered wintergreen, common bearberry, dwarf bilberry, twin-flower, two species of pussy-toes, heart-leaved arnica, and white hawk-weed. The brilliant yellow-branched wolf lichen is often conspicuous on branches of mature and aged pine. Three feather mosses – *Hylocomium splendens, Pleurozium schreberi,* and *Ptilium crista-castrensis* – and a number of turf and cushion-forming species of mosses, especially of the genus *Dicranum,* are characteristic components of the ground flora of old er pine woods and of drier spruce woods.

White spruce occupies cooler, moister areas, especially on north-facing slopes. In stands that escaped the fire of 1886 in the Cypress Hills – a fire in which the entire region, except for a few isolated patches of timber, was left charred and bare – the trees reach large proportions with diameters of up to 40 inches. Vascular plants associated with white spruce stands are stiff club moss, fragile fern, sedge, bishop's cap, bunch-berry and asters. Mosses characteristic of wet soils in white spruce woods, particularly *Aulacomnium palustre* and *Thuidium recognitum,* grow here, and the light gray and blackish brown beard lichens of the

Nodding onion

genera *Usnea* and *Alectoria* hang from the twigs and rough bark of medium-aged to old spruce trees.

Fauna of the coniferous forest

Characteristic nesting birds in the coniferous forest are the familiar black-capped chickadee, Audubon's warbler, Mearn's pink-sided junco, and pine siskin. Not quite so common but of regular occurrence are the hairy woodpecker, the crow, and a pale variety of the great horned owl. The red crossbill is an erratic wanderer that often nests in the coniferous forest. A small population of ruffed grouse is present in the Cypress Hills. They are apparently not native to the Hills, and their presence is due to a number being introduced during the 1920's.

The chipmunk, white-footed mouse and skunk are typical mammals of the coniferous forest. The mule deer and white-tailed deer are both numerous and are found regularly in this habitat, as is the red fox, but the lynx is an uncommon visitor. The familiar chatterbox of the coniferous forest, the red squirrel, has been introduced and is now quite common.

Aspen groves and woods

Groves of aspen and aspen woods are found mainly on the top of the plateau, but they also occur lower down where they merge with balsam poplar on the moister soils on valley bottoms. Associated with the aspen are wild gooseberry, saskatoon-berry, wild strawberry, pincherry and chokecherry, which are sought for their fruit. Brome and wild rye grasses help to carpet the ground along with such characteristic plants as fairy bells, star-flowered Solomon's seal, prickly rose, pea vine, Western Canada violet, the large cow parsnip and Lindley's aster. The groves are usually bordered with a margin of the shrubby buckbrush.

Fauna of the aspen groves

Compared to the coniferous forests, the aspen groves support a greater variety of bird life. The mourning dove, house wren, robin, veery and yellow warbler all nest here. Macgillivray's and orange-crowned warblers occur regularly among these trees but not on the surrounding plains. Numbers of the familiar black-billed magpie, mountain bluebird and rufous-sided towhee can also be found in the aspen groves. Less abundant, but present in some numbers, are the catbird, brown thrasher, brown-headed cowbird, white-crowned sparrow and song sparrow. The great horned owl is an irregular visitor to the aspen groves, particularly in winter and Swainson's thrush is an uncommon summer resident in the higher part of the Hills. The least flycatcher, somewhat rare, can be found in shrubbery on the lower slopes. The downy woodpecker, western wood pewee and yellow-breasted chat occur irregularly in the area but they should be watched for along the lower slopes of the Hills. A scarce but interesting bird of the aspen groves is the poor-will whose range enters Canada only in southern British Columbia and in the area of the Cypress Hills. The turkey vulture may nest in the wooded area of the Cypress Hills. Its range in recent years extends as far as Many Lake northeast of Edmonton.

Typical mammals associated with the aspen groves are the varying or snowshoe hare, cottontail rabbit, chipmunk and white-footed mouse. In addition, regular visitors are the coyote, red fox and skunk, along with the mule and white-tailed deer. Amphibians and reptiles associated with the aspen groves are the wandering garter snake and the western plains garter snake.

Wetland communities

Aquatic, subaquatic, and marginal aquatic communities are found in and around the lakes, marshes and streams of the Hills. These vary from

Aspen grove

M.H.

H.

(a) Swallowtail butterfly
(b) Pronghorn
(c) Kit fox, now extinct in Alberta
(d) Elk or Wapiti

R.MC.

D.B.

C.H.

lake, pond, stream and wet meadow to forested bank communities.

Aquatic environments are found in Elkwater Lake, Reesor Lake, Spruce Coulee Reservoir, and along streams in the Hills. Along with many algae and several mosses, the submerged plants found here are naiad, pondweed, yellow water crowfoot, water milfoil and small bladderwort. By late summer masses of floating green duckweeds tend to cover the small water bodies and quiet bays of the larger lakes. Rooted in the muddy bottom, but with upper parts emerging from the water and providing cover for waterfowl, are such plants as manna grass, spike rush, bulrush, water smartweed and mare's-tail.

Wet meadows are found in many places, especially around lakes and in some places along streams. Plants found here are marsh reed grass, manna grass, many sedges, the spike and wire rush, narrow-leaved dock, purple avens, and a moss, *Drepanocladus aduncus*.

Forested stream and bank communities exist to a limited extent on north-facing slopes bordering lakes and are common along streams. Many willows, balsam poplar and some white spruce provide a forest cover. Plants found in this shaded, moist environment are many mosses and liverworts, four species of horsetail, sedges, small-fruited bulrush, northern green orchid, round-leaved orchid, many willows, water birch, swamp birch, western spring beauty, yellow monkey-flower, American brooklime and arrow-leaved coltsfoot. Common mosses of this community are *Bryum pseudotriquetrum*, *Hypnum patientiae*, and species of *Cratoneuron* and *Philonotis*.

Fauna of the wetlands

Associated with the wetlands are a number of species of ducks including the mallard, green-winged teal, American widgeon and lesser scaup, all of which nest beside lakes in the area. The marshes around the edges of open water support nesting populations of marsh birds including the redwinged blackbird, spotted sandpiper, killdeer and black tern and are feeding areas for the belted kingfisher and great blue heron. The kingfisher and heron also feed along the streams in the forested areas. The bank swallow, barn swallow and cliff swallow are regularly seen hunting for insects over any open water.

Mammals associated with the wetlands include the meadow vole,

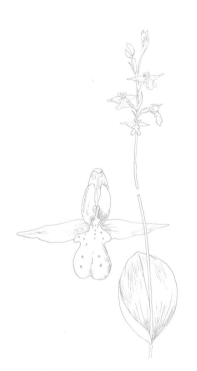

Purple avens

Round-leaved orchid

Lesser scaup duck, a species which commonly breeds in the Cypress Hills area.

muskrat, beaver and, occasionally, mink. Reptiles and amphibians in this environment are wandering and western plains garter snakes, the blotched tiger salamander, and boreal chorus and leopard frogs.

Montane elements

During the last major ice advance all of the Hills below 4,500 feet on the northern side and 4,050 feet on the southern side were covered by ice which retreated over 11,000 years ago. It is believed that little, if any, life was able to survive in the area of the Hills which escaped glaciation. After the glacial retreat, the climate was cool and moist, and a montane flora and fauna invaded the region from the south and southwest. As the climate became warmer and more arid, part of this element disappeared, while the remainder managed to survive at higher elevations, especially on the less exposed north-facing slopes and valleys.

The montane element, composed of those species of animals and plants found elsewhere only in the mountains and foothills, comprises up to fifty per cent of the biota of the Cypress Hills. Birds belonging to this element include the dusky flycatcher, Rocky Mountain orange-crowned warbler, Oregon white-crowned sparrow, red crossbill, Audubon's warbler and Mearn's pink-sided junco. The group with the highest montane representation is the land snails with four of eight species. A variety of one of the remaining species is apparently endemic to the Hills but, as the distribution of land snails is poorly known, it may also be found in the mountains. Insects have been studied only superficially, but it appears that of the butterflies and moths, at least, about ten per cent belong to this element.

Heart-leaved arnica

Thirty-nine of the 353 vascular plants, or 11 per cent of plants known to grow on the Alberta side of the Hills, have been found to be montane. Some notable examples are lodgepole pine, bluebunch fescue, bistort, western spring beauty, purple clematis, heart-leaved buttercup, western meadow rue, thimbleberry, white meadow-sweet, squaw-root, pine-drops, kitten-tails, yellow monkey-flower, heart-leaved arnica and two hawkweeds. Nine per cent of the liverworts and mosses also form part of the montane element. Leading examples are the mosses *Mnium marginatum, Encalypta procera, Timmia austriaca,* and *Lescuraea stenophylla.*

Changes caused by fire

Fires have several effects. They tend to eliminate forests and to favour grasslands, and when prairie is burnt, fescue grassland is likely to be replaced by mixed grassland. A major effect of fire in the Cypress Hills appears to have been to limit the development of a climax white spruce forest and to maintain lodgepole pine as a sub-climax. After a forest fire, lodgepole pine appears in very dense stands and maintains itself with some thinning for over 50 years before white spruce gradually makes a noticeable appearance. Fire tends to favour a short term profusion of other plants, such as fireweed, raspberry and goldenrods. The moss, *Funaria hygrometrica,* and the liverwort, *Marchantia polymorpha,* are also rapid colonizers in burned areas.

Changes caused by man

Man has the potential of causing further catastrophies, due to his habit of changing his environment. The construction of roads and fire-guards and the clearing of land for campsites and buildings have resulted in exposure of areas of soil devoid of vegetation. This disturbed soil is rapidly invaded by plants of a weedy nature. These include a number of cosmopolitan mosses and Old World quack grass, awnless brome, common knotweed, dandelion, and many mustards and clovers. Native species such as golden corydalis, crane's bill and fireweed also grow here.

Rock lichens

Man-made dams, such as the one in Spruce Coulee, cause floods and drown the vegetation of natural meadow and stream bank communities. Following the flooding, a number of years must pass before stable new communities develop. Meantime, the new banks and flats are first dominated by annual weedy species. These gradually give way to long-lasting perennial species until eventually communities typical of permanent lakes and streams develop. These new bodies of water increase the habitat for waterfowl, herons, belted kingfishers, muskrats and other species that use open water, shorelines and marsh environments. On land such species as the robin, the house sparrow and the barn swallow appear to enjoy their association with man and his activities often using buildings as nesting sites.

The gravel roads in the area provide an additional source of grit for birds, especially the seed-eaters, for grit is essential to the digestion of their food. This source becomes increasingly important in winter when, in times of heavy snow cover, plowed roads may be the only source of grit available.

Grazing and mowing, if severe, will completely change the nature of the grasslands, for over-grazing causes pasture sagewort to increase, and mowing has reduced the shrubby cinquefoil in grasslands and aspen poplars around groves. Referring in 1882 to the quality of the grassland in the Cypress Hills, John Macoun commented: "No better pasture is to be found in all the wide North-West than exists in these hills". The yield of fescue hay per acre on the plateau is about 1,000 pounds, while on the surrounding plains it varies from 250 to 500 pounds per acre.

Logging removes aesthetically beautiful mature trees and causes a drastic change in the undergrowth, since many shade-tolerant species of plants are replaced by common species. Changes in floristic competition induce similar changes in the fauna with the result that the more interesting species tend to disappear and the pest species to increase. Logging has decreased in recent years. The effect of the removal of trees is the opening up of stands, allowing more light to penetrate to the ground level. This results in the favouring of light-tolerant species over those that grow best in shaded, humid, cool habitats. Succession following logging is essentially the same as that which follows fire. Selected cutting obviously results in smaller changes than does complete removal of the tree cover.

132

Settlement in the Cypress Hills – and more especially settlement on the surrounding plains – has produced both slight and dramatic changes in the faunal population. Some species have vanished completely. Other species have been greatly reduced in numbers, and these include the pronghorn, badger, moose and trumpeter swan. The fur trade resulted in low populations of beaver, mink, and to some extent muskrat. Of late, however, the beaver population is recovering.

While some species have been reduced in numbers, others have increased. The starling and house sparrow were introduced into eastern North America and have spread westward. The ring-necked pheasant and gray partridge have been introduced as game birds. The house mouse, a native of the Old World, is well established around human habitations, and the house or Norway rat is numerous to the east of Alberta but stringent control measures along the Alberta-Saskatchewan boundary have been successful in keeping this destructive pest from becoming established in Alberta. Population figures of a century ago can only be estimated but it seems probable that such species as the mourning dove, red-winged blackbird and common crow have increased in number. The population of white-tailed deer has increased markedly in comparison with that of the mule deer.

These Hills have been referred to as "an island of cool conifer woods in the midst of a sea of dry short-grass prairie". To tourists they are a fascinating world – their geography and geology, their prehistoric fossils, their striking history, their flora and fauna – all a gift of capricious Nature – are a background to the recreational facilities and the scenic beauty of the Cypress Hills. These features are worth preserving for future generations, and continued vigilance is needed to ensure that the area receives proper management.

R.D.B.

CHAPTER SEVEN

The Aspen Parkland

CHARLES D. BIRD
RALPH D. BIRD

EXCEPT FOR TONGUES of woodland extending from Alberta into Montana, and from Manitoba into Minnesota and North Dakota, the aspen parkland is a phenomenon of Canada's prairie provinces. Its western bastion is in east-central Alberta, although a narrow strip curves toward the foothills to trail along their eastern flanks. The whole of the parkland from Alberta to Manitoba is a major vegetation zone where groves of aspen poplars, often called "bluffs", are interspersed with prairie, and large stream-valleys are clothed with fairly extensive stands of both aspens and willows. Its terrain is not level or neatly trimmed but varies from gently undulating to hilly countryside in which trees and tangled shrubbery mingle with cultivated fields.

This broad belt of parkland is one of nature's battlegrounds. To the south and east is the prairie, to the north and west the boreal and foothills forests. With each of these, the aspen parkland fights for supremacy; and within its own borders there is a never-ceasing competition between aspen groves and grassland. In biological terminology, the parkland zone is an ecotone, or area of transition.

Early history

Long before Europeans arrived, the Indian tribes of the western prairie and parkland seem to have set fire to the grasslands. In 1798, for example, the explorer and map-maker, David Thompson, wrote: "Along the Great Plains there are very many places where . . . Aspens have been burnt . . . and no further production of trees have taken place, the grass of the plains covers them; and from this cause the Great Plains are constantly increasing in length and breadth and the Deer give way to the Bison". Sixty-one years later in 1859, another explorer, Henry Youle Hind, noted that in the previous autumn, ". . . all the prairies were burned

Title picture — Aspens in autumn

135

over . . . a vast conflagration, extending for one thousand miles in length and several hundred in breadth . . . the annual fires prevent the willows and aspens from covering the country". The early missionaries, as well as explorers and travellers, were impressed by the crackling flames of the fires set every autumn by the Indians and by the bison trampling down "small wood and brush" in the parkland. Throughout the era of the early explorers and the fur traders, it seems likely therefore that the grasslands within the aspen parkland were considerably more open and extensive than they were after the bison disappeared and settlement began.

The fur traders left little or no mark on the vegetation of the parkland. Their interest was fixed on furs. They avoided the southern prairies where there were few pelts to be obtained and where the Blackfoot had formed a powerful and warlike confederacy. Instead they established a number of posts either in the parkland as at Upper Fort Garry, which became Winnipeg, or on the fringes, as at Edmonton; for in the parkland and the northern forests were the fur-bearing animals they coveted and the tribes that could be persuaded to co-operate in bringing in pelts. The fur-bearing animals in these regions were decimated. The countryside itself, except for the Red River Settlement in Manitoba and garden plots and livestock around the forts of the Hudson's Bay Company, was left undisturbed. Even the sale of the Northwest Territories to the infant Dominion of Canada in 1869 did little to affect the parkland, particularly in Saskatchewan and Alberta, until a tide of homesteaders began to pour in, just before 1900.

Effects of settlement

In the parkland of the three prairie provinces, the homesteaders checked the fires. At first, as long as either oxen or horses were the farm power, they tended to break and cultivate only the grassland. In addition, the land survey system divided the whole country into townships of 36 sections of one square mile each, left road allowances, enclosing each two sections, set aside sections 11 and 29 in each township as school property and assigned certain lands in each township to the Hudson's Bay Company. Homestead land, being free land, was occupied first, and the sections which had been reserved in each township were not sold until later. Because of this patchwork type of settlement, much of the parkland was left in its virgin state. For the same reason most of the road allowances were not disturbed, except for meandering wagon trails and narrow, graded earth roads on the main travelled routes. Under these conditions, with the bison vanished and the yearly fires checked, the aspen woodland occupied grasslands within its own territory and advanced into the southern prairie. In Alberta by 1920 the parkland had extended its range quite considerably to the south and east. But there came the tractor and next the bulldozer.

Tractors, powered first by steam and then by gasoline, appeared on western farms by about 1925. They pulled new and powerful machinery. Later, self-powered combines came into common use. The combines and threshers left behind swaths or piles of straw. Fires set for burning the straw and stubble at times escaped into stands of trees. In the same period tractors, either equipped with a cutting bar in front to shear saplings, or with heavy ploughs which they pulled through sparsely treed groves, were used to clear and break the woodland.

The major assault on the aspen groves waited until between 1945 and 1948, when the bulldozer was adopted by western farmers. This machine either pushed over full-grown trees and piled them for burning or else, equipped with a blade, cut through saplings as if they were matchsticks.

Parkland zone

136

(a)

A.K.

(a) Yellow warbler
(b) Cedar waxwing
(c) Horned grebe
(d) Catbird nest and eggs

(c)

C.H.

(b)

C.H.

(d)

C.H.

137

Aspen woodland

M.H.

In this way thousands of acres were cleared. In the meantime, there was a population increase, a massive development of automobile and truck transportation, and an equally massive surge forward in building paved highways and gravelled and graded secondary roads. As a result, roads with deep ditches and high grades – so that the snow would blow off in winter – occupied most of the road allowances in the parkland, destroying much of the native vegetation. On less important roads the ditches have often been abandoned to weeds, but in a number of places chemical herbicides have been used to kill the shrub growth and remaining vegetation. These herbicides may be injurious to animal life; and, in all cases, the removal of the vegetation has affected the wildlife which used to feed on it or make their homes in it. Yet in Alberta, because fires have been checked, the parkland has continued to invade the southern prairie.

The Alberta parkland

In Alberta the parkland covers about 23,000 square miles, or almost one-tenth of the province. In typical areas aspen groves alternate with grassland, while stands of aspen and willow mingled with conifers increase the range of the woodland along wide stream valleys. The elevation of the parkland realm varies from 2,200 feet above sea level near the Saskatchewan border to 5,000 feet in the foothills. The plains are underlaid by Cretaceous and Tertiary sedimentary rocks, with Tertiary gravels capping the Hand Hills. The results of the Ice Age glaciation may be seen in the irregular, gently rolling mantle of moraines laid over parts of the parkland, as the ice sheet stagnated and melted. From this past history arose the rather pleasing undulations and variety in the landscape.

The drainage of Alberta's parkland is eastward through the North and South Saskatchewan River systems. The only stream of any considerable size and length which travels almost exclusively through the parkland is the Battle River. Flowing out of Battle Lake, southwest of Pigeon Lake, its meandering course takes it through Ponoka and then northward to pass between Wetaskiwin and Camrose. From this point it twists and veers past Alliance, Hardisty, and Wainwright to join the North Saskatchewan River at Battleford in Saskatchewan. Lakes seem to be scattered in careless profusion throughout the parkland, varying from large and shallow waters, as at Beaverhill, Buffalo and Sullivan Lakes, to smaller expanses, usually ringed quite delightfully with trees but often surrounded by alkaline shores. Everywhere, too, are sloughs and marshes circled with willows and aspens.

In the parkland short but moderately warm summers and long, cold winters produce a mean annual temperature ranging from 39 degrees in the western districts to 34 degrees near the Saskatchewan border. There can be extremely low winter temperatures of from 50 to 60 degrees below zero, while in summer the mercury can soar as high as 100 degrees. Annual precipitation is in general greater than in the southern prairie, varying from 18 inches in the northwest to 16 inches or lower in the south and east. Winds blow frequently from the east and southeast but prevailing winds are from the west and northwest, the westerly winds, in particular, drying the soil and the plant life. Vegetation on slopes facing northeastward is usually more luxuriant than on those inclining toward the northwest, even though both are equally sheltered from drying by the sun.

Like the climate, the soil influences the type and luxuriance of the vegetation. The major soils are black, or nearly so, on top and contain more nitrogen and organic matter than the brown and dark brown earth of the southern prairie. Parkland soils were developed under fescue grassland, which is another indication that in many places aspen poplars are comparatively recent intruders. Alkaline soils, however, are found in a belt running south from Vegreville and Beaverhill Lake through Sullivan and Dowling Lakes to the prairie. As elsewhere, these soils have a hard pan underneath the surface earth which limits root penetration and holds water on or near the surface until it evaporates. Here the salt content is high enough to prevent or at least retard the growth of many plants.

The vegetation of the aspen parkland with its associated animal life is divided into four communities according to the amount of moisture in the soil: fescue prairie; aspen groves and woodland; creeks and rivers; lakes, marshes and wet meadows. A number of weeds, many of them introduced from abroad by settlers, thrive in more than one of the communities. Animals, too, being mobile, are often not limited to any one area.

The fescue prairie

Fescue or bunchgrass prairie is the most characteristic grassland of the aspen parkland. Today true fescue grassland is limited to untouched areas or to regions in which there is little grazing. In its virgin state, fescue grass spreads itself in large tussocks up to three feet in height and 20 inches in diameter. Wherever the soil is shallow or the slopes are gravelly or rocky, Parry oat and other grasses replace the fescue.

The fescue grass plant community is imposing. One hundred and forty-eight species of higher plants belong to it, of which 70 constantly occur in any stretches which are several acres in size. There are 20 grasses, three sedges, ten shrubs, 115 forbs and 30 or more mosses and lichens. One-third of the species found in the southern part do not appear in the north and west, probably because in the south soil types are more diversified and the topography rougher.

Settlement has greatly reduced the domain of the fescue prairie. Much of it is now cultivated land and most of the remainder has been

Pasture sage

altered by grazing or mowing. Under moderate grazing, rough fescue becomes patchy, although it fights a rearguard action on moister and more protected sites. In drier places, it becomes interspersed with a number of grasses, such as june, porcupine, and spear grass and blue bunch fescue along with two species of sedges, *Carex heliophila* and *Carex eleocharis.* Even in wetter regions, it may be forced to yield ground to other types, such as slender wheat grass and timber oat grass. Heavy and continuous grazing may result in the disappearance of fescue and produce a more or less worthless pasture dominated by sedges, pasture sage and pussy-toes. On the other hand, when rough fescue is mowed, it decreases more or less uniformly over the acreage and becomes less vigorous. The best hay is produced when fescue grassland is mowed not more frequently than every second year.

The shrubs, forbs and flowers of the fescue grassland are found elsewhere in the province. The shrubby cinquefoil and snowberry are characteristic, as are such forbs as common yarrow with its white flowers, cut-leaved anemone, rock cress, creeping white prairie aster, milk vetch, late yellow locoweed and goldenrod. The emblematic flowers of the three prairie provinces bloom everywhere among the fescue, the delicate tints of Alberta's pink prairie rose and Manitoba's blue "crocus" contrasting with the more flamboyant colours of Saskatchewan's tiger lily.

Mammals and birds wander freely between the grassland and the aspen groves and in many cases over the rest of the province. The burrowing rodents, although also found in the southern prairie, are particularly important in the fescue meadows. Among these, Richardson's ground squirrel, the thirteen-striped ground squirrel, the pocket gopher, and one of the principal predators of the three of them, the badger, throw up from their burrows mounds of earth which are often used as dusting places by sharp-tailed grouse. The droppings of the grouse frequently contain seeds of rose and snowberry. These seeds germinate, the seedlings establish themselves on the mounds, and patches of shrubs spread by root suckering. Seeds of aspen, too, blown by the wind, grow into seedlings on these mounds of bare earth, spread by suckering and often develop into aspen groves. In this way the burrowers are at the base of an ecological pyramid, which aids in the advance of aspen woodland into grassland.

Another mammal which in early days ranged into the parkland was the bison. Along with it came the cowbird to feed on the insects which

Pussy-toes

Common yarrow

Tiger lily

140

were associated with the "humped cattle". When the bison vanished, this bird transferred its attentions to domesticated cattle. The cowbird drops its eggs into the nests of other birds, which hatch them and rear the young.

The parkland, like the southern prairie, welcomes a host of other birds, such as the song sparrow, the vesper sparrow, the red-eyed vireo, the American goldfinch, the yellow warbler and many other species, but cultivation has destroyed much of the habitat for birds that nest in or feed on the fescue grassland. Two birds have adapted to the changed environment. The horned lark now nests in stubble, summerfallow and pasture, while the meadowlark builds its nests along roadsides and the headlands of cultivated fields. From these habitats, both birds trill their characteristic songs.

The most striking feature of the fescue grassland is the hordes of invertebrate animals. They may total over seven million individuals for each acre of ground. Of this immense multitude – except for round-worms – 98 per cent are insects, with ants as their most numerous component. Wherever there are cultivated fields, many grassland insects have been destroyed but other invertebrates, notably among the cutworms, wireworms and grasshoppers, have increased so greatly as to become pests. Long before settlement began and continuing until about 1900, swarms of Rocky Mountain grasshoppers periodically invaded the park-land and the southern prairie. In an account published in 1859, Henry Youle Hind tells of lying on his back in the country west of Souris, Mani-toba, during one of these invasions and looking upward as near to the sun as he could, where he saw "the sky continually changing colour from blue to silver white, ash grey and lead colour, according to the numbers in the passing clouds of insects".

He also relates that: "Those portions of the prairie which had been visited by the grasshoppers wore a curious appearance; the grass was cut uniformly to one inch from the ground . . ."

Since 1900 this particular species seems to have been exterminated, perhaps because its breeding habitat was disturbed by the disappearance of the bison and the replacement of dry prairie grass by green crops. Three other native species of grasshoppers continue on occasion to be almost equally destructive pests – the two-striped grasshopper, the clear-winged grasshopper and the migratory grasshopper. The first of these finds succulent crops and such broad-leaved milky weeds as species of sow thistle, blue lettuce and dandelion to its liking. For egg-laying sites

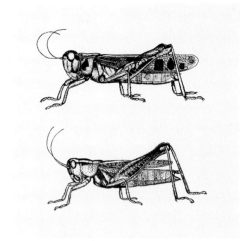

Clear-winged grasshopper
Two-striped grasshopper

Prairie rose

C.H.

C.H.

Crocus

141

it uses disturbed soil along roadsides, the banks of ditches, ridges formed by drifting soil and cultivated fields. The second, the clear-winged grasshopper, feeds mainly on grasses and grain crops and lays its eggs on roadsides and in pastures. The migratory grasshopper deposits its eggs throughout stubble fields and finds its sustenance in crops and weeds.

Other pests to trouble the farmer include the wheat stem sawfly, a native insect which finds the wheat stems an excellent place for the free movement of its larvae. In a somewhat similar way the prairie grain wireworm, red-backed cutworm and striped cutworm flourish in the loose soil of cultivated fields which permits the larvae to move freely while feeding on cereal crops.

Aspen groves and woodland

During the last century, aspen groves have invaded the grasslands in the parkland. As already noted, once a single aspen has become established on one of the mounds thrown up by burrowing rodents, new trees develop through root-suckering. If nothing adverse interferes, the result is a grove with the oldest and tallest trees in the centre and the younger and shorter trees on the outskirts. This sort of development produces a characteristic rounded profile that one notices as he approaches an aspen grove.

Aspens are unisexual. Each tree therefore is either male, known as a staminate tree, its flowers having stamens only, or female with its flowers possessing only pistils. This second type is called a pistillate tree. Since most groves intruding on the grassland are the product of a single seedling, they usually consist entirely of male or female trees. Another evidence of the common origin of the trees in a grove is that they all come into leaf at the same time. In the younger groves, dense stands are thinned through competition between the trees for moisture, soil and sunlight.

Under favourable conditions, aspens grow about one foot in height each year. Their maximum height and age can be about 110 feet and 120 years, but usually changes in climate or differences in soil interfere with growth so that the height is rarely over 75 feet and 100 years of age is seldom attained. The greatest height is found on moist and deep black earth, the least on dry, exposed sites or on gravelly soils. The diameter of aspens, if measured at chest height, usually increases at the rate of one-tenth to one-fifth of an inch each year. The larger trees in aspen stands of 35, 70, and 110 years of age give diameter measurements at chest height of about six, nine and a half, and twelve inches respectively. Furthermore, as the years go by, fungal activity thins the trees. Records show that in an area of 120 square yards, there were 500 trees in a five-year-old stand, 80 in a 20-year-old grove, and only 3 in a stand that was 110 years old.

The aspen groves and woodland nurture a fairly widespread community of small trees, shrubs, herbs, ground and tree-trunk plants. Among the small trees and large shrubs are red osier dogwood, beaked willow, saskatoon, chokecherry and pincherry. Shrubs of lower height include, along with prickly rose and snowberry, beaked hazelnut and low-bush cranberry. A few of the tall herbs which are also found elsewhere in the province, are Lindley's aster, northern bedstraw used in pioneer days to stuff bed ticks, pea vine, fringed brome and hairy wild rye. The ubiquitous Western Canada violet and wild lily-of-the-valley along with dewberry and bunchberry decorate the forest floor. Common mosses of the floor are *Mnium cuspidatum*, *Eurhynchium pulchellum*, and *Ceratodon purpureus*. Another moss, *Pylaisia polyantha*, forms stockings on the bases of practically all aspen trees.

Chokecherry

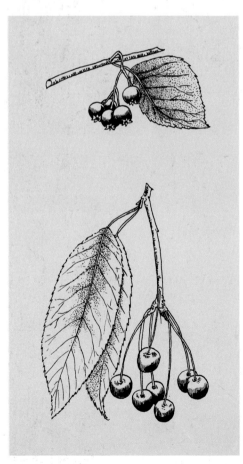

Saskatoon

Pincherry

FLOWERS OF THE ASPEN PARKLAND

(a) Wild barley
(b) Tansy
(c) Bluebells
(d) Bull thistle
(e) Three-flowered avens
(f) Mitrewort

(a)

C.H.

(c)

C.H.

(d)

C.H.

(b)

C.H.

(e)

R.D.B.

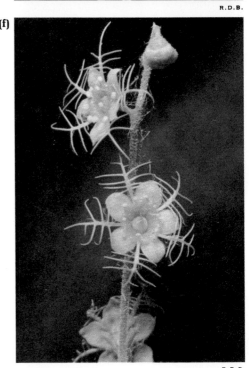

(f)

R.D.B.

Pigeon hawk in flight

Among the mammals in the aspen woodland, one of the more numerous and influential is the varying hare, so named because it turns white in winter but more often called the "snowshoe rabbit" because of its widespreading and heavily haired feet that serve as snowshoes in winter. It is noted for its peaks of abundance which occur at intervals of about 10 years. During these peaks hundreds may be found in a few acres.

The varying hare lives in thickets of hazel and saskatoon within the woodland and in dense stands of young aspen which have grown up after cutting or fire. In summer it feeds on a great variety of grasses, herbs and shrubs; in winter its main food is the bark of young aspens up to two inches in diameter. As the snow deepens, it is able to girdle these trees to several feet above the ground, thus killing them. This may result in only beneficial thinning of the stand but, during the peaks of hare abundance, whole stands of young trees may be killed.

This hare is an important item in the food supply of a variety of carnivores such as lynx, weasels, foxes, coyotes, great-horned owls and goshawks. In the periods when the varying hare is drastically reduced in numbers, these predators suffer a scarcity of food and, in turn, are reduced in numbers, unless there are enough mice and voles to sustain them. Indians and settlers also find the varying hare a source of food; but the animal is often the host of the bladder tape worm, which is a parasite of foxes, wolves and domestic dogs, whence tuleremia can be transmitted to human beings. In several ways therefore the varying hare is an important ecological factor in the aspen woodland.

Among the many birds in this woodland, the red-eyed vireo suspends well-woven pocket-type nests from branches six to 15 feet above the ground and feeds on insects and spiders. The least flycatcher, which can become quite tame, and the baltimore oriole are among the summer residents. Black-capped chickadees and two species of woodpeckers are year-round inhabitants. The ruffed grouse is frequently seen. Like the varying hare, it is periodic in abundance, fluctuating between less than one pair to six or more pairs in a square mile. This grouse nests among the litter on the forest floor, feeding on green leaves and berries in spring, summer and autumn and on buds and small twigs of aspen, birch and

144

C.H.

Magpie alighting

hazel in winter. The sharp-tailed grouse, also periodic in its number, nests on the prairies and in the woodland margins, feeding its young with grasshoppers and other insects, but winters in wooded areas, having much the same diet as the ruffed grouse. Magpies and pigeon hawks also nest here.

The slate-blue, keen-eyed goshawk, which has been briefly mentioned, also winters in the parkland. Besides varying hares its prey includes ruffed grouse, sharp-tailed grouse, squirrels, chipmunks and the mice and voles which abound in the aspen groves. The veery thrush, a summer visitor only, nests on or near the forest floor. At dusk its rich rolling song, phrased in a descending scale, enlivens the aspen groves. Like many other birds and the occasional frog which wanders into the groves, it feeds on insects.

Invertebrates are very numerous in the aspen woodland. Some, like the poplar borer beetle, injure the trees. The poplar borer drills into the heart of the aspens, inserting its eggs under the bark. The wound it makes is quickly invaded by bacteria and fungi, such as the heart rot fungus and the hypoxylon canker. These organisms may increase so rapidly that they surround the young larvae and destroy them before they can reach living tissue. Egg niches in which the larvae fail to develop subsequently heal, but stain from the fungal infection may discolor the wood for several feet outward from the wound. Periodically, too, outbreaks of the forest tent caterpillar strip the leaves from large areas of aspen poplars for several years in succession. Although the trees leaf out afresh, they are weakened by the attacks.

Sharp-tailed grouse   C.H.

Invertebrates in the leaf mold, as on the fescue grassland, are very numerous. In the latter part of June and early days of July they may reach four million individuals in each acre. Instead of ants, the most abundant species are roundworms, snails, segmented worms, centipedes, mites, spiders and insects. Ecologically, the aspen woodland supports an interesting community of shrubs, mammals, birds and invertebrates.

Creek and river communities

The valleys of streams are in general invading fingers of woodland which reach far into the parkland. Because these valleys are often fairly

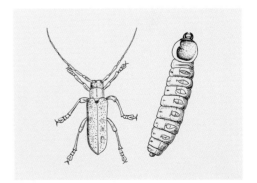

Poplar-borer beetle and larva

145

Peach-leaf willow

M. H

Mare's tail

deep, and so vary in their exposure to the sun, there are differences within them in temperature, soil moisture and humidity. Hence they nurture differing types of vegetation. As early as July 9, 1858, Captain Palliser, during his well-known expedition through the three prairie provinces, wrote a note on the Battle River near Alliance which reads in part, "the northern exposure of the river valley, as usual, was the wooded side, containing poplar, spruce, ash-leaved maple and birch, while the side of the valley by which we approached it was almost bare of wood".

Today's tree and plant life corresponds to Palliser's general statement. Valley slopes facing south and west tend to be dry, warm and occupied by prairie, but those looking north and east are cooler, moister, and covered with woodlands in which other trees are mingled with the aspens. Thus white spruce is most frequent along the north-facing slopes of the major valleys, particularly along the Battle River where it reaches from the coniferous forest near Wetaskiwin far out into the parkland. Lower in the valleys, on the wet flats near the streams, are poplars and willows. Here in the northern parkland, balsam poplar dominates, but in the southwest it shares its stands with narrow-leaf cottonwood and black cottonwood. Yellow, sandbar, and peach-leaf willows add diversity. Water or western birch, river alder and a number of herbs complete a fairly rich vegetation. Immediately along the margin of the water, there is usually a zone of tall sedges and grasses and shorter rushes. The characteristic aquatic vegetation of creeks and rivers includes algae, mosses, pondweeds, mare's tail and water-plantain. The woodland along the streams nourishes an associated animal life. As in the northern forest and the mountains, the beaver exerts a considerable ecological control on the environment by the building of dams. Low-lying lands are flooded and marshy conditions are created. Willow and aspen are cut down and, if the beaver population is not controlled by predators or trapping, the forest may be denuded for about a hundred yards back from the stream.

Before the arrival of the white man, beaver numbers were kept in balance by lynx, bears, wolves, coyotes and otters. The fur-trade period came close to exterminating the beaver and the animals that preyed on them; but with the enforcement of conservation legislation the number of beavers has again increased.

Muskrats, too, are common, but along the streams of the parkland they live in holes in the banks rather than in houses. Among the predators, mink follow the courses of the streams, feeding on muskrats, mice, voles and fish. Characteristic birds in this habitat are kingfishers and bank swallows. The latter nest in burrows in cutbanks at the water's edge. The usual insects, such as caddis-flies and mayflies, are numerous, and blood-sucking black flies are a pest. Fish are not too varied; pike, suckers, and yellow walleye are the most common species.

Lake, marsh, and wet meadow communities

When the ice sheet melted many depressions were left behind. According to their depth and the amount of water collected, these are now lakes, marshes, sloughs, or seasonal wet meadows.

Most of the parkland lakes add to the variety and attractiveness of the countryside. They are appreciated by those who enjoy swimming, boating, water-skiing and fishing; and their banks often provide secluded sites for summer cottages. These lakes vary from deep and permanent water bodies to shallow expanses, some of which are transitory. Most of the lakes are saline so that the exposed shorelines harbour plants, known as halophytes, able to live in soil with a high salt content

146

C.H.

(a) Leopard frog
(b) "Jack rabbit", really a prairie hare
(c) Silverspot butterfly
(d) Coyote hunting mice

C.H.

.D.B.

.H.

Willow-ringed slough

Among these are salt grass, samphire, sea blite, lance-leaved orache and arrow-grass.

Wave action in the larger lakes has produced firm sandy to gravelly bottoms and shorelines with the corresponding aquatic flora. In small water bodies, such as the sloughs or marshes so frequently found in the parkland, there is less wave action. In consequence, usually dense vegetation ranges from submersed aquatic and emergent aquatic plants to sedge-grass wet meadows, shrubs and poplar woods. Bulrushes and cattails are common but interesting inhabitants of these areas.

The sedge-grass wet meadow is usually flooded in the spring and summer and dry in the autumn. Rushes, the moss *Drepanocladus aduncus,* and various grasses characterize it. In the parkland, sloughs are usually ringed with willows.

The bird life which finds habitats in or around the lakes, sloughs, marshes and wet meadows is almost bewildering in its number of species and individuals. Canada geese still breed quite extensively in the more secluded parts of the parklands and the whole area has been called the main duck breeding region of North America. Mallards, pintails, shovelers, blue and green-winged teal, gadwalls and baldpates take off from the water at the approach of the visitor and redheads, canvasbacks, ruddy ducks and lesser scaups are to be seen diving for their food.

Geese and ducks are only two of the many types of birds to be found in these habitats. Red-winged and yellow-headed blackbirds, for example, nest among the cattails, bulrushes and reed grasses. During the nesting season they feed almost entirely on insects but after the young have left the nests, they descend in large flocks on the grainfields to gorge themselves with grain, weed seeds and insects. At night they return to the marshes and congregate in roosts which may accommodate thousands of birds. In the marshes are also found the American coot, horned and pied-billed grebes and the sora rail. Here, too, the pump-like call of the bitterns mingles with the squawking of black terns and the bubbling song of the long-billed marsh wrens.

As in the southern prairie, many birds, such as the white-fronted goose and the lesser snow goose, pause in the parkland only on their way to and from their nesting grounds farther north. But a number of shorebirds remain to nest. Among these are the avocet, piping plover, spotted sandpiper, willet, common snipe and killdeer. Most striking of all, perhaps, are the great blue herons. These stately birds nest in colonies in the tops of the highest trees available, adding to their huge stick nests each year until, at times, the nests become too heavy for the branches and tumble to the ground. To an observer their flight is majestic, with great black-tipped wings moving in a slow and easy rhythm, slender legs trailing behind and heads tucked in against their shoulders. They can also be seen wading in shallow water, as at Beaverhill Lake, searching for food, or posed in seemingly motionless silhouette until, suddenly, the head darts forward and downward to seize a minnow or a frog. Recently, too, the smaller black-crowned night heron has established itself in the parkland.

Mosquitoes develop in incredible numbers in the sloughs and ponds, and take to the air in June and July, a feature often noted with bitterness by early travellers who claimed that they were of enormous size. Leopard frogs, which likewise occur in numbers in these wet areas, find mosquitoes very palatable, as do many insectivorous birds such as swallows and surface-feeding ducks. Damselflies and dragonflies also consume great numbers but are in turn fed upon by kingbirds, purple martins, black terns, common terns and gulls.

Franklin's gull nests in considerable numbers in the parkland. They nest in colonies in lakes or sloughs, building their nests of reeds and grasses. This gull has adapted to agriculture and ranges for considerable distances into the fields. Flocks of them may often be seen following agricultural machinery to pick up insects. In the autumn the young gulls join their parents to work over the fields for grasshoppers and crickets. One investigator found, for example, 64 large black field crickets in the crop and gizzard of a single gull.

C.H.

Franklin's gull

The effects of man

Besides checking the annual fires, white settlement put large areas of the parkland under cultivation. Ecologically, cultivation thereby destroyed much of the natural vegetation and disrupted the food cycle running from plant and insect life up to the birds and animals. Bison, elk, moose and mule deer, together with their predators, have been either forced out of the parkland or exterminated. In their place white-tailed deer have expanded their numbers and range. Twin fawns are often produced, and triplets have been frequently recorded.

Similarly, although some species of insects and plants have been reduced in numbers, vigour or range, like fescue grass, others have benefited enormously because of cultivation. The grasshoppers, the wireworms and the cutworms have become pests. Among native plants a number have now multiplied into troublesome weeds as, for instance, the Canada fleabane and the evening primrose.

Man has also introduced so many foreign weeds that most of those which now infest fields, roadsides, and city lots have been brought in from Europe and Asia. Included among these are several species of mustard, peppergrass, Russian thistle, prickly Canada thistle, sow thistle, pigweed and stinkweed.

The settlers naturally brought in cattle and sheep which have often overgrazed the grassland and helped the weeds to spread. The introduction of the ring-necked pheasant and Hungarian partridge has turned out fortunately, but the descendants of those who, in homesickness, carried across the Atlantic Ocean the starling and the English sparrow often regret their ancestors' nostalgia.

It seems likely that in Alberta, as in the two other prairie provinces, the parkland will remain a separate zone, although its frontiers may fluctuate. Its rolling hills, wooded valleys, cultivated fields, and wave-roughened waters will continue to give it a distinctive individuality.

.H.

CHAPTER EIGHT

The Boreal Forest

GEORGE H. LA ROI
CYRIL G. HAMPSON
WILLIAM A. FULLER
EDO NYLAND

TAIGA / GEORGE H. LA ROI

Across Europe, Asia and North America stretches the broad belt of boreal *taiga,* or northern forest-and-woodland. To the north lies the tree-less arctic tundra, to the south either temperate forest, parkland, grass-land or steppe, according to the amount of precipitation. The continuous sweep of boreal taiga around the northern hemisphere is interrupted by the Atlantic Ocean, but not to any appreciable degree by the Pacific; for during the Ice Ages of the Pleistocene Epoch there were repeated oppor-tunities for the interchange of boreal as well as of arctic plants and ani-mals across the Bering Strait land bridge between Alaska and Siberia. Because of these prehistoric connections and the similarity of their habitats, the arctic tundra and boreal taiga zones of the Old and New Worlds are remarkably similar in flora and fauna.

What is taiga?

Taiga is the wooded vegetation of northern latitudes and mountain sys-tems which inhabits the climatic zone next to the colder and therefore treeless arctic and alpine tundra. Only a handful of tree species are adapted to the extremely cold winters and brief growing seasons which characterize the taiga zone. Foremost among these trees are the conifers – spruce, pine, fir and larch – and only two flowering plant genera – poplar and birch.

The northern taiga can be subdivided into three easily recognized subzones, corresponding to warmer climates from north to south.

The *Forest-Tundra* subzone is an area of transition, where tundra and taiga vegetation are intermingled. Patches of stunted trees grow only along sheltered streams and warmer habitats on a tundra landscape underlain everywhere by permafrost. The northern wooded outposts of

Title picture – Sunrise over black spruce muskeg in the boreal forest.

M.H

Boreal – Subarctic Alluvial Lowlands between Fort Smith and Fort Chipewyan. Note complex mosaic of vegetation from the interplay of the river, drainage differences and rates of successional invasion by plant population. To the left of the river are willows; behind them balsam poplars and scattered white spruce; to the right of the river are older white spruce. Much of the poplar and willow in the background may be traced to poor drainage and recent fires.

this subzone form the arctic treeline and signal the commencement of pure tundra.

In the *Subarctic Woodland subzone,* tundra vegetation is restricted to windy exposures and places where soil frost action is intense. Dense coniferous forests occur only in the most favourable sites. The subzone derives its distinctive character from vast areas where the trees grow in open formation, and the well-illuminated ground beneath is covered with low shrubs and reindeer lichens.

In the *Boreal Forest subzone,* there is no true tundra and little permafrost. Open woodlands occur in exposed or very dry regions, while spruce, larch or pine "muskegs", bogs and marshes are very common in depressions and wet flatlands. Upland areas that have escaped recent fires are occupied by dense spruce and fir forests with deep moss carpets and scattered low herbs and shrubs. Where fire has preceded establishment of the current generation of trees, then poplars, birches and pine form pure or mixed stands which are temporary in nature and are gradually replaced by those of spruce and fir.

The tundra and taiga zones extend far to the south in the higher mountain systems of Eurasia and North America, because increasing elevation compensates for decreasing latitude. Thus the alpine tundra and subalpine taiga vegetation of the mountains occur in habitats which are in many respects equivalent to those found at lower elevations to the north. Not surprisingly then, the flora and fauna of these widely-separated habitats also have much in common, especially in the Rocky Mountains of North America where subalpine taiga grades into northern taiga in Alberta and British Columbia.

Whether taiga communities first arose on northern plains or southern mountains is open to speculation. Many radical changes have taken place in regions now inhabited by such vegetation as a consequence of successive glacial and interglacial periods. During this time, there has almos

certainly been a two-way flow of evolving taiga plants and animals between the northern and subalpine parts of the zone – southbound during
glacial advance – northbound during interglacial warming. Taiga, consisting of a relatively small number of wide-ranging and exceedingly
aggressive plant and animal species, is therefore a modern evolutionary
adaptation to the ceaseless climatic changes of the Pleistocene Epoch.

Taiga in Alberta

Northern taiga forms a broad belt across North America. Starting from
the northern limit of trees at 58 degrees latitude on the Labrador Peninsula, it curves to the south around Hudson Bay and then northwest to a
northern limit of 68 degrees on the Mackenzie River delta and the Yukon
Territory. This belt averages six hundred miles in width, covering more
than half of Newfoundland, Quebec, Ontario, Manitoba, Saskatchewan,
Alberta, the Yukon Territory and Alaska.

A glance at Alberta's vegetation and topography maps will show
that subalpine taiga is prevalent in the Rocky Mountains and that boreal
taiga covers the entire northern half of the province's interior. There are
also large areas of transitional taiga in the foothills region and on the
tops or slopes of the Cypress Hills, Swan Hills, Caribou Mountains and
other isolated plateaus.

Earlier chapters have compared the climate, geology and soils of
Alberta's mountain and boreal regions. Thus we shall only emphasize

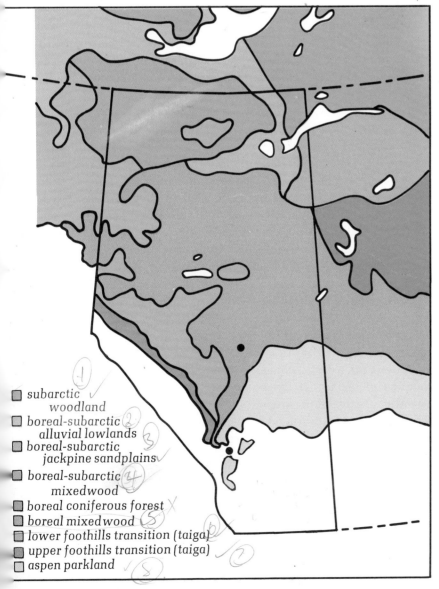

☐ subarctic
    woodland
☐ boreal-subarctic
    alluvial lowlands
☐ boreal-subarctic
    jackpine sandplains
☐ boreal-subarctic
    mixedwood
☐ boreal coniferous forest
☐ boreal mixedwood
☐ lower foothills transition (taiga)
☐ upper foothills transition (taiga)
☐ aspen parkland

**Vegetation map of the boreal forest area
(adapted from Forest Regions of Canada, by
J. S. Rowe, 1959).**

153

Slave River near its exit from Lake Athabasca in Northern Alberta.

American larch in autumn. The larch is one of the very few deciduous conifers.

what appear to be the more significant ecological differences between boreal and subalpine habitats by contrasting two typical sites. The Engelmann spruce-subalpine fir forest at an altitude of 7,500 feet in Banff National Park has more precipitation, deeper and more persistent snow cover, a shorter and cooler growing season, less extreme annual temperature variations, and more unstable soil than the white spruce-balsam fir forest near Fort McMurray. Between these two decidedly different sites there are hundreds of others which are less different in environmental conditions, and which therefore support taiga communities of intermediate character.

Although spruce-fir forests dwell in the Banff and the McMurray habitats, the species are different. Engelmann spruce is a tree of the Rocky Mountain subalpine zone, ranging as far south as Arizona. In Alberta it occurs from middle elevations to timberline, or between 5,500 and 8,000 feet. The white spruce is a boreal species, ranging from Newfoundland to Alaska. It is found throughout the northern taiga of Alberta, but is equally prominent in the foothills and lower slopes of the Rocky Mountains. Subalpine fir is mainly a tree of higher elevations, occurring in upper forested zones from the Colorado Rocky Mountains to the Mackenzie Mountains of the Yukon. It is very common in the older forests of moist upper slopes in Alberta's Rocky Mountains, but occurs in similar habitats of the foothills eastward to Lesser Slave Lake. Balsam fir is most abundant in the northern taiga of eastern Canada, but ranges westward into central Alberta where it mingles with its mountain counterpart.

Among other trees which are prominent in Alberta's taiga, the boreal jackpine yields to the lodgepole pine of the Rocky Mountains in the transitional taiga of the lower foothills and isolated plateaus. The American larch of northern muskegs is replaced by Lyall's larch in the subalpine zone of Banff, and the balsam poplar of the interior finds its mountain equivalent in the black cottonwood.

The list of pairs of boreal-subalpine species could easily be extended to other groups of organisms. From our knowledge of the history of taiga, we can safely conclude that many such pairs have a common evolutionary ancestry. Also, lest one might wrongly decide that the flora and fauna of mountain and northern taiga have completely diverged over the short duration since the last glaciation, we can point to the trembling aspen (Populus tremuloides); it is found virtually throughout the taiga

154

C.H.

Boreal — Subarctic mixedwood forest southwest of Fort Smith in Wood Buffalo National Park. Mixtures of white spruce and poplars are less susceptible to crown fires and caterpillar epidemics than are pure stands of spruce or poplar.

of North America and has a very close relative *(Populus tremula)* in Eurasia.

Only two trees of Alberta's northern forests have not been mentioned – black spruce and paper birch. Both are important species of the northern taiga, but neither is very common in the northern Rocky Mountains, nor is either of them replaced by other species in the subalpine zone farther south.

The rest of this part of the chapter will focus on those areas of Alberta which lie to the north of the aspen parkland and to the east or downslope from the subalpine zone of the mountains. In short, we shall first try to draw a general picture, then move in for a closer look at forest dynamics.

A general picture of northern taiga in Alberta

The vegetation of northern Alberta lies almost wholly within the Boreal Forest subzone of northern taiga. Only the extreme northeastern corner of the province is in the more frigid Subarctic Woodland subzone. Inside the Boreal Forest of Alberta are extensive "islands" of aspen parkland in the Grande Prairie, Peace River and Fort Vermilion areas, and some patches of transitional taiga on the isolated plateaus mentioned earlier.

Four major river systems drain most of Alberta's north country. To the west and north, the Hay River and its tributaries flow north to Great Slave Lake. To the east, the Athabasca flows north to the lake of the same name. The Peace River, after junction with the Smoky River, flows first north then northeast to its delta on Lake Athabasca. This lake is drained by the broad Slave River which, like the Hay, discharges into Great Slave Lake. The outlet of Great Slave Lake is the beginning of the Mackenzie River. Thus most of northern Alberta drains northward to

C.H.

Fort Fitzgerald rapids on the Slave River. Note the large white spruce on the islands. Their size is due to protection from fires which often swept the adjacent countryside.

Alluvial wetland vegetation surrounding islands of upland mixedwood forest and woodland near Lake Athabasca. In left foreground is a sedgewillow marsh grading to the right into a willow dwarf-birch swamp. Note raised levees along the river supporting balsam poplar forest. The ridges and low hills in the background contain spruce, birch, poplar and pine, bordered by bands of transitional vegetation due to increasing moisture.

the Arctic Ocean. The profusion of lakes, ponds, sloughs and muskegs in the region results largely from glacial modifications of the topography

Based on distinctive climate, topography, soils and associated vegetation, we can easily recognize four sections in Alberta's Boreal Forest

The *Boreal Mixedwood section* is by far the largest, covering abou 80,000 square miles and bordering on the aspen parkland. Glaciation o the underlying Cretaceous shales has produced a thick mantle of clay rich soil materials and a rolling morainal topography. Later erosion and re-deposition in postglacial lakes, which have since drained, have pro duced extensive flatlands. Fertile gray-wooded soils have developed or upland terrain, and these have encouraged the growth of moderately productive "mixedwood" forests.

Such forests contain varying combinations of deciduous poplar and evergreen white spruce, hence the name. The undergrowth is often very lush and rich in species of plants and animals, especially where poplar are dominant in the tree canopy. There is a marked tendency for white spruce, sometimes with balsam fir, to replace poplar in the older forests This trend is checked by frequent fires which encourage poplar growth by wiping out the spruce and fir and allowing reproduction by sucker from surviving poplar roots.

Vast expanses of slow-growing black spruce muskeg and larch swamp cover the poorly-drained lowlands and flats. These are associate with varying thicknesses of waterlogged peat, and the trees are widely spaced or in close formation according to the depth of the water table Very wet habitats are the willow swamps and reed marshes, the favoure breeding grounds for countless waterfowl. Jackpine woodlands are th characteristic vegetation of sand hills.

The *Boreal-Subarctic Mixedwood section* is essentially an impover ished version of the boreal mixedwood, for it is located on similar so materials in the extreme north of the province where the climate i colder and drier and permafrost is a limiting factor in many habitats Poplar and white spruce mixedwoods are common on the better uplan soils, but, since the harsh climate favours slow growth and frequent fires these usually look inferior to their southern fellows. Upland sites wit coarser soils often contain mixtures of spruce, pine and larch – but littl or no poplar. Very dry ridges are inhabited by open-growth jackpin woodlands with a patchy ground cover of low shrubs and reinde lichens.

156

Seemingly endless stretches of wet peatland dominate much of the flat terrain. Viewed from above, the alternating areas of acidic black spruce muskeg, alkaline larch swamp and watery sedge "fens" become organized into complicated geometric patterns. These seem to result from a combination of frost-action, water and nutrient flow, and a cyclical regeneration of the vegetation itself.

The *Boreal-Subarctic Alluvial Lowlands section* is very similar climatically but radically different in soil origin compared to the adjacent mixedwood sections. The Peace and Athabasca Rivers have deposited millions of tons of sediment along their lower reaches and in the west end of Lake Athabasca, forming broad alluvial lowlands and an immense delta. The valley of the Slave River is really the sediment-filled south arm of a once "Greater" Slave Lake.

The meandering of these rivers has produced an exceedingly complex and changing pattern of flood terraces, levees, abandoned channels and other distinctive features. The typical alluvial soil is a loosely-compacted silt, fairly high in nutrients and well supplied with water. Such favourable rooting conditions, when combined with long hours of summer sun, have produced habitats of surprisingly high productivity, considering the intensely cold winters of the region.

Lower and middle river terraces are nearly everywhere clothed by impressive high forests of pure white spruce or spruce that is replacing balsam poplar. The trees are often 130 feet or more tall and over 200 years old. The shrub and herb layers of these forests are very luxuriant, but the mosses are less common due to annual flooding. These impressive forests may develop following successive colonization of fresh alluvium, first by horsetails (species of the ancient genus *Equisetum*), then by willows and alders, and finally by balsam poplar and spruce. Or they may arise subsequent to fire and a different successional pattern involving birch as well as poplar. In striking contrast to the mixedwood sections, the white spruce is able to ascend quickly to a position of absolute dominance on the younger terraces of the Alluvial Lowlands section, perhaps because favourable growth conditions tend to accelerate succession rates.

The *Boreal-Subarctic Jackpine Sand Plain section* lies between the Athabasca River Lowlands and the Saskatchewan provincial boundary, where the underlying Precambrian sandstones have been glacially altered to form a lake-studded sand plain. Sandy uplands are generally inhabited by park-like woodlands of slow-growing jackpine with ground carpets of reindeer lichens and drought-resistant shrubs. In moister places, black spruce and mosses sometimes replace the jackpine and lichens. Fires are intense and frequent in the region.

The *Subarctic Woodland section* is north of Lake Athabasca and east of the Slave River Lowlands. Here lies the only continuous area of exposed Precambrian Shield bedrock in the northern taiga of Alberta. Successive passages of the Keewatin ice sheet have left great expanses of resistant crystalline rocks and little raw material for the development of mineral soil. The combination of little or no soil and truly subarctic climate has produced a remarkably austere landscape consisting of two major habitats – dry rocky uplands and nutrient-poor lakes.

The uplands feature scattered and diminutive jackpine, black spruce and paper birch, growing in rock fissures and moist pockets. The remaining rock surfaces are either partially covered by lichens or occupied by hardy shrubs or grasses rooted in crevices and decaying vegetative material. Fire has a devastating effect in this area, for it not only removes the sparse plant cover and thereby decreases the upland "catch"

M.H.

Northern river terraces near Lake Athabasca

Dry rocky uplands of the Open Subarctic Woodland subzone north of Lake Athabasca. Note grasses and drought-resistant shrubs and herbs rooted in rock fissures and small depressions, with lichens and a few mosses.

Birch clump and dwarf jackpine on the glacially-scoured Precambrian Shield of northeastern Alberta. In the foreground, yarrow and grasses are rooted in rock fissures.

of snow and its potentially valuable melt-water, but consumes most of the moisture-storing humus as well.

Transitional taiga in Alberta

Between the main region of northern taiga and the subalpine zone of the mountains, there are several large areas at middle elevations in Alberta possessing taiga vegetation which is intermediate in flora and fauna. These areas may be recognized by the appearance of lodgepole pine in burned-over places and by the dominance of white spruce in old upland stands. This transitional taiga easily falls into two sections based on elevation and on the importance of poplar in the forests.

The *Lower Foothills section* includes elevations between 3,000 and 4,000 feet in the approaches to the Rocky Mountains. It also covers the upper reaches of the Cypress Hills, Swan Hills, Pelican Mountains, Clear Hills, Naylor Hills and Caribou Mountains. Here, in upland forests following fire, trembling aspen and balsam poplar along with lodgepole pine play a prominent rôle. Black spruce muskegs identical to those of northern taiga are also present.

The *Upper Foothills section* is much smaller in extent than the Lower Foothills section but quite distinct from it. It lies parallel to the front range of the Rocky Mountains and above the lower foothills, in places reaching 6,000 feet in elevation. In this section the forests are almost exclusively coniferous, and poplars and birch are very rare indeed. The number of mountain species is large, and the subalpine fir often shares dominance with white spruce and black spruce over the other species in the older stands.

Some aspects of the mixedwood upland forest

We shall now examine more closely one of the most widespread and ecologically significant forest communities in the taiga of boreal Alberta. This is the mixedwood forest community of moderately fertile upland habitats, one with which many Albertans are familiar, and one through which visitors to the north must travel.

Perhaps the best way to begin a description of the mixedwood upland forest community is to start with an inspection of two simpler phases, the trembling aspen forest and the white spruce forest. Thus we can stress the controlling influence of the tree layer by witnessing the contrasting effects of aspen and spruce upon their environment, as first one and then the other dominates an area. Then we shall put the two simpler phases together, and develop a synthetic picture of the more complex phase where both species are present. Finally, we shall trace the theoretical natural history of an undisturbed stand over a 500-year period, and then show how fire alters the normal sequence of events. In this analysis, we shall assume that all phases and events occur on identical, rolling, morainal upland sites with moderately well-drained, gray-wooded soils and a typically boreal Alberta climatic setting.

The aspen-dominated mixedwood forest

In the trembling aspen stand the living trees are 60 years old and about 80 feet tall. They have smooth, gray-green trunks which retain no branches near the ground and are capped by shallow, convex crowns intermingling to form a stippled summer-green canopy, in which the leaves flutter on the slightest breeze. This canopy intercepts only a moderate amount of sunlight and rainfall, allowing the remainder to fall upon the stand interior. When the leaves drop in autumn, the forest becomes much more open to sun, wind, rain and snow.

Here and there amid the living trees, either fallen or still standing, are dead aspens of assorted smaller sizes in various stages of decomposition. These trees have been eliminated through the quiet but vigorous competition within the aspen population for light, water and nutrients. This struggle began with the establishment of the stand and will continue to its end. Whether this tree or that one survives depends largely on their relative growth rates and the maintenance of a sunny exposure. These two factors, in turn, are strongly influenced by reductions in the photosynthetic output of the leafy crowns, that is, in the use by leaves of sunlight combined with plant nutrients for the manufacture of food. These reductions in photosynthesis can come from insect predation or through damage by wind and ice. Another controlling factor is the relative amount of water and nutrients readily available to the root systems of the competing trees.

Moving into the warm, sun-flecked stand interior, we find that it is difficult to see the ground surface through the profusion of shrubby and herbaceous vegetation. This lush undergrowth consists of numerous shrubs reaching to the waist, even more shrubs and tall herbs reaching the calf, and under these, dense patches of dwarf shrubs and low herbs at ankle height. Pushing aside this leafy growth, we see that the forest floor is matted with moist, rapidly-decaying and nutrient-rich aspen leaves together with a sprinkling of twigs and other detritus and a host of ants, worms and other invertebrate animals. True mineral soil lies about three inches below the litter surface and is crowded with roots. Fallen logs and tree bases rise above this leafy litter, harbouring mixtures of shade-tolerant mosses.

Boreal mixedwood forest of trembling aspen and jackpine in autumn. Note the abundant aspen sprouts on the left. Dense shrub and herb layers prevent successful seedling establishment by jackpine but shade-tolerant white spruce will eventually replace both aspen and jackpine.

H.

159

Among the more abundant medium shrubs are the mooseberry, saskatoon, red osier dogwood, red raspberry and, in drier areas, hazel and buffalo-berry. The lower shrubs commonly include prickly rose, red and other currants, bracted honeysuckle and snowberry. With or just below these are large numbers of wild sarsaparilla, hairy lungwort, asters, wild pea, vetch, blue-joint, and in drier openings, pine grass. Of the many dwarf shrub and low herb species the following are most numerous: twin-flower, strawberry, bunchberry, bishop's cap, horsetails, dwarf raspberry and several wintergreens. There are signs of change in this aspen stand. Hidden amongst the shrubs and herbs one finds occasional seedlings and young trees of white spruce; but only rarely do we find young trembling aspen, though the canopy above sends down millions of seeds each year.

It is of historic and geographic interest that half of the plant species and all but one genus listed above occur in similar forests of the Eurasian boreal taiga.

The spruce-dominated mixedwood forest

The living trees in the white spruce stand are mostly about 70 years old and 80 feet tall, but the range in age and size is somewhat greater than in the aspen forest. The spruce trunks have thin, ashy-brown scaly bark retain small dead branches near the ground, and are topped by deep, pyramidal evergreen crowns. These crowns do not intermingle to the same extent as those of aspen, but they are far denser and therefore much more effective absorbers of light. Their needles also catch and return to the atmosphere much of the water in light summer showers, thus strongly reducing precipitation as well as light intensity in the forest interior throughout the year. Evidence of competitive thinning in the maturing spruce forest is similar to that for aspen, except that overtopped and suppressed trees seem to "hang on" longer before capitulating.

As we move into the summer spruce forest, we quickly notice the remarkable change in climate from that outside. The interior is far cooler and the light more subdued than in the aspen forest. The air is humid and still, thick with the scent of sun-warmed spruce needles from above and the distinctive essence of mosses from beneath our feet. Instead of wading through a mass of woody and herbaceous plants, we walk upon soft carpets of "feather" mosses, interrupted only occasionally by localized patches of dwarf shrubs and low herbs, by accumulations of spruce needles around the bases of trees, or by piles of spruce cone scales harvested by red squirrels. Medium and low shrubs are far less numerous here than in the aspen stand; those few present are straggly and bear little or no fruit.

Three feather mosses dominate the forest floor: *Hylocomium splendens, Pleurozium schreberi* and *Ptilium crista-castrensis*. These same three species produce similar carpets throughout the taiga of both North America and Eurasia. The living green part of the moss carpet in our spruce stand is about three inches thick, and is permeated with spruce needles. Below this level the moss parts are clearly discernible though colourless for an inch or so, but then begin to disintegrate along with the spruce needles into a moist, cottony fermentation layer of white or yellow fungal threads. The next two inches consist of a blackish-brown acidic peat-like material, with a network of roots lying on the gray surface of the mineral soil.

Among the more persistent and successful shrubs rooted in or through the moss carpet are green alder, mooseberry and prickly rose. The most extensive colonies of dwarf shrubs and low herbs are dominated by

Spruce-dominated forest

M.H.

bunchberry, twin-flower, horsetails, wintergreens, wild lily-of-the-valley, cowberry and northern comandra.

A careful search of the forest floor eventually finds a few very slow-growing white spruce "seedlings", some rooted in the cracks of rotting logs, others growing in places where the mineral soil has been exposed by disturbance of the moss carpet.

Environmental conditions in the mixedwood forest

The preceding descriptions of two extreme phases of the mixedwood community should make it clear that trembling aspen and white spruce trees are as different in their influence on their surroundings as they are in appearance. We are now going to look into some of the factors which seem to be responsible for the marked differences in habitat, vegetation structure, flora and fauna which distinguish the two stands. Bear in mind that the original physical environment was the same for each.

The contrasting effects of deciduous broad leaves and evergreen needle leaves are of crucial significance. The amount of solar energy reaching the aspen stand interior is greater at all seasons, and much greater after leaf fall than that percolating through the relatively unchanging spruce canopy. As a result, photosynthetic production and consumer food supply can be far higher among the shrubs and herbs under the aspen trees than is possible for the feather mosses under the spruce canopy. In the spring, direct heating of the aspen forest floor by the sun quickly melts the snow-pack and warms the soil. In the white spruce stand, the melting and warming process takes longer, since it is caused only by the diffuse light from the sky and the indirect conduction of heat by air and rain. Hence many shrubs and herbs are leafing out and flowering before the aspen canopy forms and before the last trace of snow finally disappears from the shaded moss carpet of the spruce forest.

There are other factors which add to the differing effects of aspen and spruce on the habitats and organisms beneath them. During the short boreal growing season and well on into autumn, the air and soil temperatures of the aspen stand interior are higher than those under spruce. Warmer conditions permit more rapid growth of shoots and roots and a generally faster pace of metabolic activity among organisms residing under aspen. In winter, however, soil temperatures are usually higher among the spruce because of the insulating layers of the evergreen canopy, moss carpet and deep snow. Sometimes, though, when there is no wind to accompany or follow the snow, the spruce canopy holds so much snow that the vegetation and soil profile below the crowns are exposed and therefore colder than under aspen.

About two-thirds of a light summer rain shower and one-fifth of a heavy downpour never reach the spruce forest floor but cling to the needles and twigs and gradually evaporate. The feather moss carpet soaks up most of the effective rainfall, yielding only the excess to the humus and mineral soil beneath. The comparatively open aspen canopy allows much more rain to fall through directly, as well as to collect and drip from the leaves or run down the smooth trunks. With no moss carpet to intercept it, the water can percolate through the leaf litter into the rooting zone.

The combination of water interception by canopy and moss carpet causes periodic dessication of the humus and upper mineral soil of the spruce stand, precisely where the root systems of many shrubs and herbs are most concentrated. At such times competition for moisture becomes extreme, and poorly-adapted species fail to produce seed and suffer drought damage or die. But even during periods of prolonged drought, the moss carpet simply stops growing, dries out and waits for rain. When

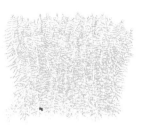

Feather mosses

Ptilium crista-castrensis

Pleurozium schreberi

Hylocomium splendens

161

C.H.

Park-like mixedwood forest near Fort Smith. Shrub and herb layers are poorly developed but feather moss carpets with patches of reindeer lichens are common. Note young trees of white spruce in centre foreground and large old jackpine in centre background.

rain does come, the mosses undergo a remarkably fast resurrection.

Of the many hundreds of seeds carried into the spruce stand by wind, water and animals, only a scant few are able to germinate and send roots down far and fast enough to escape fatal water deficits in the thick moss carpet and underlying humus layer. Even shade-tolerant white spruce seedlings cannot cope with these conditions, and far more often become successfully established on rotting logs where the water content is less variable. Most of the relatively permanent herb and shrub inhabitants of the spruce forest that we have mentioned reproduce vegetatively therein by means of underground stems, bulbs or runners, thereby avoiding the critical seedling stage. The seed-bearing fruits of these plants are eaten by or adhere to animals, so that at least some unharmed seeds are deposited in favourable germination sites outside the spruce stand.

We may well ask ourselves why there is no moss carpet in the aspen forest. One reason is that mosses have no true roots but get most of their water by direct absorption from falling rain or melting snow. Prolonged daily exposure to direct sunlight would tend to keep the moss plant dry most of the summer, thus preventing growth except for brief periods after rainfall. Another reason, perhaps more important here, is that spruce needles are shed gradually and rain down upon the moss carpet throughout the year. Because of their small size and narrow shape, they are then easily enveloped and buried by the growing feather mosses. On the other hand, aspen leaves are shed completely and quickly, often in less than a week's time. This sudden deluge of large, broad leaves produces a many-layered roof on the forest floor, enough to smother any potential moss carpet. In addition, the summer light intensity beneath successive leafy canopies of trees, shrubs and herbs in the aspen forest is very low and may in itself tend to inhibit the growth of all but the most shade-tolerant woodland mosses.

162

Old spruce needles are tough in texture and strongly acid in composition. Very few species of vertebrate or invertebrate animals will eat them. Combined with dead moss parts at the bottom of the cool moss carpet, they do form a suitable energy source for those fungi, termed saprotrophic, which feed on dead organic materials. Even the fungi, however, cannot completely utilize the needle-moss mixture, and the partially decomposed peat-like remains gradually pile up as the spruce forest grows older. As water percolates down through the moss carpet and peaty layer, it picks up free organic acids and carries them into the mineral soil. Here the acids tend to displace and leach away essential nutrient compounds. Meanwhile other nutrients are imprisoned in the substance of the peaty material and are for the most part unavailable for use by green plants. The product of interaction between spruce needles, mosses, fungi, low temperature and water percolation is an acid-rich and nutrient-poor rooting medium, which approaches or exceeds the limits of tolerance of many plant and animal species that thrive in the aspen forest.

In contrast, dead aspen leaves are quite palatable and are therefore readily eaten by many invertebrate animals. By the middle of summer, most of the previous year's leaf fall has been consumed by thousands of detritus-feeders, and the egested wastes passed on to a host of secondary consumers, from earthworms to bacteria. In this way the energy bound up in the litter of the aspen stand is largely captured by consumer and decomposer organisms, and then released as respiratory heat. As a result, the mass of organic matter in the litter declines rapidly as free carbon dioxide is respired to the air. The remaining humus materials are thoroughly mixed with the mineral soil by burrowing animals. The thorough decomposition of the aspen leaves permits a fast and efficient release of nutrient compounds which are quickly absorbed and re-cycled into use by the roots of all green plants in the stand. Thus the interaction between aspen leaves, detritus feeders, decomposer organisms and warm, moist conditions ensures the production and maintenance of a non-acidic and fertile rooting medium for many boreal plants and the organisms which live among, or feed upon them.

The hybridization of habitat

Now that we have seen what takes place in separate stands of trembling aspen and white spruce, we ask ourselves what happens in a stand where the two trees are mixed. If we assume that the size and number of trees of each species are equal, then the answer depends upon the degree of intermingling of the two populations at different places in the stand. At one extreme, they may be so thoroughly mixed that any small plot usually contains as many spruce as aspen. At the other extreme, the two species may be completely separated except along a line that crosses the area. Nature usually steers a middle course between the two extremes for a variety of reasons having to do with stand origin and the pattern of local disturbances, or with slight differences in topography or soil, or with reproductive distinctions between the trees.

Thus in our "typical" mixedwood upland stand we find small clumps of pure aspen and spruce scattered in a larger area of varying combinations of the two. The subordinate vegetation layers in the centre of the pure clumps closely resemble those of the two stands already described. Layers under mixed canopies are in many respects predictably intermediate or transitional in appearance, but in other ways quite different. For example, certain plant and animal species with only feeble representation in both spruce and aspen stands – such as the ruffed grouse – are much more common in areas where the two trees are intermingled.

Twig and cone of white spruce

C.H

Close-up of mixedwood forest floor. Note feather moss carpet, jackpine needles, narrow-leaved bearberry, round-leaved wintergreen and occasional reindeer lichens.

Other species are present here but missing entirely from spruce and aspen. These facts seem curious.

Part of the explanation appears to lie in what has aptly been called "hybridization of the habitat". There are two aspects to such hybridization – quantitative and qualitative. The former is easily understood, for it simply refers to the production of environmental conditions, light, for example, of which the intensities are between those of either pure aspen or pure spruce. Species better adapted to such intermediate habitats will prosper in them, often at the expense of competing species.

The qualitative aspect refers to the synthesis of different kinds of habitat conditions or components from precursors in the pure spruce and pure aspen stands. A simplified example will illustrate this. Some of the organic products of decomposition in a mixture of decaying aspen leaves and spruce needles do not occur in either unmixed rotting aspen leaves or unmixed old spruce needles. These "new" organic compounds form necessary links in a food chain of decomposer microorganisms which now proceed to convert the litter into a distinctive kind of humus found only under mixedwood canopies. This "new" humus in turn, is a favorable rooting medium for several flowering plants which do not occur in either the aspen or the spruce stands. The humus also tilts the competitive balance in favor of certain species which were of only minor importance in the pure stands.

In addition to the changes caused by the hybridization of the habitat and perhaps as an extension of its effects, some birds and other animals make use of both the aspen and spruce forest communities. A warbler for example, may nest in the spruce forest canopy but prey upon insects feeding in the aspen canopy or the leafy growth beneath it. Similarly large mammals like the moose use the shrub layer under the aspen as winter forage, but retreat into the spruce cover for shelter. Thus the close proximity of food and shelter in the mixedwood forest attracts new inhabitants and their associated influences which might not survive, given pure spruce or aspen.

Thus we see that the mixedwood forest community is more than the sum of its parts. The two trees which control its development have very different ecological effects on their surroundings.

The forest sequence

Suppose now that we were able to visit the same plot of upland, mixedwood forest at ten-year intervals over a period of 500 years, and that our observations and measurements began in a relatively pure trembling aspen forest like the one described earlier. We will further assume that man and his plant and animal colleagues have been absent for the whole period, to avoid interruptions of what is at the outset a very complex and poorly understood natural history. We may now ask what changes the passage of time is likely to bring.

If there are no fires and seed is available from surrounding vegetation, we shall first of all find a slowly-increasing number of shade-tolerant young white spruce trees becoming established in the lower layers of the aspen stand. Because of intense competition for light, water and nutrients with the surrounding herbs, shrubs and trees, the growth rate of the invading spruce population is at first very slow, and many seedlings perish during dry spells or are smothered under a blanket of aspen leaves. As time goes by, however, the young spruce trees begin to overtop and suppress their competition, and begin to alter their surroundings in the manner described earlier.

Meanwhile, the rate of increase in size of the short-lived aspen trees slackens perceptibly. Injuries arising from grazing animals, various insects and the weather continue to provide access to wood-rotting fungi, which subsequently prepare the trees for wind breakage. In this way, the number of healthy aspen declines, and gaps appear in the tree canopy. From time to time, slight disturbances of the forest floor cause the production of leafy suckers from aspen roots near the surface. Because these suckers cannot stand shade and animals prefer them as forage, few last very long. Consequently, as openings appear in the aging aspen canopy, they are usually occupied by white spruce, not aspen.

The replacement of one distinctive phase of the mixedwood community by another is a long process. The lingering old aspen trees continue to exert great influence on the physical, chemical and biological properties of the developing spruce stand. Even after the last veteran aspen has fallen, many years pass before the soil, flora and fauna of the aspen forest are completely succeeded by those of spruce. It seems, indeed, that the best growth of the spruce forest is made before the relatively high potential production of the aspen habitat has been depleted.

After the replacement has been effected, the white spruce-feather moss forest with its associated patches of shrubs and herbs persists for more than a century, chiefly because the life-span of the individual spruce trees often exceeds 200 years. During this period of little obvious change in anything but the size of trees, the layer of acidic needle-moss peat steadily thickens. As a result, the roots of the spruce and other plants are forced to adjust so as to maintain adequate supplies of moisture and oxygen. These adjustments, coupled with declining nutrient availability, reduce the abundance of many shrubs and herbs, permit the establishment of better-adapted species, and also increase the danger of wind-induced fall of the spruce. Although the mature white spruce trees are prolific seed-producers, few of their seedlings survive for long in the moss carpet below. Occasional stunted spruce may be seen on the rotted

165

remains of aspen or spruce, but their growth rate appears to be nil and the proportion of dead individuals is high.

Eventually time catches up with the spruce forest. Decay becomes wide-spread. Storms take their toll. Openings appear in the canopy and increasing amounts of direct sunlight reach the forest floor. Seedlings of trees, shrubs and herbs appear on the fallen trunks and mounds of upthrown mineral soil from uprooted trees. As the ground warms and decomposition rates accelerate, the moss carpet weakens and is buried here and there by the leaves of flowering plants. These plants make use of the increased light energy as well as the nutrients released by decomposition. The new generation of trees, except for a weak mixture of short-lived balsam fir and paper birch, consists again almost entirely of white spruce. This time, however, there are marked discrepancies in size and age from place to place in the stand because replacement goes on in a patchwork pattern.

The period of habitat rejuvenation is short and far from complete. Before long the thin coating of well decomposed humus is buried beneath the resurgent moss carpet and the spruce forest becomes even more austere and slow-growing than before. Because of the steady decline in productivity of the area, the span of time leading to the next destruction of the canopy is still longer. Here our story must begin to fade out, but it would appear likely that the next generation of trees will include moderate numbers of acid-tolerant *black* spruce and its associates, and that the peat-bound habitat will become more and more like that of an impoverished lowlands muskeg.

Yes, but what if . . . ?

We shall now try to deal with just two of the many questions that arise from this brief historical sketch. First, we have tacitly assumed that the surrounding countryside contained a rich fund of plant and animal species ready to participate in the sequence. For example, if there had been no spruce seed available, then the original aspen stand might well have perpetuated itself, as indeed often happens in the aspen parkland belt. Again, if only a few white spruce had become established by the time the aspen canopy began to show gaps, then the chances are that the succeeding stand would have resembled the mixedwood mosaic described earlier. In this case, the trend toward a white spruce-feather moss forest would have been delayed until the few spruce present reached maturity and released a good crop of successful seedlings.

The most precarious assumption in the sequence, however, is that the observation area somehow escaped fire for about 500 years! Anyone who has lived or travelled in central or northern Alberta knows that fire, catastrophic though it may seem, is surely a normal feature of the boreal forest. For example, the records for 1957 show that more than 20 per cent of the entire boreal forest area, including lowlands, was burned over at least once in the short interval of 15 years. Since white settlement, the frequency of forest fires has risen. Yet there is convincing evidence from burn scars on old trees and charcoal in the soil that lightning, Indians and other agents caused vast conflagrations long before the arrival of the first white explorers, fur trappers and traders.

Fires are usually more frequent and more intense and travel farther in coniferous than broadleaf forests. Crown fires in the highly inflammable spruce forest are extremely hot, and the convection winds which they generate in the lower atmosphere often drive them forward at great speed. Surface fires may or may not accompany or be accompanied by crown fires. When following a period of drought, surface fires frequently consume all litter, the moss carpet and the peat layer down to the mineral

R.MC.

FLOWERS OF THE NORTHERN FOREST

(a) Yellow paintbrush
(b) Marsh marigold
(c) Canada anemone
(d) Goldenrod
(e) Twining honeysuckle
(f) Cottongrass
(g) Canada columbine

C.H.

M.H.

C.H.

C.H.

C.H.

167

Autumn in open subarctic woodlands north of Lake Athabasca. Part of the "last frontier."

Jackpine

soil. Sometimes, however, such fires will dip under wet moss carpets and travel in the dry peat layer, killing rooted plants but sparing the mosses. Hot fires are especially common around the dry, needle and cone-strewn bases of spruce trees.

Few plants or slow-moving animals survive the holocaust which leads to a thoroughly burned spruce forest. But if the exposed mineral soil is a good one, then much of the nutrient materials released from bondage by fire in the form of ash will wash into the soil to produce a very favorable seed-bed. The area will then be rapidly invaded by a succession of fast-growing plant and animal populations. The result will be a mixed "fire-forest" dominated by seed trees of spruce, pine and birch, with occasional aspen and balsam poplar.

Even if all of the organic matter in the original spruce forest was not removed by fire, the increased illumination and amount of nutrients would encourage the growth of a multitude of plants and animals not found in the original spruce forest. Thus even a moderate fire produces a better rejuvenation than that following temporary breakup of an old spruce canopy with no fire. Barring further disturbance, however, the shade-intolerant pines and birches of the fire forest are slowly replaced by white spruce as the community reverts to the feather moss phase.

The volume of inflammable material is much less in the aspen forest, because decomposition rates usually keep up with accumulation rates, thus preventing the formation of thick litter and duff layers. Crown fires, too, are almost unheard of, for the leaves and branches of aspen are much less readily burned than are those of spruce. As a result, fires do not last long or travel fast in the aspen habitat, even after prolonged drought. Furthermore, after racing through a spruce forest, fires are frequently deflected or halted along the aspen forest margin.

As a rule, however, surface fires generate sufficient heat to kill the aspen tree tops indirectly, by girdling their trunk bases. But such fires are either not hot enough or are of insufficient duration to kill the subterranean parts of aspen and many of its associated species. Within weeks, in great contrast to the spruce forest, most of the plants of the aspen forest push forth vigorous sprouts, and virtually the entire community is rebuilt in less than 30 years. Under such conditions, the opportunity for successful seedling invasion is slim indeed.

Significantly enough, white spruce is *not* among those species which are able to regenerate vegetatively from surviving root systems. Thus at any time in the slow process of succession from aspen to spruce, the incidence of fire is disastrous for the spruce and a boon to the aspen.

In the mixedwood mosaic forest, fire may be intense in the pockets of pure spruce but light elsewhere. If so, then the aspen may expand at the expense of spruce, or the spruce may successfully re-establish itself in its old haunts by seed from unburned crowns or from nearby individual spruce trees which escaped the fire because of protection by aspen. We may therefore be pardoned for speculating that the mixedwood forest, the most common upland forest in Alberta's boreal taiga, is an evolutionary adaptation to fire, at the community level of biological organization.

SUMMER ANIMALS / CYRIL G. HAMPSON

The northern forests are by no means devoid of animal life. In spring and summer, thousands of birds wing their way to their depths to breed and nest. Everywhere can be heard the chirrup of the robin, the cheerful call of the chickadee and the nasal cry of the nuthatch, a tiny black-crowned bird that can be seen cautiously creeping, head first, down the trunk of a poplar or a birch. If we are fortunate, we will glimpse ruby-crowned kinglets among the spruce branches or glossy-black ravens on the wing, or broad-winged hawks soaring in the sky. Red-winged blackbirds nest around the margins of lakes. The myrtle warbler, the purple finch and the rose-breasted grosbeak add their delightful songs, and the northern shrike breeds and hunts its prey in these surroundings. Among the most interesting nest-builders is the ovenbird, which fashions a globular home with a rounded entrance on the side. The rusty blackbird, lesser yellow-legs, solitary sandpiper and several species of thrush may also be observed. Nighthawks nest on the forest floor, laying their two eggs in the cool moss. At dusk their erratic flight and booming power dives in search of insects are intriguing to watch. Other insect-eaters – particularly warblers and flycatchers – abound.

Peregrine falcon   C.H.

Waterfowl of many species nest along or near the shores of the multitudinous ponds, sloughs and lakes or in marshy areas. Among the ducks, the mallard, with head and neck of iridescent green, and the green-winged teal are conspicuous. Grebes are numerous in the woodland lakes and every now and then we may hear the weird call of a loon. In the trees around these woodland lakes Bonaparte's gull nests. Upon hatching, the chicks jump to the ground and are conducted to the nearest water by their parents. Other species of gulls range widely, and in the sky above the ponds and lakes soars the osprey, often called the fish hawk, watching with keen eyes for prey. With wings closed, it suddenly plummets into the water to reappear triumphantly, a fish in its talons.

Even more striking than the white and black osprey is the peregrine falcon. This is essentially the same falcon which was flown by kings and princes during the Middle Ages in Europe when the art of falconry flourished. Today, in the more open country along northern water courses, it kills its prey in the air, diving upon a duck or a grouse at air speeds said to reach 200 miles an hour. Another memorable migratory bird is the long-legged, long-necked great blue heron, which builds its bulky nest in the tops of waterside trees and is sometimes seen flapping its way across marshes and lakes.

Northern flying squirrel

C.H.

C.H

Mule deer with antlers in the velvet

C.H.

Richardson's owl in its nesting site

Some birds, like the chickadee, are year-round residents. In some parts of the forest the blue jay is a bright flash of colour in winter as well as in summer. Its cousin, the Canada jay, popularly known as the whiskeyjack or camp robber, is a friendly scamp well-known to travellers. The ruffed and spruce grouse, the Richardson's owl, hawk owl and goshawk also make the boreal forest their preferred habitat.

Mammals, too, are present. The red squirrel disturbs the silence with its chatter, and the nocturnal flying squirrel glides on its extended membranes from upper to lower branches in flights of many yards. Woodchucks dig their dens wherever the ground is suitable, porcupines stroll through the woods and we often come upon muskrat houses and beaver dams and lodges. The whole of the northern forest – and the mixedwood section in particular – is a favoured habitat of the American black bear. This powerful animal, weighing on an average between 250 and 300 pounds, can sometimes be seen fishing in the streams or hunting through the woods or in the meadows for berries, roots, snakes, insects and the rest of its well-nigh omnivorous diet.

Before agricultural settlement, the wapiti or elk used to roam widely from about Calgary and Red Deer northward through the aspen parkland and the boreal forest to near Lake Athabasca. In 1810, Alexander Henry the Younger saw large herds of elk near Edmonton and to the southwest of it. By 1903 only about 75 elk were left in the Beaver Hills. Like the pronghorn and the bison, the elk was facing extinction. In 1906, however, Elk Island National Park was reserved for them, and the remnant was saved and now has increased. Similarly, in the south where elk had once ranged as far east as the Cypress Hills, the last survivor was said to have been shot in 1927. However, in the 1920's the Alberta Wildlife Service reintroduced it to the Cypress Hills plateau. In northern Alberta, although the range of the elk is still much reduced, its branching antlers and brownish pelt can still be seen in the southwest part of the area.

C.H.

Wapiti

The elk's bulk of from 600 to 900 pounds is exceeded by that of the moose, which weighs from 800 to 1,400 pounds. The moose, too, has disappeared from the aspen parkland but is still found in the boreal forest and western foothills. It prefers regions of weedy lakes, marshes and sluggish streams. Here it feeds in summer on underwater and other aquatic plants, and can sometimes be seen deep in the water with head submerged as it searches for food. In winter it browses on deciduous shrubs and trees. The hanging tuft of hair and skin at the throat helps identify the moose, and so does its hoarse bellowing in the mating season. Mule deer also occur in much of the boreal forest and in winter the caribou retreat to it. In the northeast of the province and extending into the Northwest Territories, is Wood Buffalo National Park. Here plains bison mingle with wood bison. Both of these humped cattle are massive beasts, the wood bison being somewhat larger. This area is also the last retreat of the great whooping crane.

Wherever prey is to be found, there carnivores gather. The bark of the coyote is heard in the northern forests, but the most impressive predator is the timber wolf. Although it usually travels in family packs, at times two or more families may unite to form larger groups. These wolves are a danger to any herbivore, and their eerie howling at night, especially in winter, is a chilling sound to the camper or trapper. Through the forests, too, pads the lynx. It and the marten, which is from three to four pounds in weight, prey on squirrels, birds and the ubiquitous mice and voles. The British Columbia fisher, a carnivore normally of from eight to twelve pounds in weight, is noted for its ability to turn a porcupine over with a quick flip of its paw and, avoiding the quills, to kill and eat it. Weasels search for mice, voles, squirrels and small birds. Mink and playful otters, sometimes seen sliding down sloping banks into the streams, are as much at home in water as out of it. Muskrats and beaver are among their prey.

The animal which trappers dislike most, the wolverine, has almost its last retreat in the remoter areas of the northern forests. Chunky, powerful and the largest of the weasel family, with a weight for the males of from 30 to 36 pounds, the wolverine has been called the Indian devil, the carcajou or the glutton. There are many authenticated accounts of its seemingly wanton destructiveness. The wolverine will follow a trap line and kill and mutilate every animal found in the traps. In caches and

R.MC.

Sandhill crane chick

171

Snowy owl

cabins, it defiles what it cannot destroy. Well-endowed with cunning and caution, the wolverine often circumvents all attempts to catch it.

Many other birds and mammals as well as amphibians and insects are to be found in the boreal forest. Amphibians and the reptiles, such as the common gartersnake, are harmless; but in summer, clouds of mosquitoes swarm around the traveller. Horseflies, known locally as bulldogs, drive beasts into wild and apparently aimless dashes through the brush in their attempts to rid themselves of these scourges. Of particular annoyance to both man and beast are the diminutive blackflies. Their bite is not noticed because they first inject an anaesthetic before they draw the blood they seek, but the bite is followed by an almost intolerable irritation.

Thus we see that in summer Alberta's northern forests contain a wealth of animal life, which offers almost unlimited opportunities to the student of natural history. While some of the ecological relationships are being painstakingly worked out, much remains to be learned. Here, too, one can often observe wildlife in habitats which are almost unspoiled by man.

THE FOREST IN WINTER / WILLIAM A. FULLER

Winter in the boreal forest presents a fascinating picture of the adaptation of animals to frigid cold. The summer residents – a wide variety of birds and some species of mammals – have long since migrated to warmer habitats. Snow lies deep amid the trees and covers the ice on streams, sloughs and lakes. In the depths of this frozen stillness, the cracking of a snow-laden branch or the sudden chatter of a squirrel is startlingly loud.

Yet some species of animals migrate to – not from – the forest when winter threatens. The barren-land caribou seeks the shelter of the trees and so does its predator, the tundra wolf. The arctic fox is only an occasional visitor, but the willow ptarmigan regularly makes the northern forest its winter home.

These migrants share the problems and dangers that winter brings to year-round forest-dwellers. The most deadly enemy is cold. Throughou

(a)

(c)

(a) Goshawk
(b) Rose-breasted grosbeak
(c) Bonaparte's gull
(d) Whooping crane juvenile
(e) Sparrow hawk

(b)

(d)

(e)

173

Frost crystals

the northern forests, winter temperatures of 50 degrees below zero are common and at Fort Vermilion in northern Alberta the mercury has dropped to 78 degrees below zero, the second lowest temperature ever recorded in North America. Reptiles, amphibians, insects, spiders, worms and snails defeat the cold by passing into a dormant stage. Some mammals, like bears, avoid winter temperatures by denning up. Of the 317 species of birds known to live in Alberta, only 33 species, or a little more than one-tenth, remain active in the boreal woods during the winter, but 32 of the 90 species of Alberta's mammals, or over one-third, winter in the forest. To survive the intense cold and remain active, all these birds and mammals must keep warm. For this they all need food, and some of them need snow.

How snow is made

The production of snow is the result of one of the peculiar properties of water, namely that it can pass from the solid to vapour and back without passing through the liquid stage. This process is called sublimation. Thus ice may form either as the result of the freezing of liquid water or the sublimation of water vapour, and similarly ice may melt into water or sublime directly into water vapour. Snow is always formed by sublimation whereas surface ice on ponds or the rime that accumulates on trees and telephone lines is formed by freezing.

Sublimation tends to produce large crystals and an open-textured substance, although this does not always happen. No matter which way it forms, ice has a definite crystal structure. The molecules of

"Qali," the snow that accumulates on trees.

water arrange themselves at the points and the centre of a regular tetrahedron – a figure with four identical triangular surfaces. Six tetrahedrons will fit together to form a hexagon which suggests why all the regular kinds of snow flakes are built on the well-known hexagonal pattern. But, although snow flakes have a common pattern, anyone who has observed snow carefully knows that they come in an infinite variety of detail. We can recognize five main types of these. A simple type consists merely of flat, six-sided plates. A more complex type has arms radiating from the plates but all the arms lie in the same plane as that of the plate itself. The main arms may then have twigs of different sizes and shapes. Sometimes the arms grow out in all three planes of space which gives a third type, and sometimes the plate increases in thickness until it becomes a hexagonal column. Such columns may terminate in a pyramid-shaped end or may be capped by plates. Finally, there may be very fine needles that often form clusters.

The basic crystal may be modified between the time when it forms and the time when it comes to rest on the earth. Falling crystals may pass through a layer of supercooled water and water droplets may adhere to the flake to form pellets called graupel. They may pass through warmer or colder air or be repeatedly caught in updraughts so that, as a result of partial melting, refreezing, addition or subtraction, they are markedly modified. The conditions under which the major kinds of crystals are formed have been investigated in the laboratory and observed in nature. As an example, the typical six-armed snow flake (a plane stellar dendrite) is formed only at temperatures of 3-10° F.

What snow does in the forest

Most of us take snow for granted. We may enjoy it for skiing, but in general we plough through it or shovel it away and hope that it will soon melt. But to many of the forest-dwellers, winter's white mantle holds the keys of life or death.

Once snow falls in the forest it acts as a blanket. Heat travels upward from the ground and is lost by radiation to outer space. But fallen snow, particularly if it consists of typical flakes with arms that interlock, traps a good deal of air, thus retarding the outward flow of heat. Hence, if the snow cover is suitable, even when it is 40 to 50 degrees below zero above the snow, the air on the surface of the ground may be only a few degrees below freezing.

But snow changes with time. The upward flow of heat brings about the sublimation to water vapour of snow crystals in the layers near the ground. This water vapour tends to pass upward through the snow and, meeting lower temperatures nearer the surface, is refrozen to ice. This results in the development of a vital air space between the snow and the surface of the soil, which is very important for the smaller animals. During this same process the size of the ice crystals in the snow cover gets larger and reduces its insulating value.

Snow can be piled into drifts, although in the forest the trees prevent the wind from getting a good sweep at it. Thawing by wind and sun, followed by freezing temperatures, can bring about a surface crust. If there is another snowfall on top of this, then a second crust can be formed, a process which can be repeated until there are several crusts. Snow-crusts are important to animals that travel on or through the snow. Finally, snow collects on the branches of trees, particularly the needle-bearing trees of the boreal forest. Alaskan Eskimos refer to the snow on branches as qali, a term now adopted by scientists. Wherever there is

Barren ground caribou

R.MC.

C.H.

Flying Squirrel tracks. Arboreal mammals, such as the flying squirrel, usually place their front feet side by side when running.

qali on branches, underneath there is a snowshadow with less snow cover, known again by an Eskimo word as *qaminiq*. Both qali and qaminiq affect birds and mammals.

How mammals and birds cope with cold

To overcome cold, mammals and birds must have heat. They must somehow maintain inside their bodies a constant temperature which may at times be 150 degrees warmer than the surrounding air. With an animal, the ability to produce heat is related to the bulk or volume of its body, while it loses heat according to the surface area of that body. To step briefly into mathematics, as animals get bigger, their surface area increases as the square of a linear dimension, while their volume increases as a cube. The square of three, for example, is nine, but the cube of three is 27, so that the difference is considerable. Hence the bigger the animal, the greater the safety margin between heat-producing and heat-losing ability.

This is one reason why larger animals can cope better with cold than small ones. A second reason is that the bigger ones can grow a denser coat of insulating hair. A mouse, for instance, would be absurd in the thick coat of a moose. Boreal animals therefore can be divided into those big enough to manufacture and retain enough heat to survive in low temperatures and those not large enough. Among mammals, anything at least as large as the varying or snowshoe hare can manage the extreme cold of the boreal forest as long as it can get enough to eat because food is the fuel from which heat is produced. Mammals the size of mice, however, can only stay active and alive in winter if protected by a blanket of snow. The red squirrel, which is intermediate in size, is active when the winter temperature is moderate but, when the mercury plummets, it retreats to an insulated nest.

The basic mathematical facts in the production and loss of heat apply also to birds. No bird is as big as a moose, yet even mouse-sized birds like the chickadee, fly about all winter. So we ask ourselves why small birds can do what is impossible for small mammals. One answer is that flight requires enormous amounts of energy, and an inevitable by-product of the production of energy is heat. Birds apparently produce more heat per unit time than do mammals. The disadvantage is that birds must consume more food as fuel than mammals of the same size.

Another advantage that birds have over mammals is that feathers seem to insulate against the cold better than hair, and we ourselves use feathers, not hair, in some of our better quality sleeping robes. As long as birds are on the wing and can find enough food, they can surmount the cold; but whenever they are at rest, the surface-to-volume relationship catches up with them. All but the largest birds, like the great horned owl, must find some way to supplement their own insulating cover. Some of the grouse plunge into the snow and use it as an additional insulation. The smaller birds generally take refuge in tree cavities to huddle in groups, just like people caught in the open in below-zero temperatures. In this way they reduce the total surface for the loss of heat.

How snow helps and hinders survival

Cold and snow are twins in the boreal forest. For many sorts of mammals as well as for grouse, snow is a protection against a plummeting temperature. The short-legged, stout-bodied, short-tailed voles, for instance, spend almost the entire winter in the air space between the soil and the snow. So do the shrews and a few mice.

We know very little as yet about this world between the ground and the snow, except that its temperature seldom gets very much below freezing, and that the light is extremely dim. We can guess that it

Skunk tracks on wind-worked snow

Under this spruce is a snow shadow or "qaminiq" – a place small mammals avoid.

(a)

C.H.

(a) Coyote
(b) Least chipmunk
(c) Varying hare
(d) Long-tailed weasel
(e) Red squirrel

(b)

R.MC.

(d)

C.H.

(e)

C.H.

(c)

.H.

Blackcapped chickadee C.H.

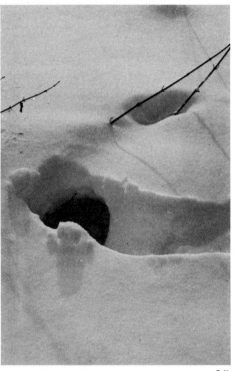

Ruffed grouse roost C.H.

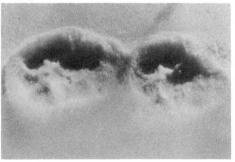

Lynx tracks C.H.

relative humidity is high and that the sounds of the world above are as muffled as the light. The group of voles living in this sort of quarter-world includes the meadow and red-backed voles which are also found in the rest of the province, the phenacomys vole and the bog lemming. Occasionally the voles build runways through the snow but usually, because of the air space, there is no need to do this. However, they often drive ventilation tunnels to the surface of the snow cover. They also bore through the snow itself from time to time, apparently in search of food particles fallen from the trees or trapped in the snow-cover. Their habitat has holes, like those in Swiss cheese, wherever there is qaminiq with snow too thin to give insulation.

While the voles use snow for survival, beavers and muskrats avoid the extreme cold of winter by living under the ice of ponds and rivers. This is the warmest place for them, since in water the temperature cannot fall below freezing. Both species move about as they do in summer, seldom coming onto the surface of the land unless their ponds are frozen to the bottom. Sealed off by snow and ice and protected by the frozen walls of their houses, they are relatively safe. But every Eden, even a frozen one, has a handicap. Winter does not prevent mink and otters from invading their habitat.

Snow can hinder as well as help. In Alberta everyone knows from experience how difficult it is to struggle through knee-deep snow. The animals of the boreal forest have solved this difficulty in various ways.

One group of mammals simply wades through the snow as we do. The best adapted animal in this group is the moose. It moves easily through two feet of snow because of its long legs and a special arrangement of muscles and bones that permits the legs to work almost straight up and down. The toes of the moose seldom leave drag marks in the snow so that it is usually difficult to tell from its tracks in which direction it was moving. The wapiti and smaller deer run into trouble at somewhat lesser depths. The predator of the moose, the wolf, also wades through the snow and, as long as it is soft and fluffy, the wolf is at a considerable disadvantage. But if a crust forms, the wolf may be able to stay on the surface while the moose keeps on wading, but with difficulty. Hence, the depth and structure of the snow mean life or death to both the wolf and the moose. Animals living in herds reduce the energy needed for ploughing through snow by playing follow-the-leader. This is the technique used by the bison of Wood Buffalo National Park, by caribou, and in deep snow by deer, when they tramp down an area to form what is known as a yard.

Another way of moving about is to float on the surface of the snow. There are floaters among both the birds and the mammals. Classic examples are the snowshoe hare and its chief enemy, the lynx. The lynx, which is about three times the size of a normal house cat, is so constructed that on each square centimetre of snow it exerts a pressure or weight, known as the weight-load, of only 35 to 39 grams, as compared to the weight-load of from 88 to 118 grams for a house cat. Where a house cat, then, will break through the snow, the lynx can float on its surface. Most of the weasel family could also be regarded as floaters, although more by their peculiar gait than because of the presence of distinct snowshoes. Among the birds, the willow ptarmigan grows feathery snowshoes which give it a weight loading of only 14 to 15 grams per square centimetre, enabling it to stay on top of the fluffiest snow. Its more northerly relative, the rock ptarmigan, has smaller snowshoes, presumably because the tundra snow is always hard packed and walking on its surface presents no problem. The introduced Hungarian partridge, however,

Great horned owl nesting in February

Deermouse R.MC.

Mule deer in deep, soft snow M.H.

Timber wolf R.MC.

with a weight loading of 40 to 41 grams per square centimetre, is incapable of moving about in fluffy snow, and unable to obtain food from the ground when the snow is firm. Hence it is limited to places with little snowfall, or places, such as the open prairie, from which the snow is removed by the wind.

Other grouse develop horny growths on the toes in winter, and these are often considered to be snowshoes. In part they are, but they are also useful in perching and moving about on the qali – the snow-laden branches of trees. Qali likewise interferes with smaller birds, squirrels, flying squirrels and probably martens and fishers. The weight of a bird landing, for instance, may cause the qali to fall, thus releasing the branch and upsetting the balance of the bird. If the qali stays in place, the bird can only hunt for food on the lower side of the branches and perhaps on only one side of the trunk. This undoubtedly explains in part why small forest-dwelling birds like the chickadee and the nuthatch can perform like circus acrobats.

Winter food problems

To find food in the snow-deep forest is still another winter problem. Often the food is out of sight under the snow, but there is evidence that some animals can detect food by hearing or smelling it. Caribou are said to smell lichens, and squirrels fungi, while foxes, weasels and coyotes can hear small mammals under the snow.

Even if snow-covered food is located, it has to be dug for, whether the snow is powdery, sugary or heavily-crusted. But birds cannot dig, and few mammals do. Foxes and coyotes paw through the snow for mice, voles and shrews, but their competitors, the weasels, can move about under the snow and pursue their prey almost everywhere. Caribou use their relatively enormous hooves to dig for lichens and other low-growing plants. Anyone who has watched bison in winter has seen them

179

C.H.

Short-tailed weasel C.H.

Bark removal by elk C.H.

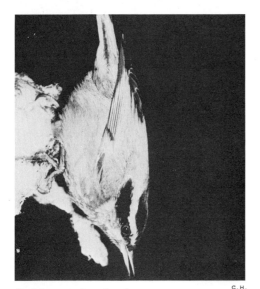

Red-breasted nuthatch C.H.

swinging their heads from side to side in an effort to clear away the snow from their food.

Most herbivores have an easier solution. They simply change from food buried in the snow to food that is in front of them. The deer family become browsers on woody vegetation, eating the terminal twigs that are the least tough and tearing off patches of bark. Even the caribou makes a partial shift to those lichens that hang from trees.

Birds, too, change their diet. Instead of food on the ground, the grouse eat the buds and catkins of trees and shrubs; and in the trees its winter toenails prove useful in foraging for food. Although the ptarmigan spends little time in the branches, it can feed on shrubs from the surface of the snow. As the snow depth increases, it is continually being brought within reach of new sources of food. The snowshoe hare and the ptarmigan may feed on the same shrubs, but the hare is more likely to eat the bark than to take the buds, catkins and tiny twigs which the ptarmigan prefers. Even the voles change their food habits. In winter they concentrate on stems of grasses and herbs or gnaw the bark from shrubs. Strangely enough, few species utilize the most abundant plant material in the boreal forest – the coniferous trees themselves. The spruce grouse however, feeds on the needles, and squirrels, crossbills and pine grosbeaks eat the seeds from the cones.

The carnivores do not show as great a shift in diet as the herbivores. Owls are able to catch voles only when the latter come to the openings of their ventilation tunnels or make brief forays on the surface of the snow and so they turn to other prey, such as squirrels and small birds, for at least part of their subsistence. The insect eaters change less, if at all. Although shrews must destroy large numbers of insects at the dormant stage that they find on the forest floor under the snow, they also include mice in their winter diet. Woodpeckers, chickadees, nuthatches, creepers and kinglets diligently search the trunks and branches of trees, again hunting for dormant insects, even though qali may interfere with their success.

For the herbivores, the winter shift in diet has its drawbacks. Although there is seldom a shortage in quantity, the quality leaves something to be desired. A piece of frozen bark, for instance, can scarcely have the same food value as seeds, berries or fresh green shoots. Just as castaways may chew on leather boots for survival, so it seems apparent although it is not yet proven, that snow-adapted herbivores go on a maintenance diet in winter. It appears to be a universal characteristic of such animals that they cannot gain weight in winter. Instead most of those studied tend to lose weight steadily.

This last fact has some interesting connotations. When an animal's weight lessens, the ratio of its surface to its volume increases so that

C.H.

Moose tracks in deep, soft snow

C.H.

loses heat faster. The more rapid heat-loss is not critical for a deer but it is for a small creature, such as a shrew or a mouse, which is already dependent on insulation by the snow cover. There must therefore be some advantage in the weight-loss to offset the greater heat-loss. The advantage appears to be in the saving of over-all energy needs. Shrews and mice are 20 to 30 per cent lighter in winter than in summer, and their total energy needs are probably reduced by about that amount.

Another side effect is that, with animals, weight lost in winter must be regained in the spring. Studies in Finland, in particular, have shown that in several species of grouse this gain in weight is closely associated with preparation for egg-laying. There seems to be a critical period in the spring during which breeding success for the entire summer is determined. If the critical period is too cold, or if too much snow is still on the ground, there will be no population increase during the summer, but favourable weather in the critical period leads to large autumn populations. Something similar occurs with white-tailed deer and perhaps other mammals. American naturalists have shown that unless female deer can get back on a high protein diet before giving birth, the odds are heavily against the survival of the fawns.

Snow, then, is a vital factor in the winter life of the mammals and birds in our boreal forests. For some, too much snow is a disaster, while for others too little snow may mean death by freezing. Besides the total amount of snow, its structure and the changes in its structure are also important. There is much that we do not know about the winter life of our small birds and mammals, and there is plenty of opportunity here for the interested amateur naturalist to make a worthwhile contribution. We need to know more about the times of arrival and departure of the snow cover and about the changes in it and the temperatures beneath it. Ideally these observations should be related to the abundance of the small mammals that are dependent on it and the game birds affected by it. We also need to know where small birds spend the cold winter nights, whether singly or in groups, and what temperatures are found in their roosting places.

Population cycles

One other aspect of animal life in the boreal forest must be mentioned. Many of the boreal species undergo fluctuations in abundance which are so regular that they are often referred to as cycles. This phenomenon has

Moose and elk must often make do with tough, low quality food in winter.

C.H.

Willow ptarmigan, nearly all white in winter, has the best "snowshoes" of any bird.

long held the attention of naturalists, but in spite of much thought and much gathering of statistics and information about the biology of the species concerned, the cycles are still inexplicable. The main cyclic species are clearly either snow-adapted or snow-dependent, so perhaps the answer to this mystery is to be found in some of the relationships already discussed.

The basic cycles involve herbivores such as the snowshoe hare, ruffed, sharp-tailed and spruce grouse and the voles. In some cases, the predators of these species also show cycles of abundance. The lynx cycle follows by about a year those of the hare and grouse which usually peak and decline in numbers at the same time. Foxes, mink and martens may also show this periodicity. All these species, except voles, have a cycle with a length of ten years, not seven as is popularly supposed. The ten-year cycle is characteristic of the boreal forests of North America and does not occur in the Old World. In the case of voles, there is a cycle with peaks in every three or four years on the average. Preliminary studies in northern Alberta and the Northwest Territories suggest that the different kinds of voles all peak at the same time. This three to four year cycle occurs in both the tundra and the boreal forest and in both the Old and New Worlds.

Theories about the causes of cycles have ranged from the extra-terrestrial – a side effect of the sunspot cycle – to sophisticated ideas of an internal control mechanism acting like a thermostat to restore the normal balance when the population gets either too large or too small. There have been attempts to correlate population changes with weather factors but curiously, until recently, no one had seriously considered the possible importance of snow, although the cyclic species are clearly snow-adapted.

Much emphasis has been placed on disease. Diseased animals often appear during the decline, but no single disease shows up at each peak and it is generally thought now that the diseases that occur are merely side effects. Some believe that predators control the numbers of the species on which they prey and then die of starvation when their food source disappears. But most studies have shown that predators cannot remove the prey fast enough to control them during a population peak. Hence the predators do not control the prey, although it seems likely that the prey controls the predator.

The thermostat theory holds that, when the animals are abundant, they interfere with each other in subtle ways that result in all the animals being under a kind of social stress. The individual animal reacts

(a)

J.M.

(a) Black bear
(b) Cinereous shrew destroys many insect pupae in summer and winter
(c) Red-backed vole
(d) Muskrat

(c)

C.H.

(b)

.H.

(d)

к.D.B.

Ruffed grouse which grows winter nails to help it move on the snow and on snow-laden branches.

to this stress by altering the output of hormones from certain of the glands of internal secretion. One of the effects of the altered hormone balance is interference with the ability to reproduce; adult animals stop breeding, and young ones do not attain puberty at the normal size or age. Hence the population stops increasing and all the mortality factors, such as predators, disease, fighting and adverse weather, act with varied intensity to produce the crash. Then, when the animals are no longer crowded, the hormone balance returns to normal, breeding recommences and the population begins to build to another peak.

This attractive theory is supported by some field observations and much laboratory work. Unfortunately it is subject to several criticisms. The populations studied in laboratories have been subjected to a degree of crowding which is much greater than ever occurs in nature. In nature one finds some but not all of the symptoms that occur in laboratory populations. If crowding were the sole explanation, we would also expect that the control mechanism would begin to act at about the same density in each successive upswing so that the peak population in each cycle would be about equal. But this is clearly not so.

So we close this part of the chapter on a note of mystery. We know that in 1967 the drumming of the ruffed grouse will be heard here and there in the boreal forests of Alberta. By 1970 the whole forest will resound to their spring drumming, but in that year, or in 1971 at the latest, there will be another population crash, and for several springs thereafter we will be fortunate to hear a single grouse. The same sort of thing will happen with hares, lynx, foxes, martens, and perhaps owls and some of the smaller birds. Meanwhile, zoologists will be counting, measuring, examining, recording and experimenting in a renewed attempt to solve what the first Head of the Zoology Department of the University of Alberta, Dr. William Rowan, called "Canada's premier problem of animal conservation".

MAN AND THE FOREST / EDO NYLAND

In the early days of settlement, homesteaders and railroaders found the forest an obstacle. During the early part of this century in Alberta, great fires, set by man, blazed along the right-of-way of railroads or fanned out from settlements. Shortly after Alberta became a province, enormous conflagrations raged uncontrolled throughout the north until the Alberta Forest Service was able to build an effective fire-fighting service and to develop a forest-conservation educational programme. Many forested areas were burned away to provide land for farming. Tragically, it was found that considerable areas of the land that had been cleared proved to be practically useless for the growing of crops. Today, for example, abandoned farms can be seen west of Edson, where the roadbed of the defunct Grand Trunk Pacific Railway runs, and in the bush north of Fort Assiniboine or along the McLeod River near Whitecourt and in many other border areas of the forest zone. Even in recent years, due to public demand, land in forested areas which is marginal or even sub marginal in quality has been opened for agricultural development. Forest soils tend to be stony, too poor in quality, and too subject to erosion and the topography too rough for good farming. Besides these disadvantages the number of frost-free days in much of the northern forest is not always enough for crops to mature properly.

Forest management

During much of the first half of this century, timber stands were sold to the highest bidder, logging was haphazard and throughout large areas only the usable trees were removed. Few tenants cared about the condition in which the logged-over areas were left, or how much debris

.G.

Crown fire in boreal forest

logged the creeks and rivers. Not until proper forest management was introduced on a province-wide basis in 1956, through the completion of a timber inventory, did Albertans begin to realize that the province's forests were not inexhaustible. Information about the species of trees, the rate of growth and age of each species and the condition and volume of timber in the different areas of the forest-land was collected. A continuous inventory of these data is maintained and modified by new information obtained concerning changes in the quality of the forest. As a result, the principle of sustained yield was put into practice.

Sustained yield (which has been a feature of forest management in Europe for many years) simply means that stands of timber are harvested in such a way that enough new wood grows each year to replace the amount destroyed by fire or removed by logging, thus ensuring a perpetual supply of forest products. There are, naturally, problems to be solved before this ideal of sustained yield can be achieved. A preliminary step is to log timber stands where the trees are too old and ought to have been removed 50 or even 100 years earlier. In such salvage operations, more timber is sometimes felled than can possibly be replaced by new growth in a single year.

The introduction of timber quotas in Alberta in 1966 was an important step toward proper forest management. Under this system, timber operators are assigned in perpetuity a definite annual volume of

M.H

Cattle grazing in forest reserve

timber to be cut, together with an area sufficiently large to grow that volume.

As another step forward, a scientific evaluation of forest soils has been made by the Research Council of Alberta. One objective of this survey was to determine which forest soils are suitable for agriculture, which for grazing and which should remain forested. Using this information, the Alberta Government has compiled a map delineating the permanent boundaries between the province's forest-lands and lands to be made available for settlement.

Thus, in addition to the principle of sustained yield, modern forest management accepts the concept of multiple use of the forested areas. This means that, besides the production and care of trees for logging, other factors, such as watershed management, grazing, flood control, game management, mineral exploration, recreation and aesthetic values must be taken into account. For example, indiscriminate logging on the eastern slopes of the Rocky Mountains, where many of Alberta's rivers have their headwaters, would endanger Alberta's water supplies and would affect those of Manitoba and Saskatchewan as well. Therefore, in this area, wood harvest is strictly controlled. Grazing, however, is a legitimate use of some forest areas, especially along streams where the soils are deep and from natural causes forest growth is absent. These fertile and often beautiful meadows usually grow such a thick mat of grasses that tiny conifer seedlings are stifled. Many of these meadows being small, difficult of access and uneconomical for use because of the cost of providing roads and other facilities, are sensibly left to deer and elk. But in the forest reserves of the eastern Rocky Mountains, since they are adjacent to ranchland, closely supervised grazing is permitted. Each summer, wherever the forest is sparse, these reserves support about 25,000 head of cattle. No damage is done to the forest but it is sometimes startling to come upon herds of cattle where one would expect deer and elk.

Economic aspects

The economic impact of Alberta's forest industry is considerable. The current annual wholesale value of forest products is about 27 million dollars, but it is estimated that this sum must be multiplied by about five to give the true total worth of the finished products – houses, bridges, plywood and pulpwood. Thus the forest industry influences the economy

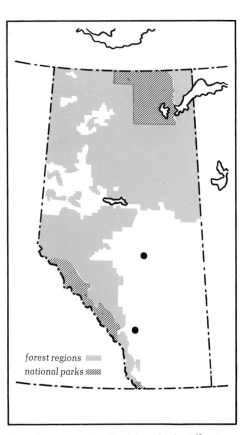

forest regions
national parks

Forest areas and national parks in Alberta

186

of the province to the extent of about 135 million dollars annually. At present, less than one-fifth of the annual capacity of Alberta's forests is being used and, as proper forest management ought to at least double the capacity, the province's ultimate potential is over ten times its current production. There is thus a good chance that the ideal of sustained yield will be attained. Besides the direct commercial value of forest products, there are other important benefits to be obtained from such forest resources as sport fishing, hunting and tourism.

In this province, white spruce is the forest tree with the greatest commercial value because its wood is quite light, is easily worked and holds paint and glue well; hence white spruce provides most of Alberta's sawn lumber for local use and for export. It is also excellent as pulpwood for the manufacture of good paper.

The lodgepole pine also has an important place in our catalogue of forest resources. The tall, slim trunks of these trees were once used as teepee poles and this same characteristic makes them popular as power and telephone poles, railway ties and fenceposts. Lodgepole pines are also utilized for pulpwood, plywood and sawn lumber, especially since its wood is ideal for treatment with preservatives. The graceful needles of this tree make it a popular Christmas tree. The wood of two other trees, balsam poplar and trembling aspen, has also been found to make good plywood.

Erosion problems

Forest soils are particularly vulnerable to erosion wherever the cover of the forest floor is disturbed. For example, the site of each oil or gas well requires a denuded area of three to four acres. Here the problem is not severe, but the filled in ditches for oil and gas pipelines are subject to erosion unless erosion control measures such as cross-ditching and seeding to grass are used. Seismic lines require close supervision. These lines, roughly cleared straight paths for the passage of seismic equipment to be used in exploration for oil and gas, reach into almost every corner of Alberta's northern forests. They cause erosion on hillsides in particular. Furthermore, in fertile soil, these lines are soon taken over by grass so dense that seedlings can scarcely compete. In consequence, whenever the grass is dry, forest fires can flame along these seismic lines farther and more rapidly than under normal conditions.

Those interested in forest conservation often find roads an erosion menace. Where roads are required, trees must be removed to provide a right-of-way. Some unfortunate results of this clearing may follow. For example, water from a swamp may have been draining slowly into a creek through layers of peat-moss. But now the ditches alongside a road through the swamp may create a completely new exit for the swamp water. In consequence the water runoff may turn the road ditches into canyons, yards deep. Similarly, rain falling on a forested hillside may have been percolating slowly, year after year, through the soil to a creek or a river in the valley below. A road cutting transversely along the hillside may trench through the slow subsurface seepage and, as a result, the seepage may be changed to a surface runoff. Now erosion along the road will probably occur and, in addition, the soil on that portion of the hillside below the road will lack moisture and the vegetation may be forced to change. Roads and other cleared rights-of-way may also cause blowdowns of timber. A wind blowing across them does no harm, but one that funnels straight down a road or right-of-way topples tall trees right and left, especially in wet soil areas where their roots have only a shallow grip.

Fills placed in a creek or a river, particularly in winter, as a crossing

Immature lodgepole pine forest

for vehicles, create still another problem. Often when spring comes the creek or river is compelled to change its course with the result that tons of soil are washed downstream. Today those concerned are fully aware of the problems and eager to co-operate in solving them.

Water storage

In forested areas we often find the need to create water storage for either hydro-electric power or for flood control and here, too, conservation must be considered. The Water Resources Division, Provincial Department of Agriculture has been surveying a number of possible dam sites on the major rivers of Alberta. The streams which run northward through the forest, such as the Hay, Peace, Slave and Athabasca Rivers are being given special attention at places where their courses might be changed to flow eastward through the prairie provinces. A future generation, or even the present one, may well see profound changes in the direction and pattern of the river systems of northern Alberta.

It may be necessary in the creation of such reservoirs to inundate many square miles of forested land. Development of large lakes in this manner is usually beneficial to recreation if the water level is relatively stable. This, however, is not always a characteristic of dams built for power or flood control. A changing water level can create large mud flats which make access to the water difficult when the level is low. Also, in a flooded area where trees were not removed beforehand, decomposition of the trees removes a large part of the available oxygen from the water, killing fish and spoiling the lake as a sport fishing area for many years.

The prevention of forest fires

While forest fires can devastate our forests, they are not always a disaster. As noted in the description of the mountain and boreal forests, fire is a major agent in the continuance of the valuable and attractive mixed wood forest and in the rejuvenation of stands of various conifers. Fire in these instances, is nature's method of clearing away over-mature forests and disease-infested humus. An aged white spruce stand may tower majestically, but it is replete with fungal rot and insect pests and is almost barren of wildlife. Without a fire the over-mature trees will be blown down eventually, and the result is what foresters term a "silvicultural slum" of rotting logs, weed-infested areas and disease-filled layers of decayed material. This slum can last for decades, since grasses take over and crowd out seedlings of trees. If fire has swept a stand, the forest has a chance at a second youth.

But a fire out of control can also rage through young and vigorous stands of timber. Each year thousands of acres of excellent forest are ravaged by holocausts caused either by lightning or by man. Alberta spends up to four million dollars a year in fighting these forest fires. Occasionally, however, the Alberta Forest Service is conducting experiments in the use of controlled fire to get rid of dried-out debris left after logging, or to prepare a seed-bed for reforestation.

Reforestation

The essence of the sustained yield ideal is reforestation. One method satisfactory but expensive, costing more than twenty dollars an acre is planting young trees. Lately a new "container planting" system has been developed. In this technique, one or two seeds of a species are placed in a three-inch-long plastic container filled with the right soil mixture for that species. The seeds in their container germinate and grow in a greenhouse. When the seedlings are at least eight weeks old, they are planted in the area to be reforested, still housed in their container. A slit in the side of each container allows the growing root to burrow into the

C.H.

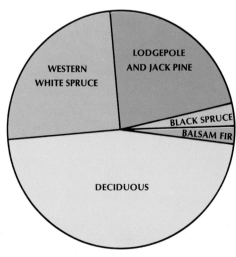

Blowdown of trees caused by road clearing

soil, and experiments have shown that during this period of early growth the containers prevent the seedlings from drying out. Later the plastic disintegrates and the young tree is free to grow as it likes.

Another method of reforestation is known as clearcutting. In this technique, all merchantable timber is removed from a previously surveyed and usually rectangular patch of ground. If the plot is one of white spruce, enough trees must be left standing to provide seed for the patch to be reforested. If the area is of pine, a larger stretch can be cut, since pine seed is found after logging on the limbs and branches of the felled trees. Whether the patch is of white spruce or pine, a seedbed is prepared by cultivating the forest floor with bulldozers, a process known as scarification. This method removes the competing vegetation growing in the humus, so that the seeds will have a good chance to germinate and survive. Sometimes scarification is followed by hand seeding to ensure a thick enough growth. This type of reforestation has proved to be very satisfactory in Alberta and is being increasingly practised.

Partial cutting is still another reforestation technique. In this method, an average of about forty per cent of the total volume of the trees in the selected plot are removed; these are marked with either paint or an axe-blaze. Trees that are diseased, crooked or damaged are the first to be marked, and the rest of the cutting is spaced so as to open up the stand and permit growth. Thus partial cutting is used in immature stands of timber which need thinning, thereby leaving the better quality trees to

Volume per cent of timber in Alberta

provide the future forest. In the logging of these stands, a process in which the remaining trees must not be injured, horses have proved better than modern machines.

Reforestation programmes are expensive but essential. At present, hundreds of thousands of acres of potential forest in Alberta – much of it brush land, logged-over stretches and burnt-over areas – are without trees. By not restocking these huge expanses at this time many years of growth of merchantable timber will have been lost, for it takes at least 60 to 70 years for trees to reach maturity.

In an attempt to add further variety to Alberta's forests, cautious experiments are being made to introduce exotic trees into gardens called arboreta. In our severe climate we cannot expect to introduce a tree as prolific as the Monterey pine, which grows better in its new home in New Zealand than in its native California and reaches merchantable size within twenty-five years. In the cities, however, the Colorado blue spruce and the Douglas fir have been accepted, and the Scotch pine is popular for shelter belts around farm dwellings. The Manitoba maple, found by early explorers in southern Alberta, is now – along with the green ash – an inhabitant of the whole province. The bur oak, although it is a curiosity rather than a useful tree, has been introduced and has survived as far north as Lesser Slave Lake and the town of Peace River.

Aesthetic values

Alberta's forests are a delight for recreation, from the conifer-clad mountain slopes of the national parks to the wide reaches of the northern forest or the woodlands of the plains. In them, nagging civilization can be forgotten and the spirit can be renewed.

Other forest benefits, such as the preservation of wildlife, have already been noted. The fact that forest soils act as a filter to assist in regulating stream flow is not so obvious a contribution; nor is the air-purifying quality of trees sufficiently realized. Forests and green hills

Clearcut areas with intervening strips of timber near Hinton.

M.H.

Forest reflections in boreal muskeg. Note white spruce, black spruce and the autumn colouration of the tamarack.

Logging with horses, 1906.

Logging with a horse today

are nature's dispensers of oxygen. Hence such large cities as London, England are now surrounded with what is known as a "Green Belt". Such a belt, which will finally involve 41,000 acres of land, has been planned for Ottawa. The time may come when green belts will become imperative for Alberta's cities.

The rôle of Alberta's forests in the present and for the future is important and manifold. Those forests will continue to host a varied plant and animal life. Their timber resources will become increasingly valuable. Their function as a recreational and aesthetic refuge will be extended, and their contributions to clear water and pure air are essential. Happily, once the ideal of sustained yield is reached, the province's forests should last in perpetuity.

CHAPTER NINE

Mountain Habitats

THE ROCKY MOUNTAINS, towering to altitudes of 12,000 feet, form over half of the western boundary of Alberta. From the United States border their ranges sprawl northwestward for approximately 450 miles, and leave Alberta near the headwaters of the Smoky River. Because the Rocky Mountains intercept the moisture-laden winds from the Pacific Ocean, and because of the width and variety of their terrain, they create a series of unusual physical conditions that produce associations of plants and animals not found elsewhere in the province. The major valleys parallel the mountain ranges, and at various points the ranges have been cleft by drainage systems, allowing the exit of waters from these valleys. Thus major river systems leaving the eastern slopes of the Rocky Mountains in Alberta flow in an easterly direction. The resulting conformation of the whole area creates a mosaic of habitats along the length of this mountainous region. Characteristically, the mountains are clad in coniferous forests. These forests may give way to mixed deciduous-coniferous or pure deciduous forests, and even to grasslands and tundra, depending upon the aspect, slope and altitude of the particular region.

The effect of fire and insects on forests

The influence of fire is to be seen throughout the mountain and foothills regions. Fire is a natural component of most terrestrial environments, and its impact is felt in various ways. The mountain forests have been consumed by fire from time to time, and in their place have come temporary associations of plants and animals whose characteristics are different from those of the original forest. Subsequent to fire, a community of mosses, lichens, low broad-leaved plants, grasses, shrubs and associated animals is formed, but by a continuous orderly process the forest

DAVID A. BOAG
W. GEORGE EVANS

Title picture – Valley of the Snake Indian River.

C. H

Fire has eliminated the canopy of conifers from this forested area, leaving the forest floor open to re-invasions by sun-loving species of plants.

slowly returns. The nature of the new forest trees will depend on the available seed source or viable underground roots. This sequence of events will continue until the last stage or climax vegetation matures.

Insects play a major rôle in the dynamics of a forest community. At all stages of forest growth, insects are very abundant both in numbers of individuals and in numbers of species. They feed on all parts of a tree. A group called "borers" mine channels through bark and sapwood, through roots, twigs, cones and seeds. Many different kinds of insects feed on leaves or needles, and they either chew the tissue, as in the case of the forest tent caterpillar, or they suck the sap, as do aphids and scale insects. Other insects form galls on leaves, needles, cones and roots. A very specialized group, called leaf miners, bore into the leaves of broad-leaved trees and leave typical irregularly shaped tracings or blotches between the upper and lower surfaces of the leaf. Sometimes, however, these miniature mines are intriguingly geometric in design, as, for example, the excavations of the aspen leaf miner. These examples of the complex interactions between insects and plants would not be complete without including the further interactions between insects and their enemies. These include viral, bacterial and fungal diseases, parasites consisting mostly of other insects, and predators, which may be other insects, birds or mammals. All animals in the forest interact with plants so that what may appear to be a loosely connected community of independent organisms is actually an intricate association of many plants and animals interdependent for their existence.

Even though insects may be classified by some foresters as pests because of the damage they can do to potential timber stands, they are an essential part of the forest environment. The rôle of the insect is similar to the rôle of naturally occurring fires which destroy vast areas of standing wood, of winds which cause extensive blowdowns, and of such other destructive factors as hares, beavers, plant diseases, and severe winter storms. All these factors contribute to the changing cover of a climax forest in which rejuvenation is constantly taking place. Trees killed or weakened by lightning, wind, insects, fire or other causes eventually fall to the ground. The fallen trunks are soon attacked by wood-boring insects, such as the larvae of long-horned beetles and metallic wood-boring beetles, which are accompanied by their parasites and predators. These in turn are followed by a regular succession of other insects which utilize the changing stages of the decomposing log. In a relatively

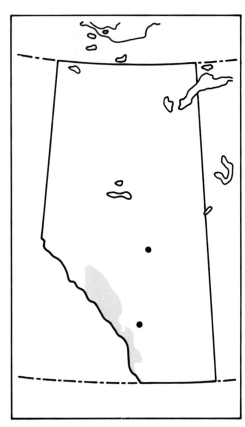

Mountain and tundra zones

194

short time the wood is reduced to humus which provides a seedbed for new seedlings, thus starting the cycle of regeneration once more.

Life along the river valley

Entrance into a mountainous region usually follows the way of least resistance which is along the floor of a valley. Mountain valley floors are invariably dissected by streams. The gradient of the stream will govern its depth and width as well as its current. Characteristically, these streams are cold, clear and cascading. From the point of view of living organisms they are relatively barren, being inhabited only by an impoverished flora and fauna. These few species of plants and animals have special holdfasts that enable them to cling to the rocky stream bed, or they may be shaped in special ways so that they resist being swept away in the current. Among the insects inhabiting these waters are the larvae of caddis-flies in their own cases which are made of sand particles glued together, and the nymphs of mayflies which cling to the undersides of rocks.

In the foothills the lower reaches of mountain streams are characteristically wide, shallow and fast moving but lacking in waterfalls or rapids. It is here that the streams often break into a series of channels with long narrow gravel bars between them. These bars often support the pioneer species of plants that will lead eventually to the stabilization of the habitat. Among the invading plants will be colourful broad-leaved fireweed, mat-forming yellow dryad and water-loving willows. These river bars are ideal habitats for a number of birds and mammals that are associated with the stream banks.

The willows provide a home for the white-crowned sparrow, an elusive buff-coloured bird with a striking black and white striped crown and a long tail. In early spring its clear oft-repeated song is a delight to hear. The male bird usually sings from a dead twig atop some willow clump, its voice often blending with the gurglings of the water passing

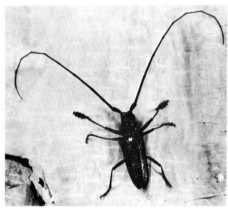

Adult long-horned beetle

The upper Red Deer River, in changing its course, has left exposed gravel bars which are soon colonized by plants and animals.

195

Mountain water shrew

Harlequin duck

over the rocky stream bottom. The female sparrow, coloured much like her mate, nests in the security of the tangled willow stems, using the bountiful food sources nearby to feed her growing brood. While the sparrows find the willows to their liking, spotted sandpipers prefer the matted low-growing dryads for their nesting sites. The eggs of this small gray and white bird with a speckled breast are so beautifully camouflaged in mottled grays, buffs and browns that often only the flight of the parent bird from the nest will attract attention to them. As with most members of the sandpiper clan, only four eggs are laid. This sandpiper, which lives on minute aquatic organisms, has the amusing habit of see-sawing its body whenever it comes to rest after a run along the stones or a short flight. Because of its behaviour, it is sometimes called the "teeterer".

A co-inhabitant of the gravel bars is a tiny mammal, the mountain water shrew. Often the gravel bars have acted as catch-alls for floating logs and other materials washed into the rivers at time of spate. It is among these materials and under the overhanging willows at the water's edge that the mountain water shrew travels in search of insect prey. These minute mammals, each weighing about as much as a fifty-cent piece, are admirably suited to this streamside habitat. They are equally at home on land and in the water, being capable of swimming, diving and running, either on the stream bottom or on its surface. They feed largely in the water, relying on a constant supply of aquatic animals. The fur of the shrew is intriguing, for it never seems to become wet. This is because the hair is so fine that the air caught in it forms a surface film preventing the entry of water between the hairs. The young of this creature are born in nests tucked away in safety under logs and other debris.

Life in the gorges and canyons

Farther into the mountains the streams become narrower, often cutting gorges through strata of softer materials such as shales. In these canyons the stream is characteristically a series of deep pools alternating with rapids or waterfalls. Vegetation is sparse along the banks because of their instability, but the waters provide a feeding ground and the steep walls a nesting spot for two typical mountain birds. In May, harlequin ducks migrate from their winter grounds on the Pacific coast to take up summer residence along these stretches of mountain rivers. This colourful species was so named because the plumage of the male bird was thought to resemble the costume of a clown. The dark blue, chestnut black and white markings are very striking. These ducks are most often seen feeding in fast water. In the early part of the season they are in pairs and seem to alternate their diving so that one of the birds is constantly on the watch for potential danger. Should they become alerted, they merely allow the current to carry them downstream until they are out of harm's way, and then once more they continue in their search for stream-bottom animals. From some vantage point above them, these little ducks can be observed submerging, wings partly open, and paddling upstream against the current, using wings as well as feet. While moving against the current, they probe with their bills among the gravel of the bottom and dislodge such bottom-dwelling insects as cranefly larvae and stonefly and mayfly nymphs, which they quickly devour.

These fast and turbulent reaches of the river also contribute nesting sites. The female lays a clutch of pale buff eggs in natural cavities on the rocky walls. Later in the season, neither the height of the nesting site nor the turbulent waters below it deter the female and her newly hatched brood from leaving the nest and tumbling into the stream below. The ducklings float like black and white balls of fluff, following their mother

often these industrious, amphibious mammals block streams with their ingeniously constructed dams. Each dam creates a pond into which the beavers can escape from predators and in which they can spend the winter. Beavers are rarely seen during daylight hours but at dusk and dawn they become active, leaving the pond to fell trees and shrubs along the shore. Bark and smaller twigs of deciduous plants are used for food. There is little difficulty in determining where beavers are working, for they leave characteristically gnawed, pike-like stumps and piles of chips beside the runways down which the lengths of branch and trunk are pulled to their ponds. These sections of trees are either incorporated into the dam or are cached underwater near their houses as winter food reserves. The work of these rodents, which is admired by engineers for its efficiency, plays a significant rôle in the conservation of water, and in the provision of additional habitats for associated organisms.

Two water birds take advantage of these temporary habitats—the sora rail and the solitary sandpiper. The sora rail is a shy bird not much bigger than a robin. It skulks about in the marsh grasses and sedges bordering the pond, where its olive-striped body and black and blue-gray face and neck may be glimpsed. The bird is rarely seen in flight, preferring to run off through the vegetation to avoid its enemies. Far more frequently its presence may be detected by the loud and raucous laugh which runs down the scale to its conclusion. By contrast, the solitary sandpiper feeds in the shallow waters at the edge of the pond. This long-legged wading bird is smaller than the rail and is distinguished by a gray-brown back, lightly speckled with faint gray spots, a white ring around the eye and a pale breast. It is aptly named, for rarely is more than a single pair seen on any one pond. Unlike the rail, which nests in the

Poplar tree felled by beaver

The headwaters of mountain streams appear as narrow rills which flow quietly between flower-strewn and mossy banks.

M.H.

River terraces, representing former levels of the stream, create a variety of habitats for plants and animals in close proximity to the water course.

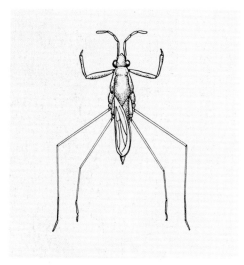

Water strider

grasses along the shore of the pond, the solitary sandpiper nests in trees. It builds no nest of its own but lays its four eggs in the abandoned nest of some other bird. Favourite nests, since these often retain their form into the following year, are those of the robin and rusty blackbird. Both species of marsh birds, which are migratory, feed on the abundant aquatic life during the summer.

A very rich and distinctive insect fauna can be found in beaver ponds, even though the habitat is temporary. Because of the fairly severe seasonal and annual fluctuations in the size and depth of these ponds, insect communities are established very quickly during the spring and summer by migrants from other ponds. Water striders skate on the surface of the water; water boatmen and backswimmers scull along; phantom larvae, diving beetles, whirligig beetles and water scavenger beetles swim in the water. The larvae of midges, caddis-flies and crane-flies, and the nymphs of dragonflies and mayflies will also be found crawling in and on the mud and debris at the bottom of the pond.

The river terrace habitat

Away from the stream bank the valley floor rises in a series of benches or river terraces to meet the slopes of the surrounding mountains. These benches represent former levels of the stream bed as it cut its way down to its present level. They receive varying amounts of precipitation and varying intensities of temperature and wind, depending upon their situation. Those benches that face south and west tend to be grasslands; those that face north and east are likely to be forested. This is because, in the areas facing south and west, water is lost at a greater rate through higher temperatures and increased evaporation, and thus trees are less easily established.

On the grassland benches several species of grasses, such as rough fescue and Parry's oat grass, are prominent. In the spring and summer these benches harbour a colourful array of broad-leaved forbs. Among

200

M.H.

The impact of topography on vegetation can be seen along Vicary Creek. The north-facing slopes are forested; south-facing ones are largely open.

Wapiti fawn

R.MC.

the more spectacular flowers in the southern mountain area are the perennial lupine, a beautiful sky-blue flower which grows in a raceme and produces bean-like seed pods; the wild sticky geranium, a lilac-coloured, rose-like flower, the stems of which are tacky to the touch; and the brown-eyed susan, a common member of the sunflower family often growing in exposed and disturbed areas of the grasslands.

A wide variety of animal life frequents these areas of low herbaceous growth. The rich vegetation provides a staple diet for grazing forms. Large game animals, such as bighorn sheep, rely on grasses the year round. The wapiti, a large member of the deer family, makes heavy use of grassy slopes at lower altitudes only during the winter. The mule deer comes to the open slopes in early spring to graze the new green shoots of early plants like the diminutive sedges. All these large animals follow the contour of the slope as they graze, their progression accentuating the natural slumping of the soil on the hillsides. This helps to produce the stepped or terraced nature of the slopes. Animals associated directly with the grasslands tend to be social species and either travel in herds, like the large grazers already mentioned, or live in colonies, like the numerous Columbian ground squirrels which burrow into the soil.

The Columbian ground squirrel can be distinguished from other members of its tribe by its reddish legs, face and underparts and grizzled gray back. Any intrusion upon the colony sets off loud chirpings at the burrow entrances, a danger warning to other members of the colony. At the sound, all the squirrels retire quickly to the safety of their burrows. They pass the winter season in a state of hibernation, living on extensive fat deposits built up during the summer months from the nutritious food which abounds in their environment. The duration of their active season is surprisingly short. Emerging from their burrows in late April, often before the last snows of winter have melted, the adult squirrels forage among the dead vegetation for seeds and new green

201

shoots. They breed in early May and the young are born underground a month later. The young are first seen at the burrow entrance in late June and early July, and their amusing exploratory antics can be enjoyed by anyone who has the patience to sit quietly nearby and watch. Their inherent reluctance to leave the security of the burrow is repeatedly overcome by the new smells, sounds and sights immediately around them. The adults return to hibernation in August, followed a month later by their young, and all spend the next eight months sealed off in subterranean cavities.

In the southern mountains of Alberta, another burrowing rodent shares the grasslands with the ground squirrels. This is the pocket gopher, also found on the prairies of the province. It is a soft-furred, slate-gray rodent with heavy digging claws and expansive hair-lined cheek pouches. Unlike the ground squirrels, this mammal never leaves the entrance to its burrows open. Instead the pocket gopher accumulates earth from its tunnelling underground, waits until the light fades and then, opening up the burrow, pushes the accumulated soil out into a pile. Having cleared its tunnels, the gopher next plugs the entrance, cutting off access to its underground passages from potential predators. Because its life is lived largely in the dark, the gopher has no need for well-developed eyes. It senses objects with its whiskers and the hairs at the tip of its tail. The tail is used for steering while travelling in reverse. This mode of travel is further assisted by body hair that lies equally well in a backward or forward direction. These subterranean rodents feed on the roots of such plants as the dandelion, though, when possible, they will pull the whole plant into the burrow with them and eat it all. Insects found in the soil form another important component of their diet.

Avian predators, such as the golden eagle, take advantage of the hunting grounds provided by these open grassland areas. This magnificent bird of prey personifies the wild mountain areas. Its piercing cry, given while riding the updraughts on outspread wings, echoes from cliff to cliff. It has keen eyes and powerful wings which may measure up to six feet across. The nest is built on some inaccessible cliff face from whence the nesting bird can survey its domain and quickly take advantage of any prey which has ventured too far from protective cover. Investigations into its food habits in southern Alberta have shown that Columbian ground squirrels comprise about three-quarters of its diet. The rest of its food consists of such items as grouse, ducks and smaller birds and mammals which the golden eagle takes when opportunities arise. While the eaglets are in the nest, the parents bring to the eyrie about one ground squirrel a day for approximately two and one half months. Just before the eaglets are ready for their first flight the parents stop bringing food to the nest, causing the famished eaglets to complain loudly. Their plaintive calls can be heard for long distances. Eventually their hunger pangs overcome their instinct to cling to the eyrie and they take their first faltering flight, usually awkward and of short duration. They are rewarded, however, by a meal taken with the parent birds at their kill. Soon after this the family hunts together.

The mixed forest of the ravines

Conditions favourable to the establishment of trees and shrubs are found in some of the ravines which dissect the grasslands. Throughout much of the mountainous region, deciduous trees clothe these ravines. The commonest tree is the aspen poplar, with balsam poplar more abundant on the moister sites. In time, there is every likelihood that white spruce will become established under the poplar canopy. The paucity of white spruce reflects a history of fire, because, although fire will kill all the

202

C.H.

Golden eaglets in nest

M.H.

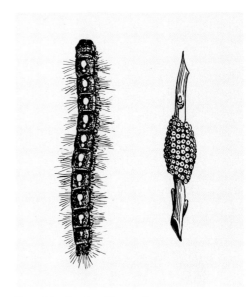

Forest tent caterpillar and egg mass

trees in the ravine, only the poplars have the ability to sprout again immediately from the roots in a multitude of suckers, forming dense single-species stands. Instead the spruce must rely on seeds from some source which has not been touched by the fire. The distance from this source will vary, and the greater it is the longer it will take the spruce to re-establish itself. The forest floor in these ravines is usually strewn with the trunks of dead trees, killed though not consumed by fire and then toppled over by the wind to lie and decay. Close inspection of these logs will usually reveal charring from either before or after the death of the tree, together with the trails, borings, galleries and faeces of insects associated with decaying timber.

One of the more prominent insects which defoliate the mixed forest is the forest tent caterpillar. Outbreaks of this insect last two to three years and are followed by periods when the population is so low that it is difficult to find any of them. The period between outbreaks varies from seven to eleven years. Apparently parasitic insects are responsible for the periodic reduction in the number of forest tent caterpillars. In 1962 more than 75,000 square miles of northern Alberta were infested by forest tent caterpillars, but by 1964 the population was declining. These insects feed on the leaves of many broad-leaved species, such as alder, birch, poplar and willow. The egg masses encircle small twigs of the host tree and are easily seen in winter. The caterpillars hatch in the spring and commence feeding on the new foliage. At first, the larvae are a nearly uniform black colour, with conspicuous hairs, and measure about a quarter of an inch in length. Later, as they grow and moult, they become pale blue in colour with a row of keyhole-shaped white spots down the middle of the back and pale yellow stripes on the sides. Unlike

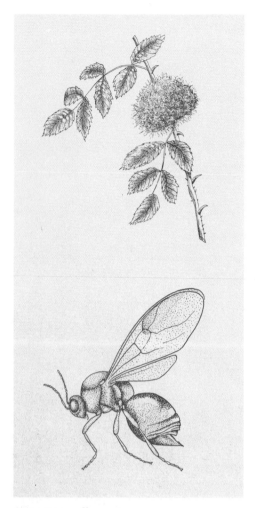

Rose stem gall
Gall wasp

Gall of the Cooley spruce gall aphid

several of its Canadian relatives, such as the eastern tent caterpillar and the western tent caterpillar, both of which construct tents in the crotches of branches, the forest tent caterpillar merely spins a felting of silk at the base of the main branches. The caterpillars congregate in this loose web at night or on cool cloudy days. Eventually they transform, first into pupae, and then into buff-brown moths about one to one-and-a-half inches in wingspan. After mating, the females spend their short life of five to six days laying eggs.

Another tent-making insect is the ugly-nest caterpillar, which feeds on the leaves of chokecherries and other shrubs of the rose family. It forms dense webs, especially over long protruding shoots. The gregarious yellow larvae feed and eventually transform into dull orange moths inside the tents.

Many insects in the forest make themselves known only by the results of their activities as, for example, the boring trails made by bark beetles, the flat-headed wood-boring beetles and the round-headed boring beetles. A walk through a mixed stand of trees and shrubs in late summer will also reveal many different varieties of galls made by insects and mites. Galls produced by insects are found on the leaves, stems, twigs and roots of practically all plants, and develop from a secretion injected either by the female insect when she lays her eggs or by the larvae. The secretion irritates the plant tissue, and a malformation or swelling results which protects the insects from their enemies and provides food for their young. These galls are seldom harmful to the plant, even though a great number may be found on one branch. Typical gall makers in the mountain forest are the gall wasps, which make galls on broad-leaved trees; aphids, such as Cooley's spruce gall aphid, commonly seen from Alberta to California, which forms cone-shaped galls on the terminal twigs of spruce; and gall midges, minute flies of which the larvae live in galls developed on many different kinds of shrubs.

Also best seen in late summer are the discoloured blotches or trails in leaves which indicate the activity of leaf miners. The aspen leaf miner with its serpentine trail has already been mentioned, but there are many more species found in the leaves of poplar, birch, willow and annual plants. All leaf-mining activity is done by the larvae, since the adults live only for a short time, and this is spent in mating and egg laying. Representatives of leaf miners are included among the larvae of butterflies and moths, beetles, flies and wasps. Although the adults in these groups differ considerably, the larvae are very much alike because of the common environment in which they live. In four widely separated groups of insects, life between the upper and lower surfaces of leaves has led to an evolutionary convergence of characteristics. The larvae have lost their legs, have become colourless, the head and body are flattened, with the head tapered into a wedge for use as an excavating tool, and the eyes and antennae are reduced. The mines in the leaves vary, however, and can be classified according to whether they are linear, serpentine or blotchy in form, or whether all of the tissue between the lower and upper surfaces is mined, or only the spongy inner cell layer, or the palisade layer of columnar cells just inside the outer covering. Leaf miners are very specialized insects but they are still subject to attack by natural enemies. Birds, mice and squirrels feed on them, and insect predators and parasites attack them. During the fall migration of warblers, it is a common sight to see these birds pecking continually at birch or poplar leaves. A closer examination will reveal that they are extracting the larvae from mines in the leaves.

Another sign of insect activity is the appearance in the spring of

(a)

C.H.

(a) Balsam poplar
(b) Alpine fir
(c) Lodgepole pine
(d) Engelmann spruce
(e) White-barked pine

(d)

C.H.

(b)

M.H.

(e)

C.H.

(c)

C.H.

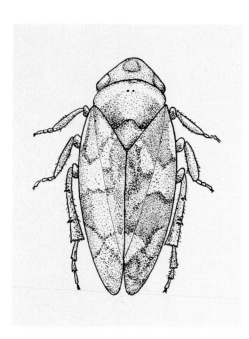

Spittle bug, or froghopper

Larval galleries of the aspen leaf miner

white spittle-like material encircling the twigs of pine trees. These spittle masses are secreted by the female spittlebug when she lays her eggs. The spittle serves to protect the hatched nymph while it feeds on the sap of the tree through its piercing-sucking mouthparts. The western pine spittlebug is found at higher elevations than other spittlebugs, and the blunt-headed adults can be found in July flying and performing their special feat of hopping up to six feet at a time.

In spring the mixed forests are filled with activity, for they provide a wide spectrum of habitats from the soil surfaces to the tree tops. On a quiet morning in early May, when the smell of damp leaves on the sunny forest floor and the odour of opening poplar buds is in the air, a sound resembling a great heartbeat can be heard. This is the drum beat of the male ruffed grouse, a shy bird which must be approached with extreme care if its performance on the drumming log is to be observed. The court-ship display is carried on from a log. The bird stands very erect and with each forward and upward beat of its wings creates a resounding thud. The drumming log is the focal point of the bird's activity during the breeding season. Evidence for this can be seen in the piles of droppings beside the drumming site. At this time of year small groups of these grouse can be seen in the aspen poplars just at dusk. They feed on the buds of these trees, which are a source of highly nutritious food eaten prior to the onset of laying by the females. While the males select fallen logs as drumming stations, the females may also use them as a protective cover for their nests. The clutch of buff eggs is laid in a nest of dead leaves and usually is only found by flushing the female from the nest.

In the woods nearby there is always a plentiful supply of old hollow trees and stumps in which woodpeckers excavate their nesting cavities. If a person taps lightly upon such a hollow tree, he may be rewarded by the appearance of either the red-shafted flicker or the pileated wood-pecker. The latter, a large black and white bird with scarlet crest, is a familiar bird in these woods where its loud call and resonant hammer-ing can sometimes be heard. One is sometimes surprised, however, by the appearance of a duck's head at the opening. The new tenant is likely to be a Barrow's goldeneye, one of our most interesting diving ducks. When the eggs hatch, the female duck flies to the ground nearby from whence she calls to her newly hatched ducklings. These little balls of fluff strug-gle to the opening of the cavity from which they launch themselves toward their mother's entreating call. They tumble to the ground, usually bouncing visibly on impact, but soon join their mother who im-mediately leads them to the nearest water.

A colourful inhabitant of these aspen groves from early June on is the lazuli bunting, a small sparrow-like bird with a sky-blue head and back and a chestnut and white breast. Its bubbling song is most often given from some tall dead tree top. This is the male's singing perch, and is usually in the middle of a territory which he defends against all other males of his species. The female, a sombre unmarked buff bird, is seldom seen unless frightened from her nest of grasses in some low shrub. The eggs are white and usually number five.

The buff-bellied chipmunk is common in the southwestern mixed woods during the snow-free period of the year. It uses fallen logs, brush heaps, dead stumps and old woodpecker holes as places in which to escape predators, make nests, store food and hibernate over the winter. This small golden-brown rodent with black and buff stripes is active only during the daylight hours. Spring, summer and autumn find it always at some purposeful business. In spring the chipmunks breed, a process preceded by much chasing back and forth through underbrush and

C.H.

around hollow logs and stumps. The young are born in May and are cared for in the nest for about a month. They emerge and join the adults in the search for food – the seeds of grasses and dandelion heads. They cut the seed heads and then shell them, holding them between their front paws much in the fashion of a child eating a cob of corn.

Female Barrow's goldeneye taking her flotilla of black and white ducklings for a cruise.

The coniferous forest

The typical coniferous forest of the mountains is found on slopes which face north or east, on the relatively flat terrain of the valley floor and high on the mountain sides below the timberline. In its mature state this forest is dominated by Engelmann spruce, white spruce and alpine fir. These conifers all produce single needles, but here the similarity ends. The needles of the spruce are four-sided and prickly to the touch, where- as those of the fir are flat and soft. The cones are also dissimilar. The spruce cones hang down from their branches, while the fir cones stand erect.

A mature spruce-fir forest is a place of gloom. Because of the con- stancy and thickness of the overhead canopy and consequent lack of light, there is a paucity of flora in the coniferous forest. Mosses and lichens are the main components of the ground flora, of which a feather moss *Hylocomium* often forms a carpet up to ten inches deep. The forest floor supports only a few shade-loving species of flowers, as for example the dainty twin-flower which forms a loose mat of trailing stems. Its paired pink nodding flowers are a common sight. Equally common on the forest floor is the pink wintergreen, with its persistent green leathery leaves and raceme of rose-coloured flowers. A third plant, which adds a touch of transitory colour, is the little pink lady slipper. Just as the num- bers and diversity of plants are reduced in this mature forest, so are the associated animals. Only those which are directly dependent on the conifers for a food source, or their predators, are to be found in any numbers.

Some of the mountain or boreal forest insects of Alberta are notori- ous for the damage they can inflict on trees to the point of weakening or actually killing large stands. Alberta is fortunate so far in being free from really serious losses from these insects. In eastern Canada where the problem is serious, large-scale insecticide treatments have resulted only in creating hazards to other forms of wildlife and in little diminution of the pest. It is to be hoped that the forests of this province will not be attacked by insects to an extent that such insecticide treatment will be deemed necessary.

The most destructive insects of western coniferous forests are the bark beetles or engraver beetles. These small insects, averaging a quarter

207

Coniferous forest in winter

H.R

of an inch in length, make characteristic galleries between the bark and wood of the tree. These tunnels or tracks are made by the female when she lays her eggs and are later enlarged by the larvae as they feed on the cambium or growing layer. When the bark is pulled off dead trees or logs, these galleries are very noticeable, and sometimes the beetles and larvae are exposed. Often tell-tale sawdust from the boring and excrement can be seen in cracks in the bark of living trees. Healthy trees, however, can resist the attacks of these insects through the extrusion of pitch which drowns the young larvae. Dead or weakened trees are readily attacked, and in these cases the bark beetles are beneficial. The related ambrosia beetles are so called because they feed on ambrosial fungi, growing in galleries made by the females. The spores of the fungi are brought by the beetles to galleries constructed in dying or freshly killed trees and in unseasoned lumber. The fungus, which is of a specific kind for each species of ambrosia beetle, then grows in the tunnels and is eaten by the developing larvae. In Alberta two types of ambrosia beetle are found in conifers, and a third in poplars.

During summer in the mountain forest, there are always interesting insects visible to anyone willing to notice them. Flies seem to be every-where; large bluebottles and fleshflies buzz whenever food is unpacked for a picnic. Hoverflies, midges, craneflies, horseflies, deerflies and mosquitoes are constant companions to the visitor and so profuse in numbers of species that specialists could be kept busy for years just identifying them. Bumblebees, wasps and ants all belong to the order known as Hymenoptera, and are as much at home in the mountain forest as they are elsewhere. Ubiquitous, predatory ground beetles can be found by looking under stones or logs where they spend their time between hunting periods, or in the gravel near streams where they are abundant. Dung beetles, as the name implies, inhabit droppings of various herbivorous animals. Both the larvae and the adults are easily seen when the dung of moose, elk and domestic animals is examined. At certain times of the summer, the tiger swallowtail butterflies are prevalent near wet spots in clearings, or are seen flitting along trails or streams. In similar situations the beautiful parnassius can be found; this white to dusky coloured butterfly, with red spots on the wings, is a very common resident of the mountain forest.

The red squirrel, because of its dependence on the seeds of conifers, has ample scope in the spruce-fir forest, which is often made noisy with its chattering. If the squirrels are silent, there is always ample mute evidence of their presence in the shelled cones at the bases of trees. Another but less vociferous member of the community is the pine marten, which dwells in these forests because it preys on red squirrels. Birds are not abundant, although in spring one often hears above the chatter of the squirrels the loud and ringing song of the ruby-crowned kinglet. This tiny olive-gray warbler, with its almost invisible scarlet crest, spends most of its time in the high canopy of the conifers. Here it builds its semi-pendent nest and constantly searches for insects, their eggs and their larvae. The loudness of its song comes incongruously from a bird so small and insignificant. Another songster of the mature spruce-fir forests is the winter wren, also an insignificant bird, which compensates for lack of visual appeal with the tinkling beauty of its song. Instead of preferring the canopy, this chocolate-brown, short-tailed little songster finds its home among the lower lichen-festooned branches and tangled debris near the forest floor, often where a spring flows through the mossy roots.

Effects of fire

Throughout much of Alberta's mountain area the coniferous forest is not yet mature. This again is the result of fire—an important and natural element in the lives of all organisms associated with mountain forests. Lightning-caused fires occur mostly on the slopes and tops of mountains. Once started, the spread of a fire depends upon a number of factors. The weather is very important, since high winds and low relative humidity promote a rapid spread of the flames. The influence of topography is another factor. South-facing slopes tend to be drier and more susceptible to burning, while a fire on the bottom of a slope ignites the trees farther up because of heat convection. An abundance of highly combustible fuel —for example, windblown, insect- or disease-killed timber—naturally increases the rate of combustion.

Once a fire is well-established, the effect on plants and animals is catastrophic. Those animals which cannot fly or run away are killed. After the flames have subsided, the blackened trunks of the smouldering trees and the ashes and burnt snags are all that seem to remain. But this apparently sterile desert is actually a habitat for a number of different insects. Among the most common insects associated with forest fires in Alberta is one called the stack beetle, belonging to the family of metallic wood-borers. This fast-flying and agile insect, with its short antennae, is a charcoal-coloured beetle about half an inch long. It is commonly

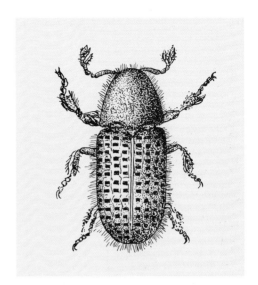

Bark beetle

Galleries made by beetle larvae

209

seen flying near campfires in the mountain and boreal forest areas of the province, and it is also very abundant near such heat sources as scrap burners at logging and plywood plants, oil fires and burning refuse heaps. When landing on the bare neck or arm of a person, these beetles tend to bite with their strong mandibles, though not painfully. Fire beetles have the unique habit of flying to forest fires, where they buzz around burning snags and crawl over the very hot surfaces of logs. These insects can detect forest fires from a distance of several miles by means of special sense organs through which they perceive the infra-red radiation emitted by fire. When they reach the site of a fire they become very active and apparently excited. Mating takes place on log surfaces quite close to the glowing embers and hot ashes. The female then deposits her eggs under the undamaged bark of scorched coniferous trees. The larvae soon hatch and feed on the inner bark, making long, winding trails filled with undigested excreta. When winter arrives they hibernate, and in the spring feeding resumes until the larvae are full grown and the pupal stage is reached. The adults emerge in a few weeks and the cycle starts once more. The ability of these insects to detect infra-red radiation means that they are able to arrive at the site of fire-killed trees before other wood-boring competitors, and so initiate the breakdown of the wood, often before the fire is out.

Forest fires attract other insects, most of which are predators or scavengers which feed on dead insects or on those deprived of their sustenance by the fire. Ground beetles are also typical inhabitants of burnt-over forest areas. These small, shiny beetles are probably predators. Flat-bugs, too, are common at fires, where they have been found crawling in the warm ashes. Empidid flies are even more common than fire beetles. These small flies swarm near still-glowing piles of logs and, although they have not been studied, the larvae are suspected of being predators. Long-horned beetles and other metallic wood-boring beetles are also seen flying rapidly near fires.

One effect of fire is to open the canopy and permit the growth of a greater diversity of plants. Fire has created a mosaic of plant communities over much of the eastern slopes of the mountains in Alberta. Each community represents a stage in a succession that culminates in the mature spruce-fir forest. One of the commonest of these stages is a forest dominated by lodgepole pine, the needles of which grow in pairs. This pine is especially adapted to fire because the cones containing the pine seeds are exceedingly durable and, under normal circumstances, require several years to be broken down before releasing their seeds. Fire scorches the parent tree, killing it but rarely consuming it completely. The cones, which are retained on the branches, are swollen by the heat and subsequently open to release relatively large numbers of seeds which have remained viable within the cone. These seeds soon germinate on the scorched forest floor and grow into seedlings which form pine stands. A natural thinning process then begins with the elimination of the weaker and smaller trees which fall and slowly decompose on the forest floor. Characteristically, deciduous trees grow with the lodgepole pine especially on wetter sites. The canopy coverage of the lodgepole pine is often sufficiently open to allow enough light through to support a shrub layer, and thus alder and willow may be found. The resulting plant community supports a much more diversified fauna. The pines create a forest canopy, the alder and willow form a dense shrub layer, and the forest floor supports such plants as blueberry, the fruit and leaves of which are used heavily by a number of species of birds and mammals.

Among the characteristic birds is the quiet and confiding spruce

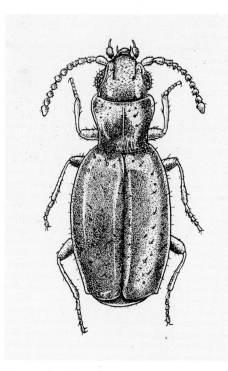

Ground beetle

(a)

.H.

(a) Canada jay
(b) Franklin grouse
(c) Blue grouse
(d) White-tailed ptarmigan
(e) Solitary sandpiper

(b)

D.M.

(c)

H.

(d)

D. A. B.

(e)

C. H.

211

grouse which blends superbly with its background, and is often passed by because it remains perfectly still when danger appears. The pine trees provide all its basic needs: a constant food supply, an escape from ground predators, a display perch during courtship, and a protective guise under which to nest. In the pine stands in May, a sound that resembles two twigs snapping in rapid succession is often heard. This sound is, in fact, the wing claps of spruce grouse as they perform one of their courtship displays. This particular display begins from a branch some feet off the ground. The bird launches itself from this perch on rapidly beating wings, flying obliquely toward the ground. The short flight culminates in two wing slaps over the back just prior to alighting. The sounds are penetrating and are often repeated by other birds in the surrounding forest.

This young mixed forest also supports many of the large mountain animals. Moose, wapiti and deer find browse abundant here. Black bears feed heavily on the fruit of shrubs and on insects, particularly ants, which abound in the fire-killed trunks of the former forest. Many species of small song birds find their best living conditions in the mixed vegetative growth. MacGillivray's warbler is a characteristic frequenter of the edges of the alder-pine growth. This greenish-yellow warbler with a bluish-gray head and neck is difficult to observe for any length of time because its constant search for insects keeps it moving restlessly through the foliage and tangled stems of the shrubs. It has a loud song which seems never to be given twice from the same spot. In this way it confounds its enemies and at the same time delineates its own territory. Another member of this community is the dusky flycatcher, a nondescript, olive-coloured bird whose two-syllable song is a common sound in the pine forests. Unlike the active warbler, this little songster sits quietly on a branch, only darting out to intercept a passing insect and then returning to its vigil. Like all members of its tribe, this flycatcher has the habit of flicking its tail every so often while it perches.

Ice worms and snow insects

Certain insects inhabiting forests are very well known either because of their specialized habits or because of the attention given to them by foresters and entomologists, due to their potentially destructive capabilities. Some of these insects are restricted to the mountain forests while others are found in both the mountain and boreal forests. Still others occur in all zones from the river valley bottoms to the exposed tundra.

A very famous insect is the ice-worm, well known to entomologists the world over and one which put Alberta on the map of the zoogeographers. Two specimens of this insect were first found in June, 1913, by Professor E. M. Walker of the University of Toronto on Sulphur Mountain at Banff. Because of its unique characteristics, it was placed in a new family, the Grylloblattidae. It has been designated as a living, though specialized, representative of an ancient group of insects that gave rise to a present order of insects, the Orthoptera, which includes cockroaches, grasshoppers and crickets. Since 1913 other genera and species of this strange group of insects have been found in Siberia, Japan and in the western United States, but Banff retains the honour of being the site of the first discovery of this new family.

The ice-worm is a pale-yellow, slender, wingless insect measuring from three quarters to one inch in length, with chewing mouthparts, cockroach-like legs for fast running and an ovipositor for egg-laying like that of a cricket. Very little is known of its biology. Most specimens have been collected in cool, moist localities, in the spring or autumn of the year when the temperatures were not much above 32 degrees fahrenheit

MacGillivray's warbler

(a)

FLOWERS OF THE MOUNTAINS

(a) **Red Indian paint brush**
(b) **Yellow lady's – slipper**
(c) **Western anemone**
(d) **Calypso orchid**
(e) **Saxifrage**
(f) **Moss campion**

(b)

(d)

(e)

(c)

(f)

213

under stones and in logs where they generally hide. In the summer months, they probably retreat deep into the talus slopes whenever it becomes necessary for them to avoid high temperatures and low humidities. It is generally thought that ice-worms are scavenger-predators which feed on dead insects or the helpless larvae of wood-borers, caterpillars and maggots. Ice-worms were once thought to be so rare that for many years the Department of Entomology at the University of Alberta paid a dollar for each adult specimen brought in, but it is now known that specimens can easily be located if they are hunted at the right time and in the right place. Specimens have been found in many locations near Jasper. In October they can be seen under stones and in logs from the Athabasca River (altitude 4,500 feet) all the way up the slopes, amongst the trees and in clearings to a height of over 7,000 feet in the alpine meadows above the Edith Cavell teahouse, where they may be seen walking on the snow.

Other insects are unusual in that they are associated with the snow on mountain sides and tops. These "snow insects", as they are called, are able to survive below-freezing temperatures on the snow surface, and are easily seen wherever snow is present either among the trees or in open areas of the forested zone as well as on the open tundra on high plateaus. *Boreus californicus fuscus,* belonging to the order of the scorpion flies, can be found walking on the snow in the mountains in late spring and early autumn. These insects are small and black and feign death when approached. They may be predators of insects which become too cold to fly and fall on the snow.

Chionea alexandriana is a wingless, long-legged, dark-coloured fly belonging to the primitive craneflies. This insect is also a snow dweller and, like *Boreus,* feigns death and remains motionless for five minutes or longer after it has been disturbed. This is presumably an adaptation for protective purposes, since these dark insects are easily visible on the snow surface. *Chionea* is usually found in the forested areas of the mountains, though occasionally it has been found at high altitudes in the tundra zone. Little is known of its biology.

The most ubiquitous snow insects are the snow-fleas or springtails. Great numbers of these small, almost microscopic, wingless, primitive insects can often be found on the snow surface in the spring and autumn. Many species of snow-fleas are known in Alberta, including those that inhabit only woodland soils, bogs and gardens, but two species, both of which are found in Edmonton, have also been reported in snow from the 4,000-foot level near Missoula, Montana. Little is known of the habits of these insects except that they feed on vegetation.

The rocky outcrop areas

Extensive areas of rock outcrop are found throughout the mountain slopes well below the timberline, and on the exposed crests of foothills. Those areas which face south or west support a distinct vegetation complex. Here Douglas fir and limber or Rocky Mountain pine are the dominant conifers.

Beneath both the Douglas fir and limber pine patches of bearberry form an evergreen mat. The small pink flowers and red fruit of this low, shiny-leaved plant form a favourite item in the diet of blue grouse. These large, slate-coloured grouse, found only in the foothills and mountains, engage in an intriguing annual movement, wintering at high altitudes at or near the timberline, and migrating to the lower slopes for the breeding season. While on the winter range they subsist largely on conifer needles. They continue with this fare upon arrival on the summer range in April, but soon turn to newly sprouting vegetation on the forest floor.

Douglas fir

Limber pine

(a)

ANIMALS OF THE MOUNTAINS

(a) Bighorn sheep
(b) Hoary marmot
(c) Columbian ground squirrel
(d) Golden-mantled ground squirrel
(e) Rocky Mountain goat

(b)

(d)

C.H.

(c)

(e)

R.MC.

These birds are most easily observed early in spring when vegetation of the forest floor is still meagre and they call attention to themselves by a series of elaborate courtship displays. At dawn and dusk on the fir- and pine-clad slopes, there may be heard the muffled hoots of the male birds. These hooting sounds, which have a ventriloquial quality, are given in series of five and are emitted through the throat of the male grouse, usually from the ground and often at the centre of his territory. This territory he will defend, either by emitting threatening hoots or by adopting threatening display postures. The posturings include much head bobbing, the erection of the scarlet coloured combs over the eyes, the spreading and upward tilting of the tail, and the exposure of deep red patches by retracting the white-based neck feathers to form a large circular rosette. In this posture the bird parades slowly back and forth in the shadows of trees. Should a female grouse arrive in the territory, the display changes in subtle ways: the combs return to their normal yellow colour, the rosettes flare even wider, and the tail is tilted forward over the back. The male then rushes towards the female in a wide sweeping arc. The last few yards of the rush are accompanied by the dragging of the wing feathers to create a loud rustling noise. Just prior to reaching the female the male emits a single loud and penetrating hoot. It is in the broken rock of these outcrop areas that the female places her nest, choosing a spot where a rock overhang will protect her. In August the adult males and non-breeding members of the population return once more to the alpine reaches for the winter; they are followed in early September by the adult females and their young.

The harsh cries of another common bird, Clark's nutcracker, may also be heard in this region. This noisy pearl gray bird with black and white wings is an impertinent member of the crow family. It lives in close association with the limber pine, for the cones of this tree form a large item in its diet. Furthermore the twisted and dense foliage of the pines provides a favoured nesting site. It is from these precarious spots that the strident, relentless begging of the young nutcrackers is often heard as they demand ever more food. These birds descend to the valley floors in winter to feed, like other members of their clan, on whatever is available.

Another characteristic sound of the rock outcrop regions is the rambling but beautiful song of Townsend's solitaire. Usually the song is sung as the bird flies in lazy circles high above the rocky outcrop, like a leaf suspended on an updraught. The song ends and the male bird plummets earthward much in the style of the lark. Occasionally, however, the same delightful warbling song may be traced to a dusky gray bird, with a conspicuous white circlet of feathers around the eye, perched on the upper branches of a dead tree. From this vantage point it warns others of its kin that a particular stretch of broken rocks and trees is its particular domain. The bird is a member of the thrush family and, except in spring, is quiet and gentle. Unlike its relatives the solitaire builds its nest on the ground, usually under a cutbank or overhanging rock. The young solitaires, in true thrush style, wear spots – although these are white, rather than dark — and cover the whole body.

Among the mammals which frequent the rocky outcrop regions are two rodents and an animal of the rabbit family. One of the rodents is the golden-mantled ground squirrel, closely resembling a large chipmunk even to the black and buff stripes on the sides. Unlike the other ground squirrels which inhabit the grasslands, this species is found among shattered rocks and on broken cliff faces. They are less gregarious than their kin, but still have their sentries on lofty lookouts to warn of approaching danger by chirping loudly. Should danger threaten, they soon

Male blue grouse in hooting posture

Clark's nutcracker

H.

Serenity and grandeur of the mountains reflected by Roche Miette.

sappear into convenient crevices or under overhanging rocks. They are relatively confiding little rodents and quickly reappear from hiding to continue their activities. Much of their time is spent in searching for food, usually tender new shoots of plants or their flowers and seeds. In late summer they busy themselves caching fruit and seeds which they carry in expansive cheek pouches and deposit in nooks and crevices in the broken rock.

The golden-mantled ground squirrel shares this rocky habitat with the pack rat. The squirrels are active only in the daytime, the pack rats at night. Hence contact between the species is minimized. The presence of pack rats is often detected first by a musty smell resulting from their habit of always urinating in the same spot. This in turn produces an accumulation of a viscous odoriferous tar-like substance that can often be found staining rock faces. These rats seem to be afflicted by a mania for collecting objects to place in their nests. Hence one often finds huge stick nests wedged into a cavity on a cliff face or in a rock slide. Frequently these nests contain human artifacts, if any such have been dropped in the vicinity. Pack rats are sometimes called "traders" because of their intriguing practice of replacing any object they collect with a twig or pebble. The rats themselves are handsome animals with soft gray coats, white bellies and bushy gray tails. Their energy and activity are prodigious. One rat can create the impression of many through its constant comings and goings along the rock ledges at night.

The third mammal found on the broken rock and talus slope is the "rock rabbit" or pika. Among the rock slides this little gray animal, no larger than a ground squirrel, is active all year round. The summer months are spent cutting vegetation and carrying it to sheltered, sunny spots beneath overhanging rocks. Here the vegetation cures into hay and

Pika

217

Between the high mountain forests and the bare rocky peaks, is found the remote and beautiful alpine tundra.

becomes the major food supply for survival in winter. When disturbed these animals emit a loud bleat, a sound not readily associated with a rabbit-like creature. The cry, often given from a lookout point in the rock slide, seems to function as a warning to the other members of the species which quickly scamper for cover.

The alpine tundra

Between the coniferous forest and the barren rocky peaks of the mountains is a zone in which herbaceous plants exist but in which no trees of any significance can grow. This is the alpine tundra. It is a fascinating environment where conditions are harsh but where, in summer, the slopes are a riot of colour as specially adapted forms quickly flower and fruit in the short growing season. Here many of the plants take on special growth forms to make the most of what heat and moisture falls upon them. Thus we find prostrate forms which grow along the surface of the ground, cushion plants that wedge themselves in crevices, and leathery or hairy-leaved forms which are adapted to conserve water in their tissues. Two very common plant species on these alpine slopes are the mountain avens and snow willow. The former grows in dense patches and in June the pale green leaves and cream-coloured rose-like flowers create a beautiful carpet. The willow, which grows but a few inches tall, produces large pinkish catkins which are visited by numerous insects.

It is to these lonely alpine meadows that flocks of bighorn sheep, mountain goats and herds of wapiti come in summer to graze on the nutritious vegetation. A number of birds are seasonal inhabitants of the alpine tundra. Brewer's sparrow is the most beautiful songster of the area. This small, sandy streaked sparrow utters its long and tumbling song from the fastness of some prostrate shrubbery. Here it nests and raises its brood, taking advantage of the relative shelter and warmth to be found a few inches above the surface of the ground. Another sparrow which returns to the alpine tundra from the valley floors to breed, is the rosy finch. This is a chocolate-brown sparrow, with a rosy wash on the flanks and rump and a gray patch above the eyes; it nests and feeds among the rocks where the plants thin out and leave only the hardiest among the sheltered crevices.

A permanent resident of the alpine tundra is the white-tailed ptarmigan. This small grouse is well equipped to withstand the rigours of the environment. Like its arctic relatives, it changes plumage with the season

218

C.H.

Male ruffed grouse performing his spectacular drumming.

In winter, it is pure white with the exception of the beak and eyes. At this time it blends superbly with the snow. As an adaptation for the conservation of heat during the cold of the alpine winters, it has feathers growing right down to the tips of its toes. Feathered feet also aid the ptarmigan in walking on the snow. In winter the species relies heavily on the buds of willows, exposed on the wind-swept ridges. In summer the plumage becomes a mottled yellow, gray and black – a combination which blends ideally with the surrounding lichen-encrusted rocks. In spring the male birds may be heard uttering their harsh calls as part of their courtship ritual. In summer one may have to climb until broken rock is reached to catch sight of the well camouflaged female with her brood.

On this high exposed tundra one of our rarest carnivores, the grizzly bear, may, with good fortune, be seen. Constant harassment by man and the usurping of much of its former range has driven the grizzly into the remote mountain tundra. Here throughout the summer, it can hunt for food in relative peace. A favourite item in its diet is the fleshy root of the legume, yellow hedysarum. Occasionally the bear may unearth a ground squirrel or a hoary marmot, or it may feed on insects such as wingless grasshoppers. The marmots are large rodents, related to the common groundhog or woodchuck, and are usually found on the high exposed rocky areas at or above the timberline. Here they spend their active season from April to September alternately grazing and sunning themselves on rocky terrain. Should anything cause them to take alarm, they utter a high piercing cry which has been likened to the sound of a boy's tin whistle.

In summary, the vast mountainous region of Alberta contains such a series of varying habitats, from valley floor to mountain peak, that one finds many species of plants and animals common to the prairies, the parklands and the boreal forests. On the other hand, some animals, particularly insects and birds, are to be found only in the mountains, and some tundral forms never leave their high, treeless and seemingly desolate environment. Alberta is indeed fortunate in possessing its mountain habitats.

Grizzly bear

C.H.

CHAPTER TEN

Aquatic Life

RODNEY J. PATERSON
LORENE L. KENNEDY
R. C. B. HARTLAND-ROWE
MARTIN J. PAETZ

AQUATIC HABITATS / RODNEY J. PATERSON

In previous chapters we have seen something of the immense variety of topography, climate and soils in Alberta. The character of aquatic habitats is dependent upon these features, and therefore we can expect to find a similar diversity in types of aquatic habitat and in aquatic life. To describe in one chapter the whole spectrum of aquatic life in the province is not possible. Instead we can only hope to provide brief glimpses of the fascinating communities of living organisms found in our lakes and streams.

Water has certain unusual properties which are of profound importance to all organisms living in it. Perhaps the most important of these is the unique fact that water is more dense at a temperature of 39.2 degrees fahrenheit than at any other temperature. If water were like other liquids, it would be most dense when frozen, and ice would sink to the bottom. Were this to happen, lakes and rivers would freeze from the bottom upwards until, during prolonged cold weather, they would be frozen solid. This would be disastrous for all the organisms living in them, as well as for those that depend upon water for survival.

Both water and ice are poor conductors of heat. When a lake freezes, not only is most of the water in the lake trapped below a layer of ice because of the difference in the density of ice and water, but this water is also insulated from the cold air above. As a result, even though ice is rarely more than three feet thick, the difference between the air and water temperatures may be as much as 70 degrees. As far as fish are concerned, Alberta winters are never colder than about one degree above freezing.

Title picture – Cattails at water's edge

221

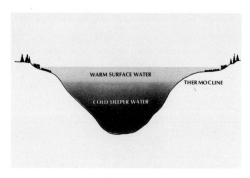

Thermal stratification in summer. The layer of warm surface water (epilimnion) is separated from the layer of cold deeper water (hypolimnion) by a region of rapid temperature change.

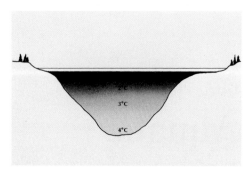

Temperatures in a lake under ice cover.

Temperature variations and overturn in a lake

Each of water's unique properties profoundly affects the behaviour of water in a standing body such as a lake. Since water is a poor conductor of heat, the sun can only warm the surface waters. The deeper waters are warmed by the mixing action of the wind, which stirs the warmed surface waters into the colder deeper waters. Since, except for the narrow range between 32-39.2 degrees, cold water is more dense than warm water, the cold water will tend to stay at the bottom of a lake and in summer there is a marked decrease in temperature as the depth increases. In winter, because water at 39.2 degrees is more dense than water at the freezing point, the warmer water of a lake will be closer to the bottom, and the coldest water will be adjacent to the ice layer at the surface. A thermometer lowered into lake waters will record a series of temperatures varying from the freezing point to a possible maximum of 39.2 degrees close to the bottom.

When lake waters are warmed in spring or cooled in autumn, for a short period all the waters of a lake will be of similar temperature and density. At this time, because of this uniformity, a lake is most susceptible to wind action and complete mixing of lake waters can occur. This mixing action is called overturn. Overturn is very important in the oxygenation of lake waters.

Oxygen in lakes

Oxygen is essential for most forms of life. This gas constitutes approximately one-fifth of the air we breathe. For most aquatic life it must be dissolved in water before it becomes usable. Water can hold only a limited quantity of oxygen in solution at a given time, depending upon the temperature, and warm water will hold less oxygen than cold water. Almost all the oxygen in lake waters is obtained from the atmosphere, and wind action is responsible for agitating the water and putting this oxygen into solution. Without wind, most of the oxygen would be concentrated in a very thin layer near the surface.

In summer, heating by the sun and the air produces layers of water of different temperatures, a process known as thermal stratification. The warm layer on the surface prevents the penetration of oxygen supplies into the deep cold layer of water, known as the hypolimnion. As a result the inhabitants of the hypolimnion must depend upon the supply of oxygen taken in at the spring overturn. In winter, ice cover prevents the absorption of any oxygen from the air, and the autumn overturn is therefore of great importance. During this overturn the lake water must take in all the oxygen necessary to support life in the lake throughout the winter. Actively growing plants contribute a small quantity of oxygen to lake waters, but in winter this contribution is only possible when snow cover on the ice is minimal, and light can penetrate the water. Decaying plants and animals use up oxygen and add less desirable gases such as carbon dioxide and hydrogen sulphide to lake waters. Winter is a critical period for aquatic life in Alberta, and the oxygen supply available may be a limiting factor for many organisms, particularly higher forms like fish.

Sunlight, nutrients and productivity in lakes

Sunlight is essential for the growth of all green plants. Light can only penetrate water to a limited degree, depending upon the amount of suspended matter and the colour of the water. Green plants will be found only at depths where adequate sunlight is available. Algae, in particular, form the "grass of the aquatic world" upon which most of the larger organisms ultimately depend. As sunlight is necessary for algal growth, the surface waters of a lake are the most productive, and deeper waters – often lacking adequate supplies of sunlight and oxygen – are much less so.

222

different depths will vary according to the surface area, the bottom contours and the wind exposure. This variation will determine the lake's suitability for certain species of plants and animals. Other species may depend upon the presence or absence of more restricted types of habitat such as weedy bays or rocky shoals.

Productivity in sloughs, saline lakes and reservoirs

In addition to lakes, there are bodies of water – some permanent and some seasonal – which are shallow but rich in aquatic life. These are ponds and sloughs. Their bottoms are rich in organic material, the decay of which may cause serious oxygen deficiency in winter along with the accumulation of such gases as hydrogen sulphide. Few fish species can survive in them. They often support large quantities of aquatic plants and invertebrates and are the nesting and feeding areas for waterfowl. Muskrats are frequent inhabitants of such waters.

In eastern and southern areas of the province, in many small drainage basins water is constantly lost by evaporation and salt concentrations gradually increase, causing the formation of saline sloughs. In some of these the salt content or salinity may reach 100,000 parts per million; that is, in every gallon of water one pound of salt will be present. Many of the more common aquatic plants and animals are unable to survive under such conditions. These sloughs therefore support a very limited range of species, each specialized for existence in such an environment.

Some reservoirs are like lakes, but they are rarely as productive as their natural counterparts since water is usually drawn off at certain seasons of the year and the surface level does not remain constant. We have seen that the littoral zone of a lake is its most productive area, but the fluctuation of water levels in a reservoir prevents the establishment of a permanent littoral zone and can seriously affect the reproduction of many species of organisms. Many reservoirs are also characterized by high water-exchange rates which tend to reduce their productivity.

Environment and productivity of rivers and streams

The physical problems of heat conduction and density change are of lesser importance to the inhabitants of naturally flowing waters. By virtue of its continually changing surface, a stream generally maintains high oxygen levels and consistent temperatures from top to bottom. As its velocity of flow decreases, so its behaviour increasingly resembles that of a small lake or pond. The very movement of water in a stream, however, presents a special problem to the organisms living in it, and only those that are adapted to this can survive.

The characteristics of a stream and the organisms which inhabit it may change many times throughout its length. The aquatic life to be found in any given stretch of stream will be influenced by the current, the nature of the bottom, the water temperature and the nature of the watershed in that region. Some of these factors may vary with the seasons but will exhibit a definite pattern which favours certain species of organisms.

Just as mountain lakes with cold water and rocky bottoms are unproductive, so also are cold, rocky-bottomed mountain streams. A stream flowing, generally slowly, through fertile agricultural land will exhibit higher summer temperatures and be much more productive. A stream in the foothills may have a moderate flow, with some stretches of rocky or gravelly bottom and with temperatures intermediate between the two extremes. Each of these types of streams may contain a completely different flora and fauna, although there will be some degree of overlap. A number of species of aquatic organisms may be found in a wide variety of streams, both large and small.

Shoreline vegetation around slough M.H.

Mountain stream. Steep gradient and underlying bedrock provide a poor habitat for aquatic organisms.

Slow-moving prairie stream M.H.

Most streams and rivers in Alberta are characterized by a marked seasonal fluctuation in flow. High rates of flow in the spring and early summer – due to the melting of the winter snows – are followed by a gradual decrease in flow throughout the summer and autumn. The lowest flows are usually recorded during the winter months. Since space is a limiting factor in population size, the "carrying capacity", or quantity of organisms which a stream can support, is governed by the lowest rate of flow of that stream. The productive capacity of a stream with a more stable flow pattern, such as one largely fed by springs, is therefore apt to be greater than one that undergoes wide fluctuations in level.

In addition to the inanimate natural forces which affect streams, the activities of such semi-aquatic mammals as beavers profoundly affect the character of many of the flowing waters of the province. Beaver construct small impoundments along streams of light to moderate flow and thus create a habitat more closely resembling that of a pond than that of a flowing stream. The resulting shallow flooded area favours the establishment of rooted aquatic plants and attracts a new fauna. As a result of increased surface area and exposure to sunlight the stream water temperature may be slightly increased. In regions where supplies of poplar and willow are limited, beaver may move to an alternative area when food supplies are exhausted and their abandoned dams may finally be washed away. Then the stream bed gradually reverts to its original condition.

Productivity and aquatic life

The productivity of a stream or lake is primarily related to the watershed in which each is situated. Productivity, however, is purely a measure of the total quantity of plant or animal matter produced; it gives no indication of the character of the life involved. The presence of particular species depends upon the presence of suitable habitats for these species. The preferred habitat of any given species involves a number of physical factors, each in varying degree. We have already seen something of these factors and their effect upon the aquatic environment. It is now possible to consider a selection of the organisms involved and the habitats in which they may commonly be found.

Beaver dam and pond

C. H

H.

Reflected reed patterns

AQUATIC PLANT LIFE / LORENE L. KENNEDY

Within Alberta, all lakes, ponds, streams and rivers contain plants, animals, bacteria and fungi that interact with one another to form a living world of great complexity and endless fascination. Those who study the plant life of lakes and streams find that there is infinite variety in the communities of plants, far more than will be found on land, and that the picture changes many times throughout the seasons. No two lakes or streams possess the same flora and fauna, since all vary in such environmental factors as depth, water chemistry, bottom sediments and other related factors to which these organisms are very sensitive. It is therefore impossible in a brief account to give a description of all the kinds of aquatic plants that occur within the province's boundaries. A much better approach is to present a picture of the pattern of communities of organisms to be found in the two markedly different natural waters – standing water and running water. In each case, some of the more common types of plants in the various communities will be selected as elements in an overall picture of life in the water.

Plant life in a lake

A fairly large and permanent body of water, such as Lake Wabamun, with a considerable depth in the centre and an extensive and varied shoreline, will illustrate plant life in standing water. Such a lake is an aqueous cosmos, a world in itself, open to the atmosphere and surrounding land, but containing within its boundaries, plants, animals, fungi and bacteria, each with a vital contribution to make to community life in the water. As we stand on the shore, we can observe some of the marginal plants and perhaps catch a glimpse of the occasional animal, but we can see little of the teeming microscopic life within the water, nor can we readily appreciate the kind of environment which is home to these organisms.

C.H.

White water crowfoot – an aquatic buttercup with finely divided leaves, well adapted to a life submerged in water.

If we now take a boat and row slowly to the middle of the lake, we note the three zones already described: first the littoral zone of shallow water; and then the open water expanse divided into the sunlight-penetrated, limnetic zone of from six to thirty feet in depth, and the dark profundal zone. At this point we become aware of the obstacles placed in the path of the observer of lake life. We cannot move around within the environment as easily as on land, and we cannot see the majority of the organisms because of their minute size. Therefore we must collect

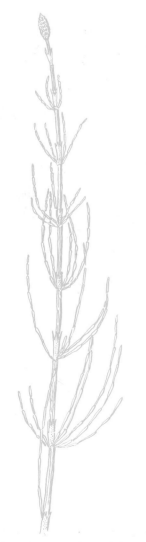

Water horsetail

Lake Wabamun. Communities of rooted, floating and submersed vascular plants ring the shoreline.

M.

the organisms from the various habitats and study them under the micro scope. From these observations we must create a picture of the aquati world, much as a person puts together the pieces of a jig-saw puzzle Such studies involve regular sampling of the water by means of fine net towed through the water, or by water bottles lowered to different depth: together with the examination of all such submerged surfaces as leaves stems, stones and the lake bottom.

Rooted plant communities of the littoral zone

If we turn first to the shoreline, we notice that the rocky or sandy beache lack visible plant growth. This is caused by vigorous wave action whic prevents the plants from becoming established. Elsewhere, in protecte bays, there is a luxurious growth of rooted aquatics – vascular plant that grow in relatively shallow water. At the margin, and extending ou to a depth of around three or four feet, grow tall cattails and bulrushes o the genus *Scirpus,* with rootstocks in the waterlogged mud and lon stems partly in water, partly in air.

These sturdy, emergent plants are really terrestrial forms adapted t a marshy habitat, as most of their leaves and their flowers are borne i the air. It is difficult, however, for the seed of these plants to germinat in the oxygen-deficient mud or water. The pioneer plants would hav started from seed, but their multiplication is by means of fleshy, under ground stems. These spread rapidly, leading to extensive stands of bul rushes or cattails, often derived from one initial plant. Although thes two plants are very common, two other rooted aquatics – reed grass o the genus *Phragmites,* and water horsetail of the genus *Equisetum* – forr extensive growths around certain of our lakes. Reed grass may grow to height of ten feet. The size of these plants, together with their larg flower clusters, or inflorescences, covered with long, silky hairs, make them a striking shoreline vegetation. Water horsetail is readily recog nized by its hollow, jointed stems lacking leaves and sometimes toppe with a spore-bearing cone.

As the water becomes deeper, floating plants make their appearance

he most conspicuous member of this group is the yellow water lily of
ne genus *Nuphar*, with its golden yellow flowers and its broad leaves
ttached to a thick, spongy rootstock. Not so striking a plant, but much
more common, is duckweed, a tiny flat plant about the size of a pea which
onsists of two or three lobes and a short root. The duckweeds multiply
o rapidly by budding that they frequently cover the surface of shallow
vater to form a vivid green carpet, thus imitating some of the larger algae.

Farther out, we leave behind the rooted aquatics which need strong
ght, and look down through the water into a tangled growth of sub-
nersed plants dependent upon the dim light which penetrates clear water
p to twelve feet. In this aquatic meadow are found water milfoil, with
:s leaves divided into pairs of smooth, tooth-pick-like segments, horn-
vort with whorled leaf segments toothed on one side, and pondweeds,
ecognized by their limp, ribbon-shaped leaves, associated in some
pecies with broader floating leaves attached to the single stem. Often
nese underwater plants are unattached, floating in dense masses near
ne bottom of the lake and marking the outer limits of the littoral zone.
Jot every lake will show these three communities of rooted aquatics,
ince their distribution is controlled by a variety of factors such as the
ype of lake bottom, and chance establishment of the plants.

Algae of the littoral zone

n the littoral zone algae are much in evidence, for here grow a variety of
ttached and loose-lying species, some of which form extensive growths
risible to the naked eye. In contrast to the algae of the open water, these
plants are adapted to a stationary existence and, while strong winds may
:arry them out into the centre of the lake, they do not flourish there. This
ittoral community of algae, known as the benthos or bottom forms, is
:omposed of numerous smaller communities distributed according to
preference for certain microhabitats, like mud or rock.

As one wades through the shallow water around the bulrushes or
:attails, floating mats of filamentous algae are often encountered. If,
vhen picked up and examined, this growth is bright green and is silky in
exture, then the alga is *Spirogyra* or one of its close relatives – plants
nade up of a single row of cells and enclosed in a gelatinous sheath
vhich makes them slippery to the touch. If the strands are yellowish-
green and rough to the touch, then the alga is a species of *Cladophora*,
he alga with the coarsest filaments. This alga may form extensive living
blankets in shallow water. The roughness comes from horny material
:alled chitin in the cell wall. Chitin makes the surface of the filaments

E.B.

A Cladophora blanket

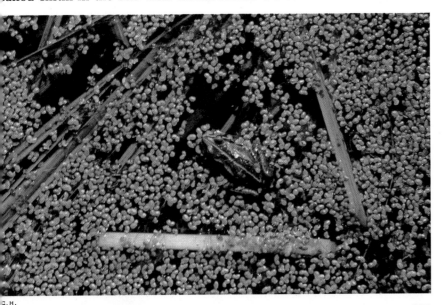

C.H.

**Producers, a green carpet of duckweed, and
a consumer, a frog, in an aquatic habitat.**

229

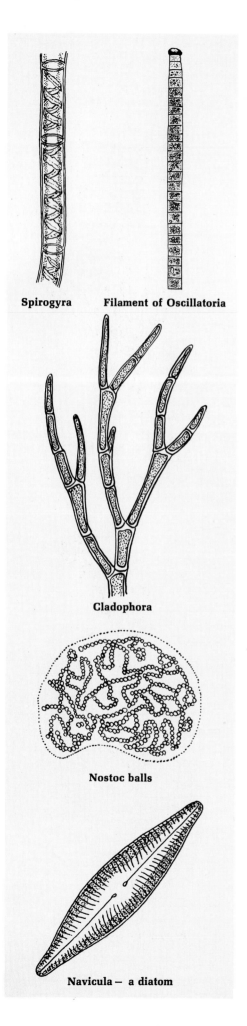

Spirogyra **Filament of Oscillatoria**

Cladophora

Nostoc balls

Navicula – a diatom

jagged and, incidentally, provides an attaching place for numerous, microscopic, stationary algae. In some lakes – for example, Pigeon Lake – *Cladophora* plants lying on the sandy bottom at the lake-edge are rolled into small balls by the lapping movement of the water. At the onset of winter these larger algae either produce a thick-walled dormant cell or a few thick-walled short filaments filled with reserve food which survive the winter in the mud below the ice, while the green vegetative cells die when the water freezes.

Another very common alga which, like *Cladophora*, may float in the water or lie loosely on the mud just under the surface is *Nostoc*, which occurs as greenish-brown spheres about the size of a grape or small plum. In this alga, filaments of bead-shaped cells are embedded in a tough gelatinous matrix resulting in so-called *Nostoc* balls which, on rough days, may be seen bobbing along in the water like ping-pong balls.

All algae show seasonal growth cycles which result in their appearance in considerable numbers and subsequent disappearance several times throughout the growing season. For example, *Spirogyra* is often present in quantity during the spring when the water is cool, well-oxygenated, and relatively high in minerals; it then disappears in mid-summer, but makes a second appearance in the autumn coincident with lower temperatures and the mixing of the waters. Therefore a description of species selected from different habitats does not imply that these or other algae are present throughout the entire growing season.

Closely associated with the larger, floating algae are two widespread algae attached to the mud or sand beneath the water and clearly visible. One, *Oscillatoria,* forms dark, bluish-green films on the bottom composed of numerous filaments stuck to the mud and each other by copious mucilaginous material. Sometimes the oxygen trapped between the adhering plants causes the whole mass to rise to the surface, and on a windy day it may be carried out into the lake. The name "*Oscillatoria*" refers to a unique feature of these plants – the slow oscillation of the upper part of the filament in the water. *Oscillatoria* reproduces by fragmentation of the filament; the sections so produced also show motility, moving away from the parent plant to colonize new areas. These puzzling movements involve no organs of locomotion, and appear to be somewhat like muscle movement, in that alternating waves of contraction and relaxation pass up and down the strand of cells. The second alga of this habitat, *Chara* the stonewort, grows erect, being anchored to the sediment by short, colourless out-growths. It usually occurs in dense stands forming a kind of underwater meadow. This pale green plant has a central axis and whorls of cylindrical segments attached at intervals along the axis which reaches just to the water surface. As the name "stonewort" suggests, the surface of these algae is rough or brittle due to a coating of lime, a feature which, together with their garlic-like smell, allows them to be distinguished from the submersed seed plants to which they bear a superficial resemblance.

In places lacking macroscopic or large algae, we may notice that the the surface of the bottom shows a green or rich brown colouring caused by dense populations of microscopic algae that are lightly attached to the sediment particles by their sticky surface. The majority of these microscopic algae are diatoms – one-celled plants with glass-like walls. One can imagine how often these cells must be disturbed and partially buried by wave action. Hence it is not surprising to find that most diatoms are motile. The extremely common diatom, *Navicula,* moves backward and forward on its axis in a manner similar to a large ocean liner when it is docking. When *Navicula* becomes buried, it responds by moving upward through the silt until it is again resting on the surface.

The rooted aquatics around the lake shore play host to a diversified algal community in which the cells attach themselves to the underwater stems and leaves. Pull a reed or cattail stem from the water, run your hand over the surface, and notice the streaks of brown caused by the diatoms you have dislodged. Such diatoms as *Tabellaria, Cocconeis,* or *Synedra,* live somewhat precariously stuck to these surfaces, for they are frequently washed away by water movements. Further study of the cattail stems frequently reveals bright green, globular colonies of *Chaetophora* in which branching filaments are embedded in a jelly. Often growing along with *Chaetophora* is *Coleochaete,* which develops tiny bright green discs of cells tightly pressed against a brown stem. These cells require a hand lens to be seen readily.

Pondweeds, which grow entirely under water, harbour so many different kinds of algae that it is a wonder how all the algae can function successfully in so limited a space. If we pick up a handful of these plants from alongside the boat and separate out an individual, the encrusting algae are evident. The most noticeable growth will likely be that of *Gloeotrichia,* which forms brown tough gelatinous nodules crowded along the stems and partly encircling them. Under the microscope, these growths can be seen to consist of tapered filaments so arranged that they radiate outward like the spokes of a wheel. *Gloeotrichia* is related to *Nostoc* and *Oscillatoria,* the so-called blue-green algae, which are the simplest of green plants. They lack specialized cells of any kind and perhaps represent the most primitive of plants.

It is interesting to note that some of the blue-green algae can absorb atmospheric nitrogen and produce soluble nitrates, a process shared with only one other group of organisms, the nitrogen-fixing bacteria which grow in legume roots. Both these groups of organisms add nitrates to their habitat, improving it greatly for neighbouring plants. Associated with *Gloeotrichia* are numerous single-celled and filamentous algae like *Stigeoclonium, Characium,* and many diatoms. Even a limited study of the littoral zone makes it evident that this part of the lake is the richest in variety of plants, although it represents a relatively small portion of the lake area.

Plants of the limnetic zone

Microscopic drifting algae, called phytoplankton, live in the open water of the lake. Their presence is noticed only when they occur in such immense numbers that they colour the water. Since we cannot see the individual plants, it comes as a surprise to learn that their numbers and contribution to the food supply far outweigh that of visible plants in the lake. Within the open-water region the bulk of these organisms occurs in the upper nine to twelve feet of water, the depth varying according to the turbidity of the water, which controls light penetration. We can picture vast populations of these algae suspended in the water, carried about by water movements, and adjusting to changes in light by vertical movements within the zone of light penetration. On a cloudy day they may be found concentrated near the surface, while a sunny day sends them deeper into the water.

To observe the details that give individuality to these tiny algae, we have to use a microscope with a magnification of about four hundred times. If we place a few drops of lake water under the lens, a fascinating array of tiny green or brown organisms comes into focus. Some are single cells which move rapidly through the water or slowly jerk themselves about. Others are rows or clumps of cells floating in the water. All possess features as distinctive as those of larger plants. Some of the

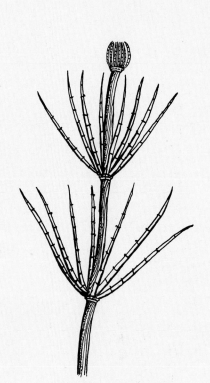

Chara – the stonewort

Potamogeton – a pondweed

231

common plankton algae of Alberta lakes are true aquatic plants, for they live surrounded on all sides by water and must obtain all requirements for life from water.

It is natural to compare these algae with the more familiar land plants, and to think of them as simple, unspecialized organisms far down on the evolutionary scale. This is to do them an injustice, for their structure reflects successful adaptation to the particular environment in which they live. This environment is a very large volume of water in which are dissolved small amounts of carbon dioxide, oxygen, minerals and organic compounds, and through which a certain amount of sunlight penetrates. In this medium, the algae must remain suspended in the upper layer so that each cell receives sufficient light to carry on photosynthesis. The general pattern of growth is readily understood as a response to these conditions. The small size of the individual plant, the lack of thickness, and the increase in surface area which results from shapes such as lobed cells, plates of cells, simple filaments, spines, and tooth cells, and flagella – lash-like structures – all these help to increase the buoyancy, and therefore ensure that all cells receive maximum exposure to light, dissolved gases and minerals. However, some unknown factor associated with the living protoplasm is also involved in keeping the cells suspended in the upper water because dead cells sink rapidly, a factor important to bottom-dwelling organisms which depend upon them for food.

When one becomes familiar with some of these algae, several questions come to mind. How do they grow and reproduce? Does each kind have a different life history? Is their existence much the same from month to month, or do they have periods of active growth alternating with dormant periods as do most land plants of the temperate zone? Phycologists, or students of algae, seek the answers to such questions by combining regular sampling of algal populations throughout the year with the growing of different kinds of algae in solutions in the laboratory.

The life histories of three of the more common plankton algae will serve to illustrate the general pattern of life in these plants, as well as to point out individual differences. Let us look first at *Scenedesmus*, found in nearly all bodies of water, which consists of a flat plate of ellipsoidal cells. There is no division of labour amongst these identical cells, each of them carrying on essential processes independent of the others. When a cell has built up a food reserve, the living contents divide to form a miniature adult plant which is released into the water by the splitting of the parent cell wall. This simple multiplication process may take place once in 24 hours or less, so that, under favourable conditions, a large population of plants may build up rapidly. *Scenedesmus* appears to make no preparation for unfavourable growing conditions, a few plants surviving from one period of active growth to the next.

In *Asterionella* – and indeed in all the diatoms – reproduction also involves only cell division and limited enlargement, but the process is complicated by the unique cell structure of this diatom. In these one-celled, brown-coloured plants, the wall is constructed of two overlapping halves which fit together as do the top and bottom of a box. Incorporated into the intricately sculptured cell wall is silica from the water. The walls are resistant to decay organisms, and empty cell walls or shells accumulate on the lake bottom, building up deposits called diatomaceous earth. When the cell is ready to divide, the protoplast (the living contents of the cell) expands, causing a partial separation of the overlapping halves of the wall. Then division takes place, and each new protoplast constructs a new cell wall along its inner face so that in each

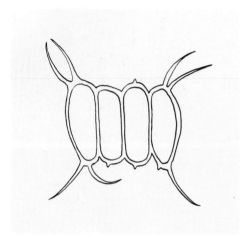

Scenedesmus

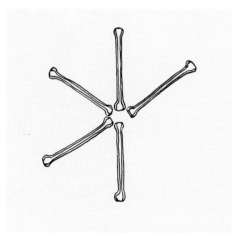

Asterionella – a diatom

ew cell the parent cell has contributed the top part of the wall while the bottom is new. Diatoms, like many other algae, survive the winter months as vegetative cells floating in the water or lying on the sediments.

Rapid cell division at certain times is common to all plankton algae, but some kinds, as for example *Cosmarium,* respond to the onset of unfavourable conditions by forming a protected cell unlike the vegetative cell. Unfavourable conditions for continued growth, especially low concentrations of certain required minerals, induces plants of different strains to come together in pairs. Pairing is followed by the separation of the two halves of each cell, allowing the living contents to flow out and fuse to form a compound protoplast, which develops a thick, resistant wall and sinks to the mud below. When favourable growing conditions return, the dormant cell cracks open to liberate two vegetative cells which initiate a new population of *Cosmarium* cells.

Seasonal cycles

Many people in Alberta have observed the sudden increase in cell numbers of some of these algae, which results in the lake water becoming distinctly green or brown. Such accumulations of microscopic plants are known as water blooms, and it is at these times that we are made aware of the drifting life of the open water. After a few days these water blooms may disappear.

In Alberta, lakes with sufficient depth to undergo spring overturn show a diatom bloom in early spring, which may cause the water to appear brown or muddy. This spring maximum in diatom population has been the subject of many studies, and the explanation for its occurrence is known. During the winter when the lake is covered with ice, there is a wide-spread breakdown of dead plant and animal cells by bacteria and fungi, which are the decomposer organisms. This results in the release of mineral nutrients into the water. At this time the number of plants which use these nutrients is at a minimum, since lack of light and low temperatures limit their activities. Therefore the concentration of minerals in the deeper part of the lake, especially at the mud-water interface where the decomposers are most active, is very high by spring. When the ice melts, there is a circulation of the water which brings these nutrients to the surface layers. Their abundance, combined with favourable light and temperature, leads to the rapid multiplication of the few diatom cells which have survived under the ice. This results in a large population or diatom bloom within a few days. The bloom will persist until such time as the water becomes deficient in required nutrients, particularly silicates and nitrates; then cell division slows down so that too few new plants are formed to balance the losses from grazing by animals, parasitism by fungi and the death of cells. Hence the diatom population decreases to the point where relatively few cells are present in the water, and the bloom disappears.

This diatom bloom is generally followed by early summer growth of a variety of green plankton algae which, in our lakes, seldom occur in numbers sufficient to colour the water. The water blooms caused by certain blue-green algae are the most widely known, since these generally take place toward the end of July or in August during the height of the holiday season. In Alberta lakes, this type of bloom – which makes the water resemble thin pea soup – is the visible result of a tremendous increase in cell numbers of either *Microcystis* or *Aphanizomenon,* which dominate the open water to the exclusion of practically all other algae normally found there. If it is a *Microcystis* bloom, the water appears to be full of bluish-green tapioca, while *Aphanizomenon* forms flakes floating in the water, which often accumulate along the beaches and look

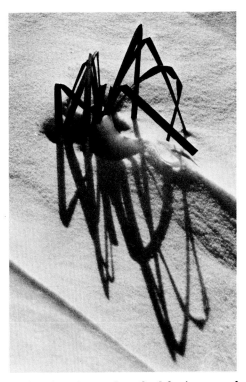

During the winter when the lake is covered with ice and snow, dead plant material below the ice is broken down by decomposer organisms such as bacteria and fungi.

233

like flakes of bluish-green paint. Both these algae have pockets of gas or vacuoles in the cells, a unique feature which allows them to float in dense layers at the water surface. Such blooms are found in shallow, somewhat alkaline lakes or ponds, or in the sheltered bays of large lakes, which possess mostly mud bottoms. They develop during periods of warm weather, if the water has become polluted with nitrogenous wastes.

There have been a number of reports of the death of farm animals, shore birds and fish caused by water blooms, and there is little doubt of their authenticity. In the case of farm animals and birds, sickness or death results from drinking water containing a toxin liberated by the algal cells. The fish may suffer both from the toxin and from lack of oxygen, as the large numbers of bacteria associated with these blooms use up the oxygen in the water. While fish are confined to the aquatic habitat, it is only necessary to provide land animals with fresh water to prevent losses.

There are no reliable reports of toxic effects of water blooms on human beings, and it is indeed unlikely that anyone would drink such water or even swim in it. The blooms may disappear quite suddenly, especially when the weather becomes cooler and the surface water temperature is lowered. There have been numerous attempts to get rid of these water blooms by the application of chemicals toxic to them, the most popular one being copper sulphate. More often than not, the effects have been unsatisfactory. Either all life in the lake is harmed and a very unhealthy lake results, or else the decrease in population of one kind of alga allows some resistant species, present in insignificant numbers, to dominate the habitat. We require a much more comprehensive knowledge of the variety of organisms in the lake and the factors that affect their growth, before we can hope to exert a controlling influence. It is regrettable that so many people think of algae in connection with water blooms, and therefore as organisms to be eliminated. The presence of algae in normal numbers and variety is essential to life in the water.

The lake in winter

We all know that in northern climates most terrestrial plant life becomes dormant during the winter months. What happens to the aquatic organisms? In connection with their survival, the most important single factor is the reaction of water density to falling temperatures. Since the resulting insulating ice cover prevents the lake from freezing to the bottom, algae can survive under the ice either in the water or on the bottom. Samples of water taken from under the ice have been found to contain active vegetative cells of plankton algae such as *Scenedesmus, Chlamydomonas,* and diatoms, sometimes accompanied by dark green *Nostoc* balls. Samples from a lake bottom, when covered with water and left at room temperature in the light, develop growths of *Oscillatoria, Spirogyra* and other algae which had survived on the bottom in a dormant condition. It is likely that many of the lake algae sink to the bottom in the still water under the ice, and survive in the dark on stored foods or, possibly, on organic compounds in the water. Others, particularly forms with some buoyancy mechanism, can maintain a position just under the ice. These active green cells provide oxygen and food for the animal life of the lake.

Rôle of plants in a lake

Awareness of the great variety of plants in a lake arouses curiosity as to what part they play in its economy. First and foremost, it is the green plants which trap the energy from the sun, convert it into chemical

Shorebirds are sometimes killed by the toxins liberated by water blooms.

nergy, and store this energy in organic compounds where it is available to all other forms of life in the lake. Plants are thus the producers of this complex aquatic community, since only they can combine carbon dioxide, water, solar energy and minerals to form the carbohydrates, fats and proteins which supply other organisms with energy and building materials. Without green plants there can be no life in the water, for they provide the energy to keep this system running, and are the first link in the food chain.

Of the various kinds of plants present, by far the most important producers are the algae, for they occur throughout the lake at all depths within the reach of sunlight. Furthermore, in most lakes the microscopic drifting algae exceed the other aquatic plants in food production per unit area. Living algal cells serve as food for a whole series of animals from protozoa to fish which live in the littoral and limnetic zones. Some of these animals, such as the protozoa, crustacea, insect larvae and young fish, graze on the algae, while others are secondary or tertiary consumers. In this way complex food chains are built up beginning with the green algal cell. In deep lakes, in the profundal zone which is too dark for plants, the animals feed on the continual "rain" of dead cells drifting down from the upper layers. In addition to contributing to the food and oxygen of the lake, the reeds, pondweeds, and such larger algae as stonevort and *Cladophora,* provide support and shelter for countless aquatic organisms, both plant and animal.

It is in the littoral zone where these plants flourish that we find the greatest variety of animals, some of them living out their lives here, many others feeding or developing to maturity where shelter is provided. Among the latter are the aquatic birds, especially ducks and geese, which build their nests along the shore and feed upon the plant life of our lakes and ponds. Indeed the activities of these birds are

The lake in winter. Below the insulating ice cover many organisms are active.

Canada geese on a pond. Aquatic birds are important agents of dispersal for algae.

C. H

chiefly responsible for the dispersal of algae from one body of water to another. Some of these algae, such as *Oscillatoria,* and many diatoms, are carried on the feet or feathers of birds, while others, notably *Scenedesmus, Cosmarium,* and *Pediastrum,* are able to pass through their digestive tracts unharmed, and so colonize new lakes many miles away.

We have spoken of two major groups of organisms in the aquatic community – the green plants and the animals. A third important group generally considered along with plant life are bacteria and fungi. These are colourless, microscopic single cells or filaments which are present throughout the water, but which reach their greatest numbers in the bottom sediments where organic material accumulates. These organisms are scarcely ever seen, and their rôle as decomposers of dead plants and animals is seldom appreciated. The bacteria and fungi complete the organic cycle within a lake, for they reduce the cells of dead plants and animals to the constituent elements, releasing these into the water along with carbon dioxide to be used once more by living green plants. Without their presence no life could exist for long in a lake. In general, the fungi live on the harder materials, such as the walls of leaf and stem tissue, insect skeletons and fish scales, while the bacteria attack the softer contents of recently dead cells. The fungi are sometimes seen as a white fuzz on fruits, dead insects, or fish floating in the water, but the presence of the bacteria is evident only from their activities.

In a lake or pond, there is a close and complex interrelationship between the producers, consumers, and decomposers of organic substances in which each kind of organism contributes to the community and takes something from it. In a healthy lake the organisms live in equilibrium with one another, an equilibrium which involves so many little understood factors that we disturb it at our peril. It is well to reflect upon this picture of an extremely complex aquatic community before upsetting the delicate balance by attempts to remove some organisms, because they may interfere for a short time with one of our amusements. For example, removal of the rooted plants gives us a bare stretch of beach, but we have done away with numerous tiny plants and animals which are part of the food chain, thus upsetting the balance in

236

he lake, and perhaps producing a body of water incapable of supporting fish or shore birds. To have a lake which will provide us with true recreation for many summers to come, we must live with the organisms in and around the lake, and not seek to destroy the occasional one which might cause us a little discomfort. This is not to say that we must never attempt to improve a lake, but it is a plea for careful study of the situation before causing a sudden change in the habitat.

Plant life in a stream

When a stream or small river is compared with a lake several fundamental differences are apparent. Perhaps the most striking feature of a stream is the continuous, directional movement of the water which presents the organisms living in it with a highly variable environment. In contrast to a lake, a stream is an open system in which the contact with land is much greater, so that any given stretch continually receives new water with dissolved gases and nutrients. In such a habitat the main problem for the organisms is to resist being carried downstream while availing themselves of substances passing by. In addition to the flow, we note that the water does not vary as much in depth as it does in a lake, and that, unless the stream is carrying a load of silt, there is usually light penetration to the bottom.

At first glance, it might appear that there are no plants in the stream, since the rooted and floating aquatics characteristic of a lake are absent unless the water is scarcely moving. However, undisturbed streams in this province are rich in algae. Their size is such that we need to wade in to look at their habitats. In any stream or river in Alberta there will be some rocky places with pebbles on the bottom or larger stones protruding from the water. It is on these hard surfaces and the occasional stranded log that plants are to be found.

The most conspicuous algae are the large filamentous species which are anchored to the rock or wood, and stream out into the water like masses of green hair. Prominent among these forms are species of *Cladophora* and *Vaucheria,* which are attached by special holdfast cells to rocks or logs and float out in tufts just under the water surface. Both these coarse algae have thick, rough cell walls and play host to a community of microscopic algae, chiefly such diatoms as *Gyrosigma, Pinnularia* and *Cymbella.* These microscopic algae are firmly attached to the filaments by means of mucilaginous pads and stalks, and are often so numerous that they must shade the cells of the filaments to some extent. Certain branched filamentous algae, such as *Draparnaldia* and *Stigeoclonium,* distinguished by their bright green colour and smooth filaments, occur in rapidly moving streams where the oxygen and nutrients are constantly high. These two algae are identified by their mode of branching. In *Stigeoclonium* the branches are evenly distributed and end in long, drawn-out tips, while in *Draparnaldia* short branches occur in clusters at intervals on a stout, main axis.

There is a second community of algae in the stream in which the whole plant is glued to the rock surface, forming a dark green or brown, smooth coating on the rocks lying under water or kept wet with spray. If some of this material is scraped off and observed under the microscope, bluish-green filaments of a *Rivularia* or *Phormidium* species can be seen embedded in a brown gelatinous material which is often coated with a variety of diatom cells. It is interesting to find that these algae always colonize the side of the boulder that faces the current, because at this point there is a reduced rate of flow which subjects the plants to less pull.

The plants of a stream are all attached forms and, although cells or

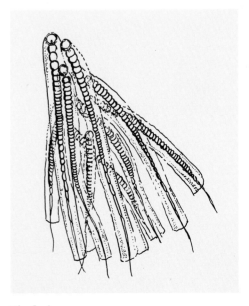

Rivularia

237

Spring breakup, which is a disturbing time for stream plants.

filaments are frequently swept into the mainstream, there is no true plankton community. In the stream, these algae serve as food for animals and provide support and shelter for numerous small animals which live a stationary life.

In comparison with lake plants, stream plants live a much more hazardous life since they are often exposed to severe disturbance of their habitat through ice formation, flooding and pollution. Most streams, unless they are very swift, freeze nearly to the bottom, and the algae survive as dormant cells on the rocks or on the bottom. In the spring when the ice breaks up, losses may occur, as then the blocks of ice, having broken free, may carry numerous attached plants downstream. The major threat to these plants is flooding, in which they are often swept from their support by torrential water from too rapid runoff after melting snow or heavy rains. Flooding may also result in the stream carrying so heavy a load of silt that light is inadequate for plant growth.

Such flooding seldom occurs if the vegetation, particularly the mosses along the stream banks, is undisturbed. These plants act as a giant sponge to control runoff so that water, free of debris, drains slowly into the stream and life there is unharmed. The third danger of life in a stream is pollution. For this we must accept responsibility, since it does not occur in streams far from man's activities. A polluted stream carries a great deal of raw waste material in suspension, too much to be effectively decomposed by the bacteria and fungi living there. This material is constantly settling out, forming a thick film on the plants and smothering them. Under such conditions the cells can no longer absorb light, carbon dioxide and minerals, or give off oxygen, and the plant dies.

Water smartweed — a plant widely distributed in shallow ponds across the province.

AQUATIC INVERTEBRATE LIFE / R. C. B. HARTLAND-ROWE

We have seen that aquatic plants form the basis for the whole economy of most freshwater environments. The living organisms in a lake or river may therefore be divided into two major categories: the producers, which are the plants that synthesize organic material from inorganic substances in the presence of light, and the consumers, the organisms which depend directly or indirectly upon the plants for food. The consumers may further be subdivided into several levels. Primary consumers feed directly on the producers, and secondary consumers feed on primary consumers. Thus one can imagine a food chain consisting of a series of different organisms, each feeding on the next link down the chain.

The conversion of food into living matter is an inefficient process and there is a great waste of energy at each link in the chain. For example, if each stage were ten per cent efficient at conversion – and this is a generous estimate – it would take 1,000 pounds of plant material to make 100 pounds of herbivorous insects to make 10 pounds of carnivorous insects to make one pound of trout. It is obvious therefore that there is a rather low limit to the number of links possible in a food chain.

In nature the situation is usually less simple than this, since animals often operate at two different levels of consumption. For example, if you have steak and green peas for lunch, you are acting as a primary consumer when you eat the peas and as a secondary consumer when you eat the steak. Many animals eat a wide variety of different kinds of foods, and the feeding relationships usually form a complex food web rather than a simple chain. But no matter how complex the system in fresh waters, aquatic plants form the lowest link in the food chain and fish usually form the top link.

Aquatic invertebrate animals

The web between these two links is the invertebrate animals that feed on plants and on one another, and provide food for fish. Some, like sponges, are sessile animals; that is, they live attached to the bottom and feed in a stationary position. Others, the benthic or bottom fauna, are more or less active animals which creep or crawl on the bottom or burrow into it. Others, again, are planktonic; that is, they live suspended in the water. Still others swim in the water (nektonic animals) or exist in other situations, such as the pond skaters which live on the surface film of the water.

239

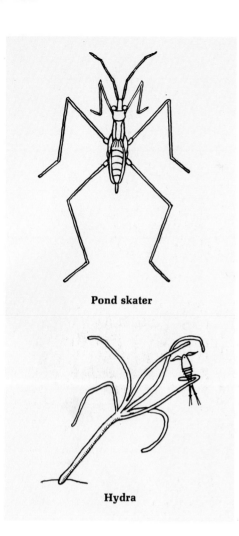

Pond skater

Hydra

Relatively few sessile animals live in our fresh waters, and the: are not important in the economy of the waters. Two are worth me: tioning, since they may be encountered in many parts of the provinc One of these is *Hydra*, a little animal resembling a bare twig half an inc tall, with seven or eight tentacles protruding from the top end and su rounding the mouth. *Hydra* is found in still or sluggish water and sits c its base with the tentacles hanging down in the water. When a wate flea or other small animal touches one of these tentacles, it is snare by means of numerous minute harpoon-like structures called nemato cysts, which are attached to the tentacles. Some of the nematocys inject the prey with poison, and others adhere to the prey, holding to the tentacles which curve round and carry it to the mouth.

These animals are not likely to be seen by the casual observer : the lakeside, but if a handful of waterplants is put in water, carrie home, and placed in an aquarium, some of the *Hydra* on the plants a likely to move onto the aquarium walls where they are visible. Fiv different species of *Hydra* have been found in Alberta, some in grea abundance.

The other sessile animal to be mentioned is the fresh-water spong known as *Spongilla*. This is barely recognizable as an animal, since lives as a thin gray or yellowish slimy encrustation on submerged log in still water. *Spongilla* feeds, as all sponges do, by entrapping minu plankton organisms on special cells, the collar cells. During the summe the sponge grows by slowly expanding over the log, but in the fall th whole animal dies except for special spherical cysts, the gemmulei These contain cells which will emerge the following spring to develo into a new sponge.

Water-fleas, fairy-shrimps and other zooplankton

Far more important than the sessile animals are those which live sus pended in the water, the zooplankton. These animals are of special im portance in lakes where they form the principal link between the plank tonic plants or phytoplankton, and fish.

If you examine a jar of water taken from a lake or a pond durin the summer, you are likely to see various members of this zooplankto community. Prominent are the red or dark-blue water-fleas. These ar likely to be *Diaptomus*, a crustacean belonging to the class Copepod: and distantly related to crabs and lobsters. We have many species o *Diaptomus* in Alberta, but all resemble one another in most respects From the head protrude a pair of large feelers or antennae which ca: be used for rapid swimming. The head also bears a single eye. On th trunk are various other appendages which are used for slow swimmin and for filtering planktonic algae out of the water and transferring then to the mouth. Many of the females will be seen to have a pair of egg-sac near the posterior end. After the eggs are laid, they will hatch into smal triangular larvae. The larva is planktonic like the adult and by moultin, a number of times it gradually assumes the characteristics of the adul Some of our species of *Diaptomus* are confined to saline sloughs, an others to lakes, but almost every body of standing water will be foun to contain one or two species. There are many related types of water fleas in Alberta, such as the very small *Cyclops*.

Also in the zooplankton, there is likely to be at least one species o *Daphnia*, another crustacean belonging to a different class, the Clado cera. These animals and their numerous relatives are enclosed by : bivalve shell which often has a prominent spine at the posterior end The female carries the eggs between the two halves of the shell. In the summer she produces eggs which are thin-shelled and hatch quickly

In the autumn a special type of egg is produced, enclosed in a protective coat to provide winter protection for the egg. Like the copepods, *Daphnia* and other Cladocera feed by filtering algae out of the water.

Another member of the community of organisms in the plankton is the phantom larva. This is the larva of a midge *Chaoborus*, and unlike the animals just mentioned, despite its innocent appearance, it is a voracious predator – that is, it feeds on other animals. The larvae of these midges, like many other planktonic animals, tend to descend into deeper water during the day and rise closer to the surface at night.

Many of the standing waters in Alberta are seasonal, existing only for a few weeks after ice and snow have thawed. Fairy-shrimps and their relatives, the tadpole-shrimps, are found in such places. These crustacea are well adapted to life in temporary pools and sloughs because they produce eggs which are highly resistant to drought and cold. There are more than a dozen species of fairy-shrimps in Alberta and three species of tadpole-shrimps. Some of them are found in fresh waters, but many of them live mainly in salt and soda sloughs, especially in southeastern Alberta. The largest fairy-shrimp, known as *Branchinecta gigas,* which may approach three inches in length, is found in this area. The fairy-shrimps feed by filtering plankton from the water, while the tadpole-shrimps are scavengers, feeding on dead plant and animal remains.

Another scavenger is the scud or *Gammarus.* Scuds are crustacea which belong to the Amphipoda, and several species of *Gammarus* are found in Alberta along with other amphipods. *Gammarus* is often seen in great numbers in lakes and sloughs where they crawl and scuttle about among the vegetation and litter at the bottom of the lake. They feed on detritus and, in turn, serve as food for fish.

One other crustacean should be mentioned, though it is not often seen. This is a true shrimp, related to the shrimps which are found in the sea. Its name is *Mysis relicta.* It occurs in deep water in some lakes like Waterton Lake and Cold Lake.

Some bottom-dwellers

Although the zooplankton is of fundamental importance in the economy of lakes, the importance of the bottom-dwelling animals must not be underestimated, especially in running waters where zooplankton cannot exist in great quantities. There are two main types of bottom-dwelling or benthic animals: those which live in the bottom material itself, usually as burrowing forms in mud; and those which live on top of the bottom material which may be mud, sand or rock. Insects predominate in the bottom fauna, although there are many other groups of animals living in this community. Among these are the segmented worms, the Annelids.

If you visit a slow-flowing river you may see, especially if the water is somewhat polluted, large numbers of greyish threads protruding from holes in the bottom mud. These threads wriggle continuously and are the posterior ends of small annelids. They belong to the family Tubificidae, the members of which can tolerate lower concentrations of oxygen than most aquatic animals. Hence they are often found in abundance where there is not enough oxygen for the more familiar animals. They are usually an indication that a river is polluted.

In the same waters as Tubificids, and in many others also, there are likely to be leeches. Although there are 16 different species of leeches in Alberta, only a very few of these will suck human blood. Some of the others cause severe damage to waterfowl and fish, but the majority of leeches are predators which feed on other invertebrate animals. The blood-sucking leeches often have three jaws by which they attack their

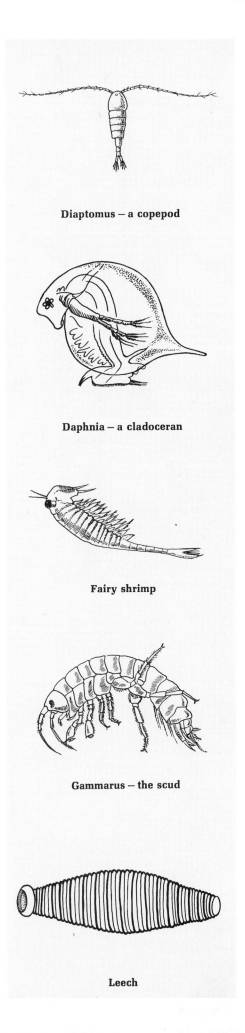

Diaptomus – a copepod

Daphnia – a cladoceran

Fairy shrimp

Gammarus – the scud

Leech

241

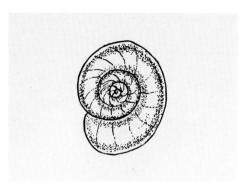

Gyraulus – a planorbid snail

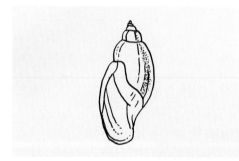

Physa – a water-snail

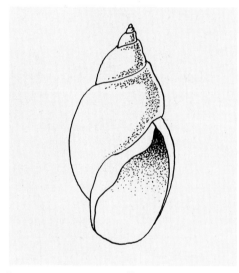

Lymnaea – a water-snail

R.H.-R.

Adult mayfly

prey. It is for this reason that a leech bite has a characteristic triangula appearance.

Water-snails

Another group of animals found in almost any body of still water ar water-snails. All the species found in Alberta are air-breathers, an hence are not greatly affected by low-oxygen concentrations in th water. In consequence, like the Tubificid worms, they may be ver abundant in polluted waters. We have three different families of snail in Alberta. Rams-horn snails, or Planorbidae, occur in ponds, slough and lakes throughout the province. The Lymnaeidae are not flattene like the Planorbids and twist to the right. The Physidae look like Lym naeids but twist to the left.

Snails are primary consumers, feeding on plants and encrustin algae by means of a special structure, the radula. This resembles a flexi ble file with rows of small teeth. It is rubbed over the surface of a roc or a leaf and rasps away particles of vegetation, which are sucked int the mouth of the snail.

Water-snails, besides their herbivorous habits, carry the larval stage of some important parasites known as flukes. Swimmer's itch result from the attack of certain of these larvae. The larvae cannot survive i the human body, but their attempts to bore through the skin may caus intense discomfort. The larvae only develop into adults inside som waterfowl and various mammals, like beavers and muskrats, whic live in or near water. The eggs reach the water from the droppings of th animals and produce larvae which burrow into a snail. Inside the snail, complex series of transformations occurs, culminating in a special typ of larva which bores out of the snail and swims about in the water seek ing a warm-blooded host in which to develop into an adult fluke, a life cycle which makes it prudent to avoid swimming in water where ther may be water-snails.

Life in rivers and streams

Most of the animals mentioned so far are found predominantly in stil waters, where they can exist without danger of being swept away. I a fast-flowing stream conditions are very different, for the bottom i rocky or stony and the flow of water presents a problem to those or ganisms which must remain in one place. Zooplankton cannot exist i any quantity in such an environment since it will be rapidly washe downstream. Therefore bottom fauna – much of which is also found i standing waters – predominates in such streams, and we find that th animals which constitute this fauna show various adaptations to thei surroundings.

If you pick up a stone from a fast-flowing mountain stream and tur it over, you are likely to see many of the important benthic animals, suc as mayfly, stonefly and caddis larvae, as well as planarian worms. Othe important members of the community live in the sand or gravel at th bottom of the stream. Since the bottom fauna is of the greatest im portance as food for the fish which live in these waters, some of thes animals merit closer examination.

Mayflies

Among the most attractive of bottom-dwelling larvae are those of may flies. There are many species in Alberta, and any mountain stream wil probably harbour at least ten species. When a stone is picked up from stream, mayfly larvae can usually be distinguished from the other in sects by their habit of running down to the underside of the stone an resting there. Mayfly larvae have three long thin "tails" trailing out fro the tip of the body, and the abdomen usually bears a series of gills along ch side. On the main body or thorax, there are small wingbuds.

Different kinds of mayflies differ markedly in shape and size. The
edominant ones in fast-flowing water are very flattened. This shape
rmits them to creep into cracks and crannies between the rocks where
e current is not so strong. One species, *Rhithrogena doddsi,* has a
rge sucker on the underside of its abdomen which, when attached to
stone, prevents it from being washed away. Other mayfly larvae are
aped like little fish and can swim rapidly from one sheltered spot to
other. In sluggish waters another type occurs, in which the gills are
vered by a protective flap which keeps them from being smothered by
ud and silt. Still others live in burrows in the muddy banks of large
ow rivers.

Most mayfly larvae feed on vegetation by browsing on the algae en-
usting the rocks, or by feeding on dead leaves which have fallen into
e water. A few species are predators, feeding on other insects, and
ve the front legs developed as grasping structures. The burrowing
rvae either ingest mud or filter plankton from the water.

When a larva is full grown it swims to the surface and within a few
conds moults to produce the first flying stage, known to fishermen as
e dun. The dun rests in trees or bushes for a few hours and then moults
gain – the only instance in the insect world where a winged insect is
own to moult. The final moult produces the spinner, or adult mayfly,
ith shiny wings held upright over the back, and two or three long tails
the tip of the abdomen. These tails serve partly to prevent the mayfly
om yawing, or swinging from side to side, in flight. They may also keep
e head upwind when the insect is resting on the water surface.

The males congregate in swarms, often in the late afternoon, and
main in flight for an hour or so. Mates are selected by the females
hich fly into the swarm of males and leave with the one of their choice.
ater, often on the following day, the females may be seen flying low
nd fast over the water, dropping eggs into the water by dipping the tip
the abdomen. The adult life of the mayfly is brief because these insects
ck a functional mouth and so cannot feed. In many species, the adult
fe is no more than a day or two, and in some the adult life-span is
easured in hours or minutes rather than days.

Mayfly nymph

R.H.-R.

toneflies

nother very important group of animals found in streams are stoneflies.
any of their larvae live in places similar to those where mayfly larvae
xist. They can always be distinguished from mayfly larvae because they
ave only two tails and no gills along the sides of the abdomen, although
ey may have them elsewhere, such as near the anus or around the
eck. These larvae usually behave differently from the mayfly larvae.
hen a rock is removed from a stream, stonefly larvae run to the edge
f the rock and then fall off, instead of running round to the lower side.

There are two main groups of stoneflies in Alberta. Most of the
naller ones, the larvae of which reach perhaps half an inch in length,
ed like most mayfly larvae by browsing on plant materials. The larger
pecies have larvae which may be one and one-half inches long, and are
ften incorrectly called hellgrammites by fishermen. (True hellgrammites
re the larvae of the Dobson-fly which does not occur in rivers but in
ow streams). The large stonefly larvae are predators and will feed
vidly on any insect they can catch. If you collect insects from a stream,
nd a stonefly larva is in your jar, you are likely to find that everything
lse has been eaten or at least nibbled on by the time you get your speci-
ens home.

Stonefly

R.H.-R.

Stonefly skeletons   C.H.

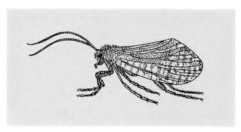

Caddis-fly

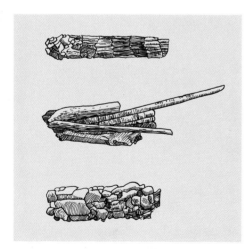

Caddis-fly houses

The stonefly larva moults to produce an adult, as in the case of ma
flies, but the last moult is a slow process. Whereas the mayfly lar
moults in a second or two while floating at the water surface, the stonefl
larva climbs onto a rock until it is an inch or two above the water a
grasps the rock firmly. After a few minutes the skin bursts and the adu
slowly appears out of the split skin. The whole process may take mo
than an hour, and since it tends to take place soon after dawn, it ofte
goes unnoticed. But most anglers have probably seen the empty skins
the larvae fixed to rocks and bridge pilings.

The adult stonefly is not as attractive as the mayfly, being usuall
brown or greenish, with two pairs of wings lying flat over the back. U
like the mayfly, the stonefly can feed and may live for days or week
Some small green stoneflies, belonging to the genus *Alloperla,* are
familiar sight fluttering from bush to bush in August and September
still later. Others are among the earliest of the stream insects to hatc
often before the snow has melted.

Aquatic insect life-cycles

The life-cycles of many of the insects are related to seasonal changes
streams and rivers in such a way that growth and reproduction occ
at the most favourable season. During the winter, when the supply
food is limited and the temperature is low, many species exist only
eggs, while others exist as larvae which show very little sign of growt
In the spring the eggs hatch and the larvae start to grow. This grow
accelerates until, by summer, the adults emerge. The eggs are laid l
the end of the summer. They may either hatch to produce small larva
which grow a little before winter starts, or they may lie dormant at t
bottom of the stream until warmer and more favourable conditions r
turn in the following spring.

This type of life-cycle results in only one generation of adults p
year. Only a few species in our climate – but many species in warm
climates – produce two generations a year, one in early summer an
another in the early autumn. Some, such as the large stoneflies, grow s
slowly that it takes two years for the larvae to develop from eggs
adults. This means that there are two age-groups of these insects prese
during most of the year. Thus in January, there will be one group
larvae which hatched from eggs the previous September, and anoth
group a year older. These older and larger larvae may be of considerab
importance to the fish in the river, since at this time the younger grou
are only eggs or small larvae.

Caddis-flies

A third group of insects of great importance as food for fish are caddi
flies. These insects resemble small moths, are usually dull-coloured ar
often possess very long antennae. The adults sit on rocks and run rapid
about when disturbed. The larvae might be expected to resemble cate
pillars, and in fact they do show similarities. However, they differ fro
most caterpillars in that they live in water and in houses which they co
struct. The houses are usually mobile and are made of grass stems, twig
sand grains, or little pebbles stuck together with silk. Each house form
a tube inside which the larva remains anchored by means of a pair
hooks at its posterior end. Some caddis larvae live in fixed tubes of si
which they spin among rocks. All of them are predators. Like the cate
pillar, the caddis larva moults to produce a resting stage, the pupa. Th
caddis pupa remains in the house that has been constructed by its larv
Eventually the pupa moults to give rise to the adult which emerges fro
the water.

Mayflies, stoneflies and caddis-flies are probably the most importa insects for the survival of fish in fast-flowing waters, although many other species are present. They are not confined to such streams, for all may occur in large numbers in ponds and lakes and are of great importance to certain types of fish in such waters.

Blackflies and mosquitoes

All the insects mentioned so far spend only a part of their life in water. In this same category are two other familiar groups of insects – the blackflies and the mosquitoes. Blackfly larvae are small bottle-shaped animals, which live attached to rocks by their bases in the most rapid currents. They feed by means of brushes of fine bristles, which are used to filter plankton and floating particles of debris out of the water. The larva moults to produce a pupa, which rests in a tent-shaped silken case on the rock. From this emerges the adult blackfly.

In contrast to blackfly larvae, which live in fast-flowing water, the familiar larvae or wrigglers of mosquitoes live in sluggish or stationary water, where they feed by means of mouth brushes or bristles. We have more than forty different species of mosquitoes in Alberta, some of them living only in freshwater pools, others being confined to saline waters. Many of the Alberta species belong to the genus *Aedes,* in which the eggs are resistant to drought. It is these species that are troublesome in the summer, since the eggs which were laid the previous autumn hatch as soon as water appears in puddles and ditches. It is perhaps some consolation to know that we only get bitten half as often as we might, since it is only the females which bite. The males feed on nectar from flowers.

Dragonflies and damselflies

The most beautiful of all aquatic insects are dragonflies, and their close relatives, damselflies. In Alberta, there are more than forty species ranging from slender damselflies, less than two inches long, to dragonflies with a wingspan of about four inches. Despite their very attractive appearance, dragonflies and damselflies are voracious predators throughout their life cycle. The adults have highly developed, compound eyes – in some dragonflies each eye has as many as 28,000 facets – and are easily able to capture other insects in flight. The larvae of both groups are aquatic and live mostly among vegetation on the shores of lakes and ponds. Dragonfly larvae vary in shape but are generally relatively stout with short broad heads. Damselfly larvae, like the adults, are more slender and possess three blade-like gills protruding from the tip of the abdomen. In the dragonfly larva the gills are in an unusual place – in the wall of the rectum. Water is drawn into the rectum and then forcibly expelled through the gills. This action not only ventilates the gills but also propels the larva forward – perhaps the first use of jet propulsion in history.

Both dragonfly and damselfly larvae have an unusual means of catching their prey. One of the mouth appendages is a long retractile structure, known as the mask, which bears toothed recurved claws on either side. When prey is sighted the larva creeps within range and then, with great rapidity, the mask is shot out to seize the prey and bring it back to the mouth.

Water-beetles and water-bugs

Of the insects which spend their whole lives in water, water-beetles and various kinds of water-bugs are the most common, although there are many other less familiar insects. Water-beetles occur in almost every type of aquatic environment, but are especially common in still water. The most abundant water-beetles belong to the two families, Dytiscidae

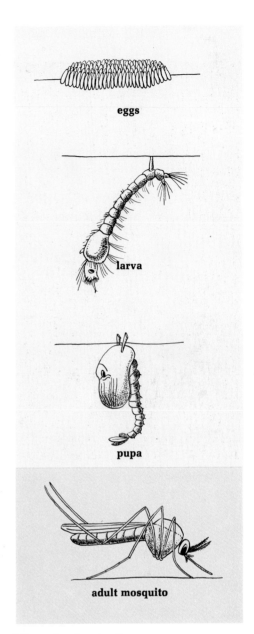

eggs

larva

pupa

adult mosquito

Life-cycle of mosquito

Dragonfly

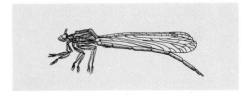

Damselfly

245

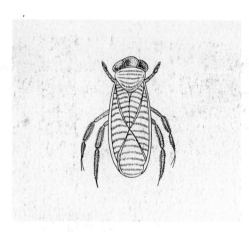

Water boatman

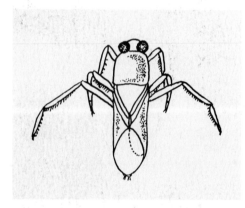

Backswimmer

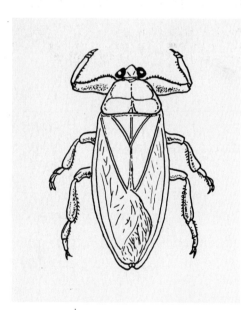

Giant water-bug

and Hydrophilidae, which, like the dragonflies, are predacious through out their lives. The larvae are usually fierce-looking animals, with broad flattened heads and a pair of large jaws which are used to grasp their prey. The adults range in size from less than a quarter of an inch to more than one and a half inches in length. They swim well, using hind-legs which bear fringes of fine bristles and act like the blade of a paddle.

Although they live in water, these beetles are air-breathers. If you watch one, you will see that periodically it swims up to the surface and breaks the surface film for a moment or so. During this time air passes into the space under the wing covers where it is stored by the beetle for use as it swims below the surface. Although most of the water-beetles live in slow-flowing streams, there are some species which are special ized for existence in those that flow rapidly. The larvae of these beetles have suckers by which they attach themselves to rocks.

The Hemiptera, or bugs, are perhaps even more diverse than the beetles. In fresh waters in Alberta we find a variety of different kinds the most familiar of which are water boatmen or Corixids. These bugs about half an inch long, have elongated hind legs equipped with fringes of hairs which are used for swimming. They are found in great abun dance among the littoral vegetation of lakes and in ponds. Some species can also live in the saline sloughs of southeastern Alberta. Like water beetles, they must come to the surface of the water to replenish their supply of oxygen.

The backswimmer *Notonecta* may reach a length of about one inch and looks like a giant water-boatman, but the hindlegs are propor tionately even longer, and the animal swims upside-down. It also differs in that it is a predator.

The most spectacular of our water-bugs is *Lethocerus americanus* the giant water-bug, which may exceed two inches in length. Like other water-bugs this insect can fly, and is most often encountered in sum mer when it is attracted to bright lights. *Lethocerus* feeds on other ani mals, even tadpoles, by means of a pointed tube, the proboscis, which protrudes from the underside of the head. If handled carelessly, the bug may give one a painful jab.

Also included in the Hemiptera are the water-striders or pond skaters belonging to the family Gerridae. They occur on slow-moving waters, such as ponds or the backwaters of streams and rivers, where they skate over the surface feeding on small insects which have become trapped in the surface film. They are able to walk on the water, because their feet are waxy and can support the slight weight of the insect with out breaking the surface film.

Worms of various sorts

Two kinds of worms are often seen in Alberta's aquatic habitat. Flat worms occur in streams, ponds and sloughs. Some of these simple worms are very small, such as *Mesostomum*, a gray spindle-shaped blob about a quarter of an inch long which is sometimes seen in sloughs Planarians are usually larger, a common example being *Polycelis corona ta* which occurs in large numbers in our cooler streams and rivers, where it lives under rocks. When taken out of water, it resembles a blob of gray jelly, but in the water it has a definite shape. Planarians are scaven gers and probably play an important part in consuming dead animals in the river.

The horse-hair worm, *Gordius,* is another interesting animal which is sometimes seen in streams or ditches as a tangled mass of brown or black filaments. It is unusual in that the adult worm cannot feed, lacking a mouth and a functional alimentary canal. It is also remarkable in

Kananaskis Falls on Bow River — one of Alberta's typical fast-moving mountain streams suitable for power generation.

having a complicated life-history, including a parasitic larval stage. The eggs are laid in the water by the adult worm and are eventually eaten by an insect. In the insect the larva of the worm hatches from the egg and burrows its way into the body of its host. Here it lives until ready to emerge into the water as an adult.

It is unfortunate that we have been able to look at only a few of the vast number of the invertebrate animals that live in Alberta's fresh waters. Those have been selected which are most likely to be seen when visiting lakes and rivers in this province, and we have excluded those extremely important but minute forms such as the protozoa and rotifers, which cannot be seen without a microscope. Nevertheless, from the few considered, it is apparent that there is a tremendous diversity in structure, size, and habits. When it is realized that all these animals, together with plants and fish, live together to constitute the whole community of a lake or a river, it will be appreciated that the interrelationships between the members of the community are of great complexity. In consequence the whole system is in a condition of unstable equilibrium, each species depending on its physical and chemical environment and on a variety of other species.

THE ANGLER'S DOMAIN / MARTIN J. PAETZ

In fresh waters, fish are usually the top link in the aquatic food chain. They are more familiar to us than most of the other aquatic organisms because of their size and because, since prehistoric times, man has used them as food. In Alberta commercial fishing is important, while angling is a major recreation.

Fish differ from the lower water-dwelling animals in that they are vertebrates or creatures with backbones. Their ancestors were, in fact,

247

G.H

Trout stream in foothills

the earliest vertebrates. Although both fish and invertebrates are cold
blooded animals, fish do possess a number of distinct advantages ove
their invertebrate neighbours. They have a more or less torpedo-shaped
body which facilitates movement through a dense medium such as water
This shape, coupled with improved powers of locomotion, enables them
to forage widely and rapidly for food, or in the case of some species
to make long journeys to spawning grounds. Fish also possess fins
scales, and a lateral line system. Fins assist in movement, particularly
in turning and balancing, while scales, when present, provide a con
siderable degree of protection from injury. The lateral line system form
a communications link with the aqueous environment. Through a pat
tern of external pores, joined on either side with a canal in the skin
which contains nerve endings, fish are able to detect vibrations and
changes in water temperature. These and other characteristics assure
fish of a much greater degree of independence from forces such as cur
rents and gravity, and from the substrate or bottom of the lake o
stream, than is possible for most invertebrates.

Primitive fish — the sturgeon and lamprey

In Alberta at the present time, 15 families of fish, which include 4
species, are known. All are freshwater forms, and all but two species ar
members of a group termed teleosts or modern bony fishes. The tw
exceptions – the lake sturgeon and the lamprey – are primitive form
which seem somewhat out of place among modern fish.

Lampreys are not true fish, but members of a group of early jawles
vertebrates called Cyclostomes which, being fish-like in form and t

248

some extent in habits, are commonly so classified. They have become well known because of their invasion of the Great Lakes, and the subsequent decline of lake trout populations in those waters. Adult lampreys are predacious, with a rasping tongue-like structure in place of jaws, which enables them to feed on the flesh of higher fish. They also have a larval form, very much simpler than that of the adult, which lives a stationary life close to the surface of the bottom mud, straining small items of food from the water. Although freshwater lampreys have not been collected in Alberta, they are believed to occur in Lake Athabasca.

The sturgeon – a fish famous for the caviar obtained from it – is a survivor of one of the early forms of bony fish. It is considered degenerate because it has lost the typical scales of its ancestors, and the skeleton is more cartilaginous than bony. In place of scales the sturgeon has rows of bony plates, a characteristic that readily distinguishes it from the higher fish forms. The feeding methods of this survivor from the past are also rather primitive. It locates food in the mud along the bottom of the lake or stream by means of a row of sensitive barbels placed ahead of the mouth. Sturgeon are declining in numbers in Alberta, probably because of the alteration of the environment by man. According to early observers they were once fairly abundant in the North Saskatchewan River, but they are now rare. Significant numbers are found only at the junction of the Bow and Oldman Rivers in southern Alberta.

Fish and their environment

The remaining 13 families that comprise the bulk of the freshwater fish are unfortunately difficult to group according to their habits. For example, some fish are generally considered piscivorous – that is, they feed largely on other fish, or perhaps even on their own young – but they will also devour freshwater shrimps and the larvae of midges. Other species are believed to depend largely on bottom-dwelling organisms, such as small clams and midge larvae, but often feed on small minnows. Although some fish have definite habitat preferences, many are found over a fairly wide range of ecological situations. Only a few fish, such as tullibee and yellow perch, are confined almost entirely to lakes. An equally small number of species, such as redhorse suckers and flathead chubs, are restricted to stream environments. The large majority of our fish are as much at home in standing as in flowing waters.

Most freshwater fish of the cool-temperate zone can live within the temperature ranges existing in the lakes and streams of Alberta, but other ecological factors – such as type of stream bottom, the presence or absence of rooted vegetation, or the amount of oxygen present – also influence their distribution. Even so, and despite the range of temperature tolerance, certain fish families have temperature preferences. It is therefore on the basis of water temperature preference that it is convenient to discuss the freshwater fish of Alberta. This basis permits their separation into three broad groups: first, the cold water species, including those which prefer waters which do not exceed 70 degrees for more than a very short period in summer; second, the warm water species which prefer summer water temperatures over 70 degrees and up to 80 degrees, which is close to the maximum temperature attained in waters in this province, and third, a miscellaneous group, the members of which can equally well occupy both cold and warm water environments.

Cold water fish

The kokanee is the only member of the Pacific salmon group found in Alberta. Its presence is due to its recent introduction into a few selected lakes by man. Kokanee are plankton feeders, usually travelling in schools

Weights and lengths of fish on following pages refer only to fish caught in Alberta.

249

Cutthroat trout
up to 22" and 10 lbs.

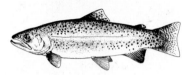

Rainbow trout
up to 25" and 20 lbs.

Brown trout
up to 24" and 18 lbs.

Golden trout
up to 20" and 4½ lbs.

Eastern brook trout
up to 22" and 12 lbs.

Dolly varden trout — a char
up to 26" and 16 lbs.

Lake trout — a char
up to 47" and 60 lbs.

through cool, well-oxygenated waters. Like all Pacific salmon the adults die after spawning. They are unlikely to reproduce successfully in Alberta, except in a few special situations, and their existence here will therefore depend mainly on further artificial propagation and stocking.

Four species of trout will be familiar to anglers in western Alberta: the cutthroat and the rainbow, both native to the province, and the brown and the golden trout which have been introduced. Cutthroat trout were found originally only in cold, clear, gravel-bottomed streams and lakes from the Bow River system to the international boundary. Their range has been extended by man to the Red Deer and North Saskatchewan River systems. The native range of the rainbow trout in Alberta was also restricted at first to the headwater streams of the Athabasca River and its tributaries. Their present wide-spread occurrence is due to stocking.

Brown trout were first imported from Europe. They are now well established in the slower-flowing, meandering streams in the area between Rocky Mountain House and Calgary. Sunken logs, overhanging banks and tangles of tree roots which occur in these streams provide many favourable niches for this wary fish. They feed on a variety of aquatic insects and frequently on other fish, doing so in the late evening and well into the night, a semi-nocturnal feeding habit not generally shared by other trout.

Golden trout, so named because of their vivid orange and gold colours, have been introduced into a few selected alpine lakes only within the past decade. In such waters this species tends to utilize planktonic organisms to a somewhat greater degree than its close relatives, the cutthroat and the rainbow.

Three species of char comprise the remainder of Alberta Salmonids. They are the brook trout, the dolly varden and the lake trout. The char, unlike most trout, are typically fall spawners. They also favour the colder waters of our east slope streams, and the introduced brook trout, though not as widely distributed, is more frequently found near the cold spring sources of a number of central Alberta creeks.

The lake trout is even more exacting in its temperature and habitat preference, being seldom found in waters above 55 degrees. It is therefore a denizen of the deep, cold lakes which are scattered rather sparingly throughout the province. Even in these, its distribution during the summer is restricted to the waters below the thermocline – that is the zone between the warm surface layer and the cold bottom waters of a lake. Its occurrence in streams is rare and due more to chance than choice. For instance, lake trout have sometimes been swept into rivers below large power reservoirs, where they must of necessity complete their life span. As adults, the dolly varden and lake trout feed largely on other fish. In Cold Lake the chief forage fish for lake trout is the small cisco.

Whitefish and tullibees or ciscoes are members of the same family. The mountain whitefish lives in streams and mountain lakes along the western border of Alberta. Like trout and char, it prefers clear, gravel bottomed streams. The lake whitefish is native to many lakes of moderate depth in the drainage basins of the North Saskatchewan River and of Alberta's Arctic river systems. Its range has been extended by introductions into the irrigation storage reservoirs of the South Saskatchewan River system. Its occurrence in streams is limited to occasional movements into and out of large rivers which flow into those lakes where they are present in large numbers.

The lake whitefish will be familiar to many as a table fish, and is the mainstay of the freshwater fishing industry in Canada. Exports of Alberta whitefish reach markets in the United States and Europe. The round whitefish is the least abundant of the group and, because of limited collections for research purposes, its range has not been well established. In body form it is more or less circular in cross-section, thus resembling the mountain whitefish more than the lake whitefish.

Whitefish are predominantly bottom feeders in both lake and stream environments. They subsist on a variety of larval insect forms, small clams, snails and crustaceans which are available among the stones or in the bottom mud. The cisco, or lake herring, may easily be mistaken for the lake whitefish, for in colour and shape they are much alike. They may be distinguished by inspection of the lower jaw and the gill rakers, the finger-like structures of bone projecting inwardly from the bony arch which supports the gills. In the cisco, the gill rakers are more numerous, finer and usually longer than those in whitefish, a structural difference that is reflected in a difference in feeding habits. Ciscoes may be termed mid-water fish, foraging freely in schools in open water areas of lakes usually in the vicinity of, or just below, the thermocline. Zooplankton, which is their main diet, is prevented from escaping through the gill openings by the gill rakers. Cisco populations are extremely variable. In Cold Lake some races attain a weight of only a few ounces, while others in Kehiwin Lake, only a few miles distant, go up to six pounds. Prior to their introduction into several mountain reservoirs in the Bow River drainage, ciscoes were restricted to the lakes of the Arctic watersheds in the province.

The single member of the sucker family, which may be considered essentially a cold water species, is the northern mountain sucker. It reaches only six to eight inches in length, is adapted to life in swift streams and is restricted to the upper portions of the drainage of the North and South Saskatchewan Rivers. It appears to feed primarily on algae adhering to stones of the stream bed.

The trout-like Arctic grayling, an attractive fish with a large colourful dorsal fin, is abundant in streams of the northern forested region in the Arctic watershed. A very sparse population also exists in the Belly River in extreme southwestern Alberta.

Warm water fish

Warm water fish may be found most frequently in the littoral zones of our prairie and parkland lakes, as well as in the broad rivers which meander across the central and southern parts of the province. These shallow lake waters and lower reaches of streams undergo considerable warming during the summer, thus providing temperatures in the range generally favoured by this group of fish.

Members of the perch family include three game fish as well as two very small fish, charmingly called darters. They all have rough-feeling scales described as "ctenoid", meaning "like the teeth of a comb", as well as double dorsal fins. The first of these fins carries very stiff supporting rays ending in sharp spines – how sharp, any fisherman may find out unless he exercises due care. The yellow perch frequents the shallow weedy bays of lakes where it feeds mainly on insect larvae, leeches and crustaceans. They are so abundant in many lakes that the populations are stunted, apparently through competition for food and space.

The darters, so called because of their habit of remaining relatively motionless and then suddenly darting a short distance before settling down again, are found in shallow waters over sandy bottoms. The males are brightly coloured in oranges and blue-greens during their spring spawning period.

A fish much sought after by anglers is the walleye, incorrectly called the pickerel, which occurs in both lakes and larger streams, but prefers

Mountain whitefish
up to 20" and 5 lbs.

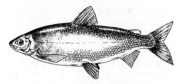

Lake whitefish
up to 25" and 12 lbs.

Arctic grayling
up to 24" and 4 lbs.

Yellow perch
up to 14" and 2 lbs.

Walleye
up to 32" and 15 lbs.

Sauger
up to 18" and 2 lbs.

Northern pike
up to 48" and 50 lbs.

Goldeye
up to 16" and 2 lbs.

251

gravelly or rocky bars beyond the weed beds. It sometimes seeks the slightly deeper and cooler waters of lakes, but returns to the shallow areas to feed on small fish, including young perch. Tagging studies have shown that some walleyes travel long distances, although the reasons for such lengthy journeys remain a mystery.

The sauger closely resembles its near relative, the walleye. Sauger adults, however, are on the average much smaller than adult walleyes, and a side-by-side comparison of the two will reveal other differences. The sauger is restricted to the Milk River and the large, sluggish rivers of the drainage basins of the North and South Saskatchewan Rivers.

The northern pike is one of our commonest and most wide-spread game fish, occurring in most of the lakes and streams capable of supporting fish life. It is a voracious feeder, usually preying on other fish, although not averse to an occasional duckling, mouse or young muskrat.

It is generally believed that fish thrive best in clear waters. While this is true for most freshwater species, it does not appear to be so for the goldeye, which is found only in the warm, silty reaches of large rivers and in similar habitats in Lake Athabasca and Lake Claire. Quite unlike the waters they inhabit, goldeyes are clean, silvery fish resembling herring in appearance, but with bright, golden eyes. They appear to be gregarious, and it is not unusual for an angler to catch a goodly number in one location and then, on moving elsewhere, to run into another school. The goldeye is probably best known because of its reputation as the "Winnipeg goldeye" of the commercial fish trade in North America.

M.H.

The South Saskatchewan River contains the sauger, goldeye, walleye, pike, cutthroat trout, quillback and northern redhorse suckers and several minnows. This drainage system is the last stronghold of the sturgeon in the province.

Suckers are bottom-dwelling fish with thick, fleshy lips with which they suck organisms from the mud of the lake or stream bottom. The four warm water species seem to do well in turbid waters unlikely to be tolerated by many freshwater species. Two of these – the quill-back sucker and northern redhorse sucker – are found only in the prairie sections of our large streams, such as the Red Deer, North Saskatchewan and South Saskatchewan Rivers. The most common species are the white sucker and the longnose sucker, the former being particularly abundant in both lakes and streams throughout the province. Occasionally the spawning concentrations of these species will be so dense in shallow streams that the water literally appears to be moving with them.

Sticklebacks are most interesting little fish, between two and three inches long. As the name suggests, they have a row of sharp spines on their backs, ahead of the dorsal fin. The brook or fivespine stickleback usually has five of these spines. A second species occurring in the province, the ninespine stickleback, generally has nine, although the number may vary from eight to eleven. Other features by which we may recognize them are their spindle-shaped bodies, lack of scales, and by the fact that the pelvic fins are reduced to spines.

The spawning behaviour of sticklebacks is of particular interest. The male builds a nest of grass stems, sticks and debris similar to a bird's nest. After the female has deposited her eggs, he diligently guards the eggs, as well as the young, for a time. Brook sticklebacks are widespread occurring in streams, lakes and even in shallow boggy ponds. They are known to survive the winter in ponds where oxygen conditions are so low as to be lethal to most other freshwater fish.

The largest group of fish in the province are the minnows. At least 14 species have been recorded and it is likely that additional ones will be discovered. The name "minnow" in proper usage applies only to members of this family, but it is often used incorrectly to refer to young fish of other families, properly known as "fingerlings". Many of us undoubtedly have heard the expression "perch minnows" and "sucker minnows" in reference to what are, in fact, small perch and suckers. Most minnows are from two to six inches in length, but exceptions – such as the northern squawfish – may attain a weight of more than five pounds. Minnows are usually most abundant in the shallow waters of lakes and in backwaters of large rivers, where they are important as food for other fish. A few species extend into the cool environments of our foothills streams and occasionally into mountain lakes and reservoirs.

The redside shiner and the redbelly dace acquire brilliant colours during the spawning season, while others remain more drab in appearance throughout life. Food habits and spawning behaviour are as varied as colouration. Some feed primarily on vegetation, others on minute animals, while still others may utilize both plant and animal life.

Several members of the group are quite undesirable. The common goldfish, frequently found in home aquaria, has been introduced into at least one lake in the province where its abundance now interferes with game fish populations. It is feared also that the squawfish, now apparently confined to the Peace River, may find its way into lakes in the system, where it may become competitive with more valuable species. The European carp, another undesirable, which is not as yet known in the province, may invade our waters through the North and South Saskatchewan Rivers. If this should occur, it will undoubtedly compete seriously with some of our native fish. Since the presence of these three species contributes nothing useful to our fish fauna, they should not be introduced or transferred into waters in which they do not now exist.

Two additional warm water fish are the stonecat and the trout perch. The stonecat is the sole member of the catfish family found in the province. It occurs only in the Milk River just north of the international boundary. Catfish have well-developed barbels around the mouth. These whisker-like structures assist them in finding food on the stream bottoms. Trout perch – so called because they bear some external resemblance to both trout and perch – are small fish which occur widely in both lakes and streams east of the foothills.

Cold or warm water fish

A few species of fish may be found as often in cold waters as in warmer environments. The sculpins and burbot are probably the best examples of this versatility. The burbot or ling, as it is commonly called, is the only true freshwater species of cod in North America. Burbot are widely distributed from the warmest of our streams to cold, oligotrophic lakes, such as Rock Lake and Cold Lake. Three sculpins are found in Alberta waters; they are the slimy sculpin or miller's thumb, the spoonhead sculpin and the deepwater sculpin. Sculpins are easily identified by their large heads and tapered bodies, and by pectoral fins which are huge in relation to their body size. They are predacious fish, feeding on such aquatic organisms as insect larvae and the fry of other fish. They are to be found foraging among the stones in stream beds and along lake shores rather than in open water. It is not unusual to find them under stones when collecting insect larvae.

Distribution of fish

There are a number of instances in which Alberta's waters offer favourable habitats for certain species of fish, yet these fish are either not found in the province or are confined to rivers in selected drainage basins. The absence of certain species and the restricted distribution of others is due to the last or Wisconsin glaciation. Because the ice eventually extended in an almost unbroken sheet from northern Canada to the northern part of the Mississippi drainage basin, fish survived only in the unglaciated areas of Alaska and the Yukon and south of the ice front.

M.H.

While the Red Deer River tends to be covered with snow during the winter, its lower reaches undergo considerable warming in summer and provide conditions favourable for warm water fish.

During deglaciation, water from the receding and sometimes stagnant ice mass ponded into huge lakes along the melting ice front. Melt-waters sometimes flowed into or out of these lakes, establishing drainage systems. These lakes and streams, as the ice continued to melt, tended to change in volume, location and direction. During this period fish from the Mississippi River basin and from Alaska and the Yukon gradually found their way into the newly formed lake and river systems. It is also believed that some species came from Pacific slope waters through lakes that at that time straddled the continental divide.

As the centuries passed, little by little the present drainage systems of Alberta came into existence. During this process, in some instances postglacial lakes, which had extended across pre-existing heights of land, receded. This meant that fish on either side of the height of land were now separated. In other cases, newly formed watersheds blocked the spread of fish into otherwise favourable environments. The stonecat, for example, probably did not invade the Milk River from the Mississippi River drainage system until the ecological environment was suitable, but by this time the present drainage system was established. Thus the possibility of its progress into the South Saskatchewan River system was prevented.

In addition to the natural pathways by which fish have redistributed themselves in postglacial times, accidental transfers and deliberate introductions by man have also affected present-day distribution patterns. A few examples of these – such as the introduction of goldfish, brown trout, and brook trout – have already been mentioned. The construction of canals to divert waters from one drainage system to another have also permitted fish to move to new territories.

Fish culture

For the past century, considerable attention has been directed toward artificial methods of hatching fish eggs and raising young fish for later release into natural waters. This practice, known as fish culture, is carried on in fish hatcheries and has been used to augment both game fish and commercial fish stocks. Emphasis has been placed on the production of cold water species, such as trout and salmon, mainly because of the demands made on these fish for sport; also, their natural reproductive potential is not as great as that of warm water fish. Unfortunately, over the years the rôle of the fish hatchery has not always been kept in proper perspective. People tended to regard the hatchery as a cure-all for declining fish populations, and have failed to recognize that the preservation of the environment and biological research are of the greatest importance in fish conservation. Today the fish hatchery is properly being recognized as an essential tool of fish management, but is no longer considered to be an end in itself.

The province operates a fish hatchery at Calgary and, associated with it, a system of rearing ponds for raising fish to the age of yearlings or older at Beaver Creek near Caroline, Alberta. Here facilities at present produce approximately three million fingerlings and half a million yearling trout annually. The majority of these trout are rainbow trout, but brook trout, brown trout, lake trout, kokanee and Arctic grayling are also produced as required. The National Parks have separate fish-hatchery facilities for stocking water within the parks. Most of the fish stocked in the province's waters are placed in lakes or other aquatic habitats where there are not suitable conditions for natural spawning. In streams and lakes, where conditions are favourable, reproduction by wild fish is relied upon to maintain stocks. Proper conservation of Alberta's waters is essential if the angler's domain is to be maintained and improved.

254

SOME OF
ALBERTA'S FISH

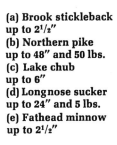

(a)

(a) Brook stickleback
up to 2$^1/_2$"
(b) Northern pike
up to 48" and 50 lbs.
(c) Lake chub
up to 6"
(d) Longnose sucker
up to 24" and 5 lbs.
(e) Fathead minnow
up to 2$^1/_2$"

(c)

M.B.

(b)

(d)

M.B.

(e)

M.B.

.P.S.

255

R.C.

Refinery effluent. Industrial effluents contain a complex mixture of chemical substances. Small fractions may be toxic to animal life.

G.N.H.

Stream destruction which has been caused by faulty road design.

WATER CONSERVATION / RODNEY J. PATERSON

Conservation has often been defined as "wise use", and this is nowhere more true than in the field of water-resource management. The growth and prosperity of a nation depend to a very considerable degree upon the intelligent use of its water.

In Alberta until recent years, the economy has been primarily based upon agriculture. Now, with increasing urbanization and industrial development, there is a fast-developing competition for the use of water. It is in such a context that water conservation becomes of prime importance. The resource must be managed on a broader basis, involving complete drainage basins, and careful consideration must be given to the needs of all its users. In this province we live close to the headwaters of several major drainage basins, and for this reason we bear an important responsibility.

Forestry operations and stream erosion

Headwater streams generally lie within the steep-sloped, shallow-soiled forested area, and here good forest management is the key to success in water conservation. In these areas the forest cover must be preserved to prevent serious erosion. On less precipitous slopes the same careful supervision of the harvest of timber is still necessary, because extensive removal of forest cover or clearance close to a watercourse can likewise lead to dangerous erosion. Most of Alberta's timber is not of sufficient quality to warrant harvest by clearcutting, and the judicious removal of marketable timber has not adversely affected the quality of headwater streams. Yet the clearcutting of blocks of forested land, as practised by the pulpwood industry, can lead to serious erosion if care is not taken to avoid stream beds and steep gradients adjacent to stream beds. Some instances of damage have been recorded. It is to be hoped that such instances will not recur.

Stream damage from logging operations is of two types. First, direct physical damage to the banks and stream bed may result from logging close to the bank or from the poor location of access roads. It may be more convenient to build an access road in or close to a stream bed, but this action may seriously damage or eliminate game fish habitat in the stream. A second type of damage results from watershed erosion following the removal of forest cover close to watercourses. Here erosion is primarily caused by the loss of the forest's moss cover. These shade-loving plants act like a sponge and restrict the movement of surface

256

water, even on steep slopes. In the absence of trees this cover is lost, and the rapid movement of surface water soon erodes the soil into the stream as silt. Trout and char require silt-free gravel on which to spawn. Silt from eroded soil smothers their spawning areas and eliminates the habitat of their primary food organisms. A stream may recover eventually from the effects of local soil erosion, but meanwhile a valuable resource is being wasted. More extensive forest clearance can cause irreparable damage to the watercourse and its flow pattern.

Agricultural aspects

Much of the prairie and parkland region of Alberta has been placed under cultivation within the last seventy years. This area is relatively flat, and the precipitation pattern is such that erosion is not a serious problem. Farmers in this area are usually more concerned with water conservation than land drainage.

The major rivers, which are subject to substantial fluctuations in flow pattern, already carry a significant silt load from the cumulative natural erosion of the drainage basin. The sluggish lowland streams are intermittent and warm, with mud bottoms. It is unlikely that either has been much changed by the advent of agriculture. Many of Alberta's most valuable trout streams, however, flow through the foothills region where the soils are only moderately fertile. Where agriculture has extended into this region, in many cases damage to the streams has resulted. Bush-covered land is cleared for cultivation or pasture, and when this cover is removed from stream banks, the temperature of the water rises. The trout encounter unfavourable temperatures and are displaced by pike and suckers. The clearance and cultivation of steep slopes give rise to silt problems similar to those encountered in forestry operations. Intensive grazing along stream banks destroys the root systems of the smaller plants to which the banks owe their stability and bank erosion ensues. A narrow, deep, well-shaded stream can be changed into one that is wide, shallow and exposed.

All this has happened, but further damage can be avoided if the

Stream destruction by bulldozing

Logging operations – Moon Creek. Forest clearance can lead to severe surface erosion and subsequent stream siltation.

natural cover close to streams is protected, and access by cattle is restricted to specific locations. In this way, accelerated erosion can be prevented and stable flow patterns maintained for the benefit of all those who use the stream.

The loss of ponds and sloughs in the parkland region of Alberta is a further serious problem. The bottoms of both semi-permanent and seasonal sloughs have been ploughed up during periods of extended drought. Those that remain contain a great variety of aquatic life and are major breeding areas for large numbers of ducks. Once the soil is broken, its waterholding capacity is seriously affected and its wildlife habitat value greatly reduced.

The impact of industry

The mining of metallic ores and of coal or gravel often involves washing operations to separate desirable material from waste material. Wash waters usually contain substantial proportions of suspended matter, and it is important that adequate settling ponds should be constructed to prevent the addition of such silty suspended matter to streams.

Industrial impact is also sustained through the construction of roads and Alberta's extensive network of die-straight highways and district roads has been built with little regard for land contours. Roads built in straight lines with wide ditches and steep banks ought to have these banks and ditches protected from the forces of erosion by sowing them to clover or to grass. Where this precaution has not been taken, the formation of gullies has led to substantial silt loads entering streams during heavy rains. Poorly constructed bridge approaches can also lead to significant erosion during periods of high stream flow. Damage of this type is most common in hilly country, where gradients are steeper.

The straightening of streams for convenience in road construction, mainly in mountainous terrain, has caused considerable loss of stream habitat in some parts of the western United States, notably in Montana, although this is not yet a problem in Alberta. Access roads in the Forest Reserve areas of Alberta have generally been constructed with consideration for watershed values, and this policy extends to other areas under the control of the Forest Service.

Local erosion can also be serious following the cutting of seismic lines. Most are straight and, in hilly country, form gullies for water erosion. Where oil exploration has been intensive, substantial silt loads may be added to streams. Companies involved in this work are being encouraged to construct diversion ditches and to seed the cut lines to grass after use.

Recreation

Much leisure time is centred around water, and much money is spent annually on travel to lakes and streams. The development of lake shore cottages has often led to the removal of aquatic shoreline vegetation, with the result that the habitat of pike and many small fish on which they feed has been destroyed.

Improved sport fishing has come from the introduction of fish not native to the province, but as a consequence some native fish have been either displaced or hybridized. For example, native cutthroat trout have bred readily with introduced rainbow trout and pure cutthroats are now found only in a few streams and high altitude lakes.

Chemical treatment of lake waters for the control of aquatic vegetation, algae and "swimmer's itch" is becoming increasingly popular. Yet the chemicals employed are in most cases toxic to fish and the organisms on which fish feed. Aquatic herbicides offer only short-term control and

258

J. P.

A heavy silt load. Wash water from gravel removal operations may carry heavy loads of sand and silt. If permitted to enter a stream without adequate settling, serious siltation will result.

etreatment is generally necessary. Control of algae is usually impractic-ble because of the severe oxygen depletion and fish kills which can re-ult from treatment of an algal bloom. "Swimmer's itch", or schistosome ermatitis, is a wide-spread problem, yet we have seen that chemical con-rol involves the use of copper sulphate in concentrations that are toxic o fish and invertebrates, and is therefore only feasible in certain con-ned situations.

The increasing demand for chemical control will doubtless lead to the roduction of chemicals which are more specific in their action and herefore less toxic to other organisms. Although this would be benefi-ial, it could also lead to the development of more extensive weed-con-rol programmes with, in certain areas, a consequent reduction in aquatic abitat. This would be a vicious circle indeed.

he problems of water pollution

lthough water pollution is not yet a major problem in Alberta, it is a rowing one that deserves serious study. The old adage "an ounce of revention is worth a pound of cure" is nowhere more true than in the eld of pollution. In this case, prevention necessitates extensive field and aboratory research so that mistakes already made in more highly popu-ated areas will not be repeated here. Pollution comes from a variety of auses and exerts a number of effects upon a stream or river. For ex-mple, pollution is detrimental to the oxygen balance.

A stream is the natural habitat of a variety of small and large organ-sms. Their survival depends upon the availability of adequate oxygen. Dissolved oxygen is consumed during respiration and in the assimilation f food. Chemical reactions occurring during the breakdown of waste naterials in water also consume oxygen. The total requirement of oxygen or all these activities may be termed the oxygen demand. When the oxy-en demand exceeds the amount of oxygen dissolved in water, then foul onditions result which are fatal to most forms of stream life. Such con-itions occur when excessive amounts of inadequately treated waste naterials are discharged into a stream. Most organisms, in fact, require certain minimum oxygen concentration and would be eliminated before his condition was reached.

The breakdown of waste material is relatively slow and decomposi-ion may take place over a distance of many miles of stream. Breakdown s dependent upon temperature and is rapid in warm water but much

slower in cold water. Under ice cover a river has no access to oxyge
supplies, and the process of chemical breakdown may continue for man
hundreds of miles downstream. This, of course, is a climatic proble
and one that limits the ability of northern rivers to purify wastes, thu
necessitating the more extensive use of treatment facilities.

The extreme fluctuations in flow of most of Alberta's rivers cor
stitute another limiting factor. It is during periods of low water flow tha
a river's ability to purify wastes is most highly taxed. These low flow
normally occur during the period of ice cover, a period when access t
atmospheric oxygen is also restricted.

Industrial and domestic wastes generally include a complex mixtur
of substances, many of which are never found in nature. Some industri
wastes contain materials which are toxic to stream life even in very sma
quantities. The tolerance of aquatic organisms to such toxic materia
differs widely, and at the present time knowledge in this field is limitec
Much more research is necessary to determine the effect of specific sub
stances upon different organisms and the mechanisms involved.

A problem which has attracted considerable attention in recent year
has been that of chemical insecticides, some of which are particularl
persistent and insidious in their effects. Their wide application over larg
areas of agricultural land makes it inevitable that at least small quantitie
of the substances enter the streams draining the areas. Small quantitie
may not be directly toxic in themselves, but they become permanentl
absorbed by small aquatic organisms and concentrate in their storag
tissues. Fish feeding on these organisms will similarly concentrate th
chemicals in their body tissues, possibly to a level which could caus
reduced reproductive success or even death. The long-term effects c
these chemicals are still unknown, but it is clear that they are having
significant detrimental effect upon the aquatic environment in man
areas of the world, particularly in the United States. Little attempt ha
so far been made to evaluate the extent of this effect in Alberta. A mor
cautious attitude to their use has, however, resulted from the wid
spread concern expressed by conservationists.

Most natural waste materials are broken down into simpler chemic
forms, and these chemicals have an enriching effect upon the strean
They act as fertilizers. Water draining from agricultural land will als
carry with it commercial fertilizers from the soil. If added in exces
these chemicals will encourage the growth of aquatic plants, algae an
fungi. Such growth may cause objectionable odours and may itself cor
tribute to the depletion of oxygen.

The nutrient effect of Calgary's wastes upon the formerly unprodu
tive Bow River has for many years provided some of the finest rainbo
trout fishing anywhere in the country. Recently, however, the city ha
been in danger of so enriching the river as to make it uninhabitable fc
these game fish. A reasonable level of enrichment may be beneficial, bu
an excess can become severely detrimental.

There are a variety of chemicals which may give rise to objectionabl
tastes and odours in water. These are often accompanied by a change i
colour and may make a stream less aesthetically attractive. Foam, suc
as that associated with pulp-mill effluents, can have a serious effect upo
the aesthetic value of a river. Minute traces of certain chemicals can als
affect the flavour of edible fish, a problem particularly associated wit
oil-refinery wastes.

Waters with wastes in them may cause changes in temperature in
stream or a change in its degree of acidity or alkalinity, or in its turbidit
Turbidity from sources such as mines or gravel-washing operations ca

M.H.

Stream in winter. Most streams in Alberta are ice-covered in winter but springs and Chinook winds maintain some open water.

be largely eliminated through the use of suitable settling ponds. Domestic wastes may carry significant quantities of detergents which do not readily break down and may hinder the action of the treatment plant. These chemicals may also serve as a physical barrier to re-aeration in the stream.

Disease-producing organisms may also enter a stream in domestic sewage. The sewage treatment process removes between 50 and 99 per cent of such organisms. Chlorination prevents their entry into domestic water supplies. There is, however, always a danger from drinking untreated stream waters.

Water pollution in Alberta

The number of towns in Alberta which have sewage treatment facilities is above the Canadian provincial average. Present pollution in most Alberta streams is low, but the climate presents certain problems, particularly in the more northerly parts of the province. The combination of low winter flow and heavy ice cover reduces to a low level the capacity of these streams to carry off pollutants. The City of Edmonton has already approached the limits that the North Saskatchewan River can support, and a portion of the effluent is now held in ponds during the period of low winter flow. The City of Calgary is imposing a severe load on the Bow River and conditions are becoming critical. The pulp industry is expanding in northern Alberta and the increasing quantity of pulp mill effluents, which have a particularly high oxygen demand, will necessitate extensive treatment facilities in order to protect northern rivers from severe pollution. Several fish kills, resulting from the escape of petroleum products and drilling fluids, underline the need for constant surveillance by the oil industry.

The outlook for the future in Alberta is good if we are prepared to take a responsible attitude towards the problems. There is a serious need for more research, with particular attention to the climatic problems of

261

Brazeau Reservoir at low water. Failure to remove cover before flooding results in the exposure of extensive areas of mud and rotting timbers.

the more northerly streams. It is necessary to build up a background of information on Alberta's streams so that potential pollution problems can be approached in an informed and intelligent manner.

Several of Alberta's major streams flow into the neighbouring provinces of Saskatchewan and Manitoba. Pollution control in these streams must soon be delegated to an independent inter-provincial authority so that control programmes can be administered on a drainage basis, and fair consideration given to the rights of all downstream users.

Power and irrigation reservoirs

The growth and development of industry has led to increasing demands for power. The construction of hydroelectric plants on many of the major rivers is assisting in meeting these demands. The South Saskatchewan River contains a series of reservoirs on its headwaters and major tributaries, and a major impoundment has been constructed on the Brazeau River, a tributary of the North Saskatchewan River. Some reservoirs effectively raise the level of pre-existing lakes, increasing both the surface area and the volume – for example, Spray Lake and the Kananaskis Lakes. These lakes are subject to substantial fluctuations in level, and the establishment of a permanent littoral zone is prevented. This leads to a paucity of the bottom fauna preferred by species of trout and char. Comparison of fish populations before and after impoundment shows that the populations of most trout are reduced, despite an increase in the size of the lake, because of fluctuating water levels and loss of spawning areas. Some reservoirs – such as Bearspaw, Ghost, Brazeau, and Waterton – have been constructed on relatively unproductive rivers, but the reservoirs do little to improve productivity and game fish are sparse because of high silt loads and fluctuating water levels. Water-level fluctuations in many reservoirs result in the exposure at certain seasons of the year of large areas of bottom mud, stumps and rotting trees. More complete clearing at the time of construction would improve the area from an aesthetic and recreational point of view.

262

It is reasonable to predict that, in most cases, the effect of future reservoirs upon the total plant and animal community will not be beneficial. In addition, some proposed schemes involve the diversion of water from one watershed to another. From the scientific standpoint, it is of value to study the natural ranges of different organisms in a drainage basin and the factors limiting their distribution. The introduction of non-native fish has already disrupted the distribution of some native species, and the construction of diversion channels will certainly intensify this situation, possibly permitting the spread of some less desirable species of fish which are at present confined to one drainage system. For example, the northern squawfish is confined at present to the Peace River drainage in Alberta, and carp are found only in the North Saskatchewan and South Saskatchewan Rivers in the province of Saskatchewan. It is undesirable that the range of either should be extended.

Reservoirs constructed for irrigation purposes in southern Alberta have been established in some cases in previously dry valleys; thus an aquatic habitat has been created where none previously existed. The reservoir waters are comparatively warm and fertile, with populations of lake whitefish, pike and suckers. They are interconnected by a system of canals, and water levels fluctuate severely in some reservoirs but are relatively stable in others. Reproduction of the fish characteristic of these waters is less drastically affected by fluctuating water levels, and they are able to make use of the bottom fauna in such conditions. As a result these reservoirs support a valuable commercial fishery for whitefish and a sport fishery for pike.

Consideration of all the above actualities and possibilities seem to make it apparent that in water conservation complacency and procrastination are attitudes to be avoided. This province is so rich in water resources that they may seem inexhaustible. But the history of man's treatment of his water supplies in other countries and civilizations has been a sad one, and mistakes once made are often irreparable. South of the international boundary, the pollution and spoilation of streams has reached a point where billions of dollars will be needed to undo the damage already done. As one looks to the future, it must be with an awareness of the necessity of conservation of Alberta's heritage of water.

CHAPTER ELEVEN

The Study of Natural History

M. T. MYRES

NATURAL HISTORY is a branch of the science of biology. Indeed biology largely grew out of the curiosity and observations of the naturalists, mainly clergymen and schoolmasters, of the 17th, 18th and 19th centuries. Until 25 years ago there was little distinction between a student of nature and a biologist. But today biology embraces so wide a variety of ideas and skills that some biologists do not know much natural history. The professional biologist who retains the greatest degree of common interest with the amateur naturalist is the ecologist, who studies the relationships of animals and plants with their environment and with one another. In fact, most ecologists and wildlife biologists were amateur naturalists in their youth.

There are good reasons why the study of natural history should be promoted more effectively at this point in Alberta's development. Here, as elsewhere in North America, a rapid growth in population, urbanization and industrialization is causing increasing pollution of our water, air and soil by human wastes and manufactured chemicals. Moreover, city-dwellers, in adapting to the possession of more leisure time, are increasingly seeking recreational pursuits outside the cities. It is cause for anxiety that relatively fewer of those visiting the countryside have any extensive personal knowledge of how the landscape is constructed or how easily the harmony of nature is disturbed. To remedy this must be the major rôle of naturalists in our time, and the enthusiasm and resources of their organizations must be used to create a comprehensive training programme, aimed at educating those who will be adults in the next quarter of a century.

Our far-distant ancestors, of necessity, developed the ability to predict changes in the weather and to track unseen animals by their signs.

Title picture – Close-up of butterfly's wing

265

In spite of our reduced dependence upon the natural environment, most of us seem to retain something of the curiosity about wild things that our forbears developed. In modern society it is the responsibility of naturalists to satisfy this interest. Children are eager to learn about living creatures and young people, when properly guided, are capable of developing a comprehensive understanding of the natural environment. The foundations of these skills must be laid while they are still at school, so a special responsibility rests with teachers. Most of a naturalist's real knowledge, however, will be acquired by individual field experience.

We study living things for the pleasure it gives, from curiosity about how animals and plants live and interact, or from a desire to understand how the plants and animals with which we share the world come to be as they are. With over one million species of animals and three hundred thousand species of plants known to exist, it is possible for almost anyone to become an authority in some field of natural history.

Methods of study

How, then, does a person begin the study of natural history? His most valuable assets will be his eyes and ears and an inquiring mind. He needs very little equipment: a notebook for recording field observations, one or more field or identification guides, some suitable equipment for collecting, and a manual or two indicating the regional distribution of the groups of animals or plants in which he is most interested.

The references at the end of this chapter include books and pamphlets which describe how to collect and preserve specimens, field guides and identification keys, and books on the regional distribution of different groups of plants and animals in western Canada. A *field guide* indicates by means of drawings or coloured illustrations the identifying features of a species. A *key* is an elaborate chain of "right or wrong" choices which, if followed correctly in a careful examination of a specimen, eventually leads the student to its identification. By consulting the relevant books on the plants or animals of the region, a naturalist can quickly determine whether the discovery of an animal or a plant in a particular locality is considered unusual.

When making field notes, the naturalist should include in the detailed account of each observation the following essential information: exact date (day, month, year); nearest town; exact locality in relation to local features, with a map-reference to latitude and longitude, or to meridian, township and range; name of the species being referred to; abundance or exact number of the plants or animals seen; and notes, as appropriate, on the time of day, habitat, weather conditions, state of growth (for a plant), and activity or behaviour (for an animal).

Most plants and animals are best studied alive, preferably in the field. But because of their small size, many have first to be collected or caught and then studied in the home or at school. Plants may be grown under suitable conditions and many animals can be kept alive quite easily in aquaria or terraria. Details of equipment used in making a collection or keeping animals can be obtained from the *Turtox Service Leaflets*. Some items can be made at home and others may be obtained locally or from a biological supply house.

To collect plants, little more is needed than a hand lens, a carrying case or vasculum, and a plant press. Detailed instructions on how to make a collection are to be found in D. B. O. Saville's *Collection and Care of Botanical Specimens*. Specimens of plants should, if possible, include the entire organism: stem, leaves, roots, flowers, fruit and seeds. But since the standard size of herbarium sheets is $11\frac{1}{2}$ by $16\frac{1}{2}$ inches, it is

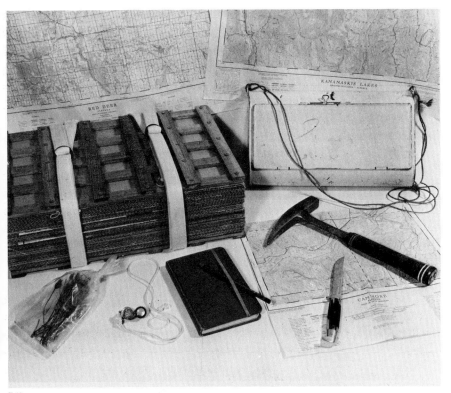

T.M.

PLANT COLLECTING EQUIPMENT

At the right is a vasculum for carrying plants, a digging tool and a knife; at the left (rear) a plant press containing corrugated cardboard, blotting paper and newspaper; at the left (foreground) a plastic bag, a hand lens and a field notebook with the page in use held open by an elastic band. Topographic maps enable the collector to provide an exact map reference for the point of collection.

only possible to preserve representative portions of a large plant. Most specimens are dried under pressure in a plant press. Solid structures like pine cones may be dried separately. Plants should be mounted on good quality, heavy-weight, white paper. Properly, the specimen is fastened to the paper with a plastic adhesive, but it is perfectly satisfactory to place narrow bands of gummed linen tape across the specimen.

To collect insects, a naturalist needs a net, pill boxes or collecting vials, a killing bottle, a spreading board, a pinning block and a storage case. There are several ways of killing insects but, as these involve chemicals or gases which are highly poisonous and can penetrate the skin, damage the eyes, or kill children or adults if inhaled or ingested, they must be used with extreme care by the beginner. The novice should therefore read carefully *The Insect Collector's Guide,* published by the Entomological Society of Alberta, and B. P. Beirne's *Collecting, Preparing and Preserving Insects.*

Fish, amphibians and reptiles may be preserved in a solution of nine parts of water to one part of formalin, each specimen in its own bottle or jar.

Every specimen, whether plant or animal, should be provided with a label stating the species, the date, locality and habitat of collection, and the collector's name.

Collection of animals, plants and fossils is forbidden in National and Provincial Parks, and is frequently regulated even outside the parks. In Alberta the collection of fish requires a permit from the Fish and Wildlife Division of the Department of Lands and Forests; the collection of birds, or their eggs, is not legal unless the collector has a permit from the Canadian Wildlife Service for species that are classified as "migratory" birds by the Migratory Birds Convention Act of 1917, and from the provincial Fish and Wildlife Division for "non-migratory" birds. To collect or keep in capitivity game or fur-bearing mammals requires a licence, and to collect small mammals such as mice or chipmunks requires a provincial permit. Banding of birds requires a permit from the Canadian Wildlife Service.

At any age a student of natural history should subscribe to one or more magazines or periodicals dealing with the natural history of his region, or with the groups of animals or plants of most interest to him. *Blue Jay,* the journal of the Saskatchewan Natural History Society, has been building a permanent record of the natural history of the prairie provinces since 1942. The *Canadian Field-Naturalist* often publishes important notes and papers on the natural history of Alberta. *Audubon Field Notes* publishes observations of prairie birds season by season.

It will take some time for a student to achieve proficiency in identifying plants or animals. When he has reached a stage at which he can identify most of the species of a particular group in his local area, he may find some species which he does not know and which it is important to have identified. He may then consult with someone at one of the scientific institutions listed at the end of this chapter. The latter may be able to confirm an uncertain identification, or identify an organism, either from personal knowledge or by comparison of the specimen submitted with specimens in the collection at the institution.

Natural history societies

Each naturalist will often get special pleasure from visiting a favourite locality, and in developing an unrivalled knowledge of its fauna and flora, or he may study a particular group of animals or plants. This pleasure is, however, enormously increased if one can compare notes with other observers. While naturalists are often individualists, they are bound together by many common interests—for example, ensuring that plant and animal communities are protected and conserved. It is not surprising therefore that there are many local societies devoted to the study of natural history.

The rôles of natural history clubs in modern society are: to interest more people in understanding their natural environment; to teach people how to identify animals and plants in the field, and how to discover more about them; to increase the available knowledge of the natural history of an area in relation to neighbouring regions; and to note changes in the distributions of plants and animals in successive years, and to put these on permanent public record.

An active natural history society holds regular meetings; conducts field trips to interesting places; and publishes at frequent intervals an informative bulletin or newsletter. It also conducts special studies of particular local habitats or species, and publishes the results as papers in one of the established journals or as a society monograph; provides other workers with local information when requested; and supports and promotes wise conservation practices and co-operates with other societies in efforts to study and conserve the natural environment. As examples, the Calgary Bird Club publishes a regular bulletin which includes recent observations by its members, submitted on a specially-designed form, and the Edmonton and Calgary Bird Clubs have in the past co-operated in the production of an annual report on the birds of Alberta. Both groups are also active in the field of environmental conservation.

The amateur's contribution

What contributions can amateurs make? First, naturalists can, collectively, contribute to knowledge by gathering data which no person could collect single-handed. For example, a biologist would not have the time or the capacity to make repeated visits to one thousand nests of a single species of bird in each of the three prairie provinces during a single summer in order to make a statistical determination of the effects of cold weather, heavy rainfall or drought on its reproductive success. But about

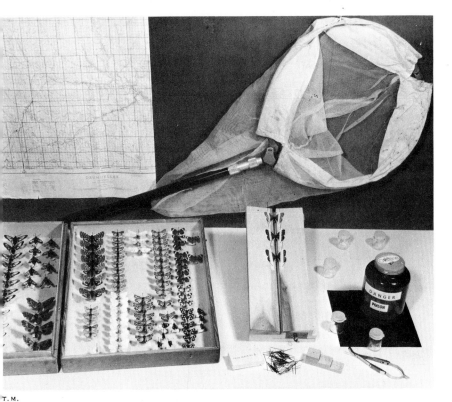

T.M.

two hundred amateur naturalists scattered across the region, each contributing just a few records, could quite easily provide such information for many species. A beginning has been made in the collection of information of this sort in the prairie provinces. Since 1958 bird-watchers have recorded information on Prairie Nest Record Cards on the nests that they find each summer, and by the end of 1965 information on about 7,500 nests had been collected. Such an achievement is quite beyond the scope of the specialist, and in the long term the results of analyses of this data will be of real interest. Likewise, although films were taken at several radar stations in 1964 and 1965 which showed bird migration over Alberta and Saskatchewan, it was possible to make reasonable identification of some of the species involved only after a number of amateur observers had reported particular species of birds in their localities on particular days.

The amateur naturalist plays a major part in mapping the distribution of each species of animal and plant in his region. Of course, naturalists particularly enjoy finding species that they have not seen before. Unfortunately, the occurrence of a rare bird is generally of little importance, since usually it has simply strayed from its migration route. But the finding of a rare species of plant, or an unfamiliar insect or other invertebrate animal frequently signals the discovery of a previously unrecorded colony. Indeed, at the present stage of our knowledge, the Alberta naturalist can often go on to show that the species is not rare at all, but only unrecorded.

The most valuable contribution that naturalists can make is in recording changes in the distribution of animals and plants. When bird-watchers fill in observation report forms they are providing a permanent and continually growing record. These reports are filed, by species, for future reference. In later years it will be possible to refer back to them and make reasonably accurate assessments of the changes that have occurred in local and regional bird populations, and the reasons for them. For example, the breeding distribution of a number of birds in the western prairies alters in response to increasingly wet or increasingly dry conditions. Thus grebes and other marsh and water birds become more widely distributed during a period of wet years, while the range of such dry-country birds as the lark bunting and McCown's longspur seems to expand in dry years. At present, naturalists all over the world are extremely concerned about the decline of birds of prey in all countries where poisonous chemicals are widely used. But until very recently, no attempts have been made to discover whether birds of prey are in trouble in the Canadian prairie provinces. Such changes in numbers of a species can be satisfactorily determined only by conducting careful and regular observations, including various types of organized and repeated census.

Naturalists must play another very important rôle. Resource biologists are dependent to a great extent upon the general public for information about abuses of the environment. For example, the general public has a responsibility to report improper use or application of toxic chemicals. An organized network of widely scattered amateur naturalists can quickly alert the authorities to local occurrences of pollution, unnecessary habitat destruction, or changes in the composition of the flora or fauna. It has been shown, for example in Great Britain, that in this way naturalists can *prevent* abuses, but in Alberta such a volunteer network is only in its infancy.

In such ways, the naturalist can contribute to the growth of biological knowledge and to conservation of the environment. Although the contribution of each individual may be quite small, the observations of all naturalists in an area, when taken together, create a sizeable body of information, and their combined activities make a valuable contribution to the conservation movement. Of course, field observations lose most of their value and significance if they are not made available to fellow naturalists through publication in the regular bulletins of a local society, or in an established natural history journal. Not to do so is to deprive our successors of necessary information if they are to learn about the changes in the flora and fauna which have occurred since our day, and if they are to manage and conserve their natural environment effectively.

Alberta's naturalists have an important rôle to play in monitoring ecological changes at the local level and should not be reluctant to call upon the knowledge and experience of biologists. Many career biologists have failed heretofore to appreciate the contribution that the naturalist can make, and appear to have felt little obligation in recent years to communicate with their amateur colleagues. In return for the considerable assistance which the latter can give him, the ecologist must be willing to advise naturalists when requested, and to show them how to spend their spare time in useful as well as interesting ways. Ecologists must establish and maintain an association with naturalists, with information being passed both ways, if we are to succeed in maintaining and conserving an unpolluted, undisturbed and healthy natural environment into the 21st century. We must also hope that, as has happened elsewhere, the day will soon come when authoritative papers and books on various aspects of the natural history of Alberta will regularly be written by amateur Alberta naturalists.

FURTHER READING—CHAPTER 11
(Compiled by M. T. Myres)

OBSERVATION, COLLECTION, PREPARATION AND PRESERVATION

Anderson, R. M. 1960. *Methods of collecting and preserving vertebrate animals*: National Museum of Canada, Bulletin 69.

Ball, G. E. 1959. *Tips on making an insect collection*: Insect Information Leaflet No. 222. Department of Entomology, University of Alberta, Edmonton.

Beirne, B. P. 1963. *Collecting, preparing and preserving insects*: Canada Department of Agriculture, Publ. 932.

Biological Sciences Curriculum Study (BSCS). *Research problems in biology: Investigations for Students*. (At least four series). Doubleday (Anchor Books), Garden City, New York, for American Institute of Biological Sciences.

Cohen, E. 1963. *Nestboxes*: British Trust for Ornithology Field Guide No. 3, British Trust for Ornithology, Beech Grove, Tring, Hertfordshire, England.

Duddington, C. L. 1960. *Instructions to young botanists*: Burns and MacEachern, Don Mills, Ontario.

Goodwin, D. 1961. *Instructions to young ornithologists, No. 2, Bird behaviour*: Burns and MacEachern, Don Mills, Ontario.

Harrison, J. M. 1964. *Bird taxidermy*: Percival Marshall, London.

Hebditch, J. R. 1965. *Binoculars and telescopes for field use*: British Trust for Ornithology Field Guide No. 2, British Trust for Ornithology, Beech Grove, Tring, Hertfordshire, England.

Hocking, B. 1959. *Instructions for sending insect material for identification*: Insect Information Leaflet No. 220. Department of Entomology, University of Alberta, Edmonton.

Hocking, B. 1960. *Insects and how to collect them*: Insect Information Leaflet No. 221. Department of Entomology, University of Alberta, Edmonton.

Hollom, P. A. D. and Brownlow, H. G. 1958. *Trapping methods for bird ringers*: British Trust for Ornithology Field Guide No. 1, British Trust for Ornithology, Beech Grove, Tring, Hertfordshire, England.

McMullen, R. D. 1964. *The insect collector's guide*: Entomological Society of Alberta. (Obtain from Department of Entomology, University of Alberta, Edmonton; Department of Biology, University of Calgary, Calgary; or Research Station, Canada Department of Agriculture, Lethbridge).

Needham, J. G. et al. 1959. *Culture methods for invertebrate animals*: Dover, New York.

Oldroyd, H. 1959. *Collecting, preserving and studying insects*: Macmillan, New York.

Saville, D. B. O. 1962. *Collection and care of botanical specimens*: Canada Department of Agriculture, Research Branch, Publ. 1113.

Siverly, R. E. 1962. *Rearing Insects in Schools*: Wm. C. Brown Co., Dubuque, Iowa.

Smithsonian Institution. 1944. *A field collector's manual in natural history*: Smithsonian Institution, Publ. 3766, Washington, D.C.

The Resource Reader: Department of Natural Resources, Regina, Saskatchewan.

Turtox Service Leaflets: General Biological Supply House Inc., 8200 South Hoyne Avenue, Chicago, Illinois 60620. (Sixty leaflets).

Wagstaffe, R., and Fidler, J. H., eds. 1955 & 1965. *The preservation of natural history specimens*: Vol. 1, Invertebrates: Vol. 2, Vertebrates: Witherby, London.

IDENTIFICATION GUIDES AND KEYS, FLORAS AND FAUNAS

Minerals

Pough, F. H. 1960. *A field guide to rocks and minerals*: Peterson Field Guide Series, Houghton Mifflin Company, Boston, Massachusetts.

Fossils

Colbert, E. H. 1951. *The dinosaur book*: McGraw-Hill, New York, for American Museum of Natural History.

Fenton, C. L. and Fenton, M. A. 1958. *The fossil book*: Doubleday, New York.

Langston, W. 1959. *Alberta and fossil vertebrates*: Alberta Society of Petroleum Geologists, 9th Annual Conference: 8-19.

Nelson, S. J. 1961. *Mississippian faunas of Western Canada*: Geological Association of Canada, Spec. Paper 2: 1-39.

Nelson, S. J. 1965. *Field methods in palaeontology*. Bulletin of Canadian Petroleum Geology 13: 1-138. (Obtainable from Riley's Reproductions Ltd., Calgary, Alberta).

Swinton, W. E. 1961. *Instructions to young naturalists, No. 4, Fossils*: Burns and MacEachern, Don Mills, Ontario.

University of Alberta. 1965. *Vertebrate Paleontology in Alberta*: University of Alberta, Edmonton.

Warren, P. S. and Stelck, C. R. 1956. *Devonian faunas of Western Canada*: Geological Association of Canada, Spec. Paper 1: 1-15.

Algae

Palmer, C. M. 1959. *Algae in water supplies*: United States Department of Health, Education and Welfare, Public Health Service, Publ. 657.

Prescott, G. W. 1954. *How to know the fresh-water algae*: Pictured-key nature series, Wm. C. Brown Company, Dubuque, Iowa.

Smith, G. M. 1950. *The fresh-water algae of the United States*: McGraw-Hill, New York.

Fungi

Bandoni, R. J. and Szczawinski, A. F. 1964. *Guide to common mushrooms of British Columbia*: British Columbia Provincial Museum, Handbook No. 24.

Groves, J. W. 1962. *Edible and poisonous mushrooms of Canada*: Canada Department of Agriculture, Research Branch, Publ. 1112.

Lange, M. and Hora, F. B. 1965. *Collins guide to mushrooms and toadstools*: Collins, London.

Smith, A. H. 1963. *The mushroom hunter's field guide*: University of Michigan Press, Ann Arbor.

Lichens

Bird, C. D. 1966. *A catalogue of the lichens reported from Alberta, Saskatchewan and Manitoba*: Department of Biology, University of Calgary, Calgary, Alberta (Multilith).

Hale, M. E. 1961. *Lichen handbook*: Smithsonian Institution, Washington, D.C.

University of Calgary. 1965. *The lichenized fungi of Alberta (A key to families and genera)*: Department of Biology, University of Calgary, Calgary, Alberta (Multilith).

Mosses and Liverworts

Bird, C. D. 1964. *A preliminary flora of the Alberta Sphagna and Musci*: Department of Biology, University of Calgary, Calgary, Alberta (Multilith).

Bird, C. D. 1966. *A preliminary flora of the Alberta Hepaticae and Anthocerotae*: Department of Biology, University of Calgary, Calgary, Alberta (Multilith).

Bird, C. D. 1966. *A catalogue of the bryophytes reported from Alberta, Saskatchewan and Manitoba*: Department of Biology, University of Calgary, Calgary, Alberta (Multilith).

Conard, H. S. 1956. *How to know the mosses and liverworts*: Pictured-key nature series, Wm. C. Brown Company, Dubuque, Iowa.

Higher Plants

Brayshaw, T. C. 1963. *Key to the native trees of Canada*: Canada Department of Forestry, Bulletin 125.

Budd, A. C. and Best, K. F. 1964. *Wild plants of the Canadian prairies*: Canada Department of Agriculture, Research Branch, Publ. 983.

Canada Department of Forestry. 1963. *Native trees of Canada*: Canada Department of Forestry, Bulletin 61.

Craighead, J. J., Craighead, F. C. and Davis, R. J. 1963. *A field guide to Rocky Mountain wildflowers*: Peterson Field Guide Series, Houghton Mifflin Company, Boston, Massachusetts.

Hardy, G. A. and Hardy, W. V. 1949. *Wild flowers in the Rockies*: H. R. Larson, Saskatoon.

Hubbard, W. A. 1955. *The grasses of British Columbia*: British Columbia Provincial Museum, Handbook No. 9.

Lyons, C. P. 1962. *Trees, shrubs and flowers to know in British Columbia*: J. M. Dent, Toronto and Vancouver.

Moss, E. H. 1959. *The flora of Alberta*: University of Toronto Press, Toronto, Ontario.

Scoggan, H. J. 1957. *Flora of Manitoba*: National Museum of Canada, Bulletin 140.

Szczawinski, A. F. 1959. *The orchids of British Columbia*: British Columbia Provincial Museum, Handbook No. 16.

Szczawinski, A. F. 1962. *The heather family (Ericaceae) of British Columbia*: British Columbia Provincial Museum, Handbook No. 19.

Taylor, T. M. C. 1956. *The ferns and fern-allies of British Columbia*: British Columbia Provincial Museum, Handbook No. 12.

Hydras

Adshead, P. C., Mackie, G. O., and Paetkau, P. 1963. *On the hydras of Alberta and the Northwest Territories*: National Museum of Canada, Bulletin 199.

Leeches

Moore, J. E. 1964. *Notes on the leeches (Hirudinea) of Alberta*: National Museum of Canada, Natural History Paper No. 27.

Molluscs

Burch, J. B. 1962. *How to know the eastern land snails*: Pictured-key nature series, Wm. C. Brown Company, Dubuque, Iowa.

Mozley, A. 1938. *The fresh-water mollusca of sub-arctic Canada*: Canadian Journal of Research D16: 93-138.

Insects

Beck, W. H., Ewen, A. B., Gollop, J. B. and Whitehead, W. F. 1954. *Laboratory manual on the aquatic nymphal and larval stages of insects, with supplementary ecological information*: Department of Biology, University of Saskatchewan, Saskatoon, Saskatchewan (duplicated).

Beirne, B. P. 1956. *Leafhoppers (Homoptera: Cicadellidae) of Canada and Alaska*: Canadian Entomologist, Vol. 88, Supplement 2.

Bowman, K. 1919. *Annotated check list of the Macrolepidoptera of Alberta*: Alberta Natural History Society, Red Deer, Alberta.

Bowman, K. 1951. *An annotated list of the Lepidoptera of Alberta*: Canadian Journal of Zoology 29: 121-165.

Brooks, A. R. 1958. *Acridoidea of southern Alberta, Saskatchewan and Manitoba (Orthoptera)*: Canadian Entomologist, Supplement 9.

Brooks, A. R. 1960. *Adult Elateridae of southern Alberta, Saskatchewan and Manitoba (Coleoptera)*: Canadian Entomologist, Supplement 20.

Brown, C. E., Robins, J. K. and Stevenson, R. 1962. *Forest Entomology – Introductory Lectures for Forest Rangers and Park Wardens*: Canada Department of Forestry, Calgary, Alberta.

Carr, F. S. 1920. *An annotated list of the Coleoptera of northern Alberta*: Alberta Natural History Society, Red Deer, Alberta.

Curran, C. H. 1965. *The families and genera of North American Diptera*: H. Tripp, Woodhaven, New York.

Ehrlich, P. R. and Ehrlich, A. H. 1961. *How to know the butterflies*: Pictured-key nature series, Wm. C. Brown Company, Dubuque, Iowa.

Essig, E. O. 1958. *Insects and mites of western North America*: Macmillan, New York.

Frost, S. W. 1959. *Insect life and insect natural history*: Dover, New York.

Hatch, M. H. 1953-66. *The beetles of the Pacific Northwest*: University of Washington, Seattle, Publ. Biology 16 (5 parts).

Hebard, M. 1936. *Orthoptera of North Dakota*: Agricultural Experiment Station, North Dakota Agricultural College, Bulletin 284 – Technical, Fargo, North Dakota.

Helfer, J. R. 1963. *How to know the grasshoppers and their allies*: Pictured-key nature series, Wm. C. Brown Company, Dubuque, Iowa.

Holland, W. J. 1908. *The moth book*: Doubleday, Page and Company, New York.

Holland, W. J. 1931. *The butterfly book*: Doubleday and Company, New York.

Jaques, H. E. 1951. *How to know the beetles*: Pictured-key nature series, Wm. C. Brown Company, Dubuque, Iowa.

Keen, F. P. 1952. *Insect enemies of western forests*: United States Department of Agriculture, Washington, Misc. Publ. 273.

Klots, A. B. 1964. *A field guide to the butterflies*: Peterson Field Guide Series, Houghton Mifflin Company, Boston, Massachusetts.

Llewellyn Jones, J. R. J. 1951. *An annotated check list of the Macrolepidoptera of British Columbia*: Entomological Society of British Columbia, Occ. Paper No. 1.

Lutz, F. E. 1948. *Field book of insects*: Putnam, New York.

Miller, C. D. F. 1961. *Taxonomy and distribution of Nearctic Vespula*: Canadian Entomologist, Supplement 22.

Needham, J. G. and Westfall, M. J. 1956. *A manual of the dragonflies of North America (Anisoptera)*: University of California Press, Berkeley, California.

Prentice, R. M. 1958-66. *Forest Lepidoptera of Canada*: Canada Department of Forestry, Forest Entomology and Pathology Branch, Ottawa (4 parts).

Quaestiones Entomologicae: Department of Entomology, University of Alberta, Edmonton.

Rempel, J. G. 1950. *A guide to the mosquito larvae of Western Canada*: Canadian Journal of Research D28: 207-248.

Sharplin, J. 1966. *An annotated list of the Formicidae (Hymenoptera) of central and southern Alberta*: Quaestiones Entomologicae 2: 243-253.

Strickland, E. H. 1938 and 1946. *An annotated list of the Diptera (Flies) of Alberta*: Canadian Journal of Research D16: 175-219 and D24: 157-173.

Strickland, E. H. and Hocking, B. 1950. *Insects of the Alberta farmstead*: Faculty of Agriculture, University of Alberta, Edmonton, Bulletin 55.

Swain, R. B. 1948. *The insect guide*: Doubleday Nature Guide Series, Doubleday and Company, Inc., Garden City, New York.

Urquhart, F. A. 1965. *Introducing the insect*: Warne, London.

University of Alberta. *Insect information leaflets*: Department of Entomology, University of Alberta, Edmonton.

Usinger, R. L. (Editor). 1963. *Aquatic insects of California, with keys to North American genera and California species*: University of California Press, Berkeley, California.

Walker, E. M. 1953-58. *The Odonata of Canada and Alaska*: University of Toronto Press, Toronto, Ontario (2 vols.).

Wallis, J. B. 1961. *The Cicindelidae of Canada*: University of Toronto Press, Toronto, Ontario.

Whitehouse, F. C. 1918. *Dragonflies (Odonata) of Alberta*: Alberta Natural History Society, Red Deer, Alberta.

Spiders

Bristowe, W. S. 1958. *The world of spiders*: Collins (New Naturalist Series No. 38), London, England.

Comstock, J. H. (Edited by W. J. Gertsch). 1965. *The Spider book*: Comstock Publishing Company, Ithaca, New York.

Emerton, J. H. 1961. *The common spiders of the United States*: Dover, New York.

Gertsch, W. J. 1949. *American spiders*: Van Nostrand, New York.

Kaston, B. J. 1952. *How to know the spiders*: Pictured-key nature series, Wm. C. Brown Company, Dubuque, Iowa.

Fish

Bailey, R. M., et al. 1960. *A list of common and scientific names of fishes from the United States and Canada*: American Fisheries Society, Special Publ. No. 2.

Eddy, S. 1957. *How to know the freshwater fishes*: Pictured-key nature series, Wm. C. Brown, Dubuque, Iowa.

Hubbs, C. L. and Lagler, K. F. 1958. *Fishes of the Great Lakes region*: Cranbrook Institute of Science, Bulletin 26, Bloomfield Hills, Michigan.

La Monte, F. R. 1958. *North American game fishes*: Doubleday Nature Guide Series, Doubleday and Company, Inc., Garden City, New York.

Lewin, V. and Nelson, J. S. 1960. *Key to the families of Alberta fishes & Keys to species of Alberta fish*: Department of Zoology University of Alberta, Edmonton (Multilith).

MacDonald, W. H. 1961. *Fishing in Alberta*: Department of Lands and Forests, Edmonton, Alberta, Queen's Printer, Edmonton.

Scott, W. B. 1954. *Freshwater fishes of Eastern Canada*: University of Toronto Press, Toronto, Ontario.

Scott, W. B. 1958. *A check list of the freshwater fishes of Canada and Alaska*: Royal Ontario Museum, Toronto.

Amphibia and Reptiles

Carl, G. C. 1959. *The amphibians of British Columbia*: British Columbia Provincial Museum, Handbook No. 2.

Carl, G. C. 1960. *The reptiles of British Columbia*: British Columbia Provincial Museum, Handbook No. 3.

Cook, F. R. 1966. *Amphibians and reptiles of Saskatchewan*: Saskatchewan Museum of Natural History, Popular Series No. 13, Regina, Saskatchewan.

Logier, E. B. S. and Toner, G. C. 1961. *Check list of the amphibians and reptiles of Canada and Alaska*: Royal Ontario Museum, Toronto, Contribution No. 53.

Stebbins, R. C. 1954. *Amphibians and reptiles of western North America*: McGraw-Hill, New York.

Stebbins, R. C. 1966. *A field guide to western reptiles and amphibians*: Peterson Field Guide Series, Houghton Mifflin Company, Boston, Massachusetts.

University of Alberta. 1964. *Key to amphibia of Alberta*: Department of Zoology, University of Alberta, Edmonton (Multilith).

University of Alberta. 1964. *Key to reptiles of Alberta*: Department of Zoology, University of Alberta, Edmonton (Multilith).

Birds

Beacham, E. D. 1964. *Check list of the birds of the Calgary region*: Calgary Bird Club, Calgary, Alberta.

Cornwallis, R. K. and Smith, A. E. 1964. *The bird in the hand*: British Trust for Ornithology Field Guide No. 6, British Trust for Ornithology, Beech Grove, Tring, Hertfordshire, England.

Cornwallis, R. K. and Smith, A. E. 1964. *Guide to ageing and sexing*: British Trust for Ornithology Field Guide No. 10, British Trust for Ornithology, Beech Grove, Tring, Hertfordshire, England.

Dorst, J. 1961. *The migration of birds*: Houghton Mifflin Company, Boston, Massachusetts.

Federation of Ontario Naturalists. *Sounds of Nature Series*: Vols. 7 and 4, "Prairie Spring" and "Warblers" (sounds of 64 prairie species and 24 species of Alberta warblers), Federation of Ontario Naturalists, 1262 Don Mills Road, Don Mills, Ontario.

Godfrey, W. E. 1966. *The birds of Canada*: National Museum of Canada, Bulletin 203. Queen's Printer, Ottawa.

Gollop, J. B. and Marshall, W. H. 1954. *A guide for aging duck broods in the field*: Mississippi Flyway Council, Technical Section (Multilith).

Harrison, C. J. O. 1964. *Instructions to young ornithologists, No. 5, Birds' nests and eggs*: Burns and MacEachern, Don Mills, Ontario.

Hickey, J. J. 1963. *A guide to bird watching*: Doubleday (Natural History Library, Anchor Books), Garden City, New York.

Houston, C. S. and Street, M. G. 1959. *The birds of the Saskatchewan River, Carlton to Cumberland*: Saskatchewan Natural History Society, Spec. Publ. No. 2.

Kortright, F. H. 1953. *The ducks, geese and swans of North America*: Stackpole Company, Harrisburg, Pennsylvania.

Munro, J. A. and Cowan, I. McT. 1947. *A review of the bird fauna of British Columbia*: British Columbia Provincial Museum, Spec. Publ. No. 2.

Nero, R. W. 1963. *Birds of the Lake Athabasca Region, Saskatchewan*: Saskatchewan Natural History Society, Spec. Publ. No. 5.

Palmer, R. S. 1962. *Handbook of North American birds*: Yale University Press, New Haven, Connecticut. (To appear in 5 vols.; only Vol. 1 (Loons through Flamingos) has yet appeared).

Peterson, R. T. 1961. *A field guide to western birds*: Peterson Field Guide Series, Houghton Mifflin Company, Boston, Massachusetts.

Peterson, R. T. 1962. *A field guide to western bird songs*: Peterson Field Guide Series, Houghton Mifflin Company, Boston, Massachusetts (3 LP Records).

Pettingill, O. S. 1961. *A laboratory and field manual of ornithology*: Burgess, Minneapolis.

Pough, R. H. 1957. *Audubon western bird guide*: Doubleday Nature Guide Series, Doubleday and Company, Inc., Garden City, New York.

Reed, C. A. 1965. *North American birds' eggs*: Dover, New York.

Robbins, C. S., Braun, B. and Zim, H. S. 1966. *Birds of North America – a guide to field identification*: Golden Press, New York.

Salt, W. R. and Wilk, A. L. 1966. *The birds of Alberta*: Queen's Printer, Edmonton.

Stevenson, E. N. 1942. *Keys to the nests of Pacific Coast birds*: Oregon State Monographs, Studies in Zoology No. 4, Oregon State College, Corvallis, Oregon.

Taylor, R. R. 1966. *Summary of the first eight years of the Prairie Nest Records Scheme*: Blue Jay 24: 180-181.

Mammals

Anthony, H. E. 1928. *Field book of North American mammals*: G. P. Putnam & Sons, New York.

Beck, W. H. 1958. *A guide to Saskatchewan mammals*: Saskatchewan Natural History Society, Spec. Publ. No. 1.

Booth, E. S. 1950. *How to know the mammals*: Pictured-key nature series, Wm. C. Brown Company, Dubuque, Iowa.

Burt, W. H. and Grossenheider, R. P. 1964. *A field guide to the mammals*: Peterson Field Guide Series, Houghton Mifflin Company, Boston, Massachusetts.

Cowan, I. McT. and Guiguet, C. J. 1965. *The mammals of British Columbia*: British Columbia Provincial Museum, Handbook No. 11.

Palmer, R. S. 1954. *The mammal guide*: Doubleday Nature Guide Series, Doubleday and Company, Garden City, New York.

Rand, A. L. 1948. *Mammals of the eastern Rockies and western plains of Canada*: National Museum of Canada, Bulletin 108.

Soper, J. D. 1961. *The mammals of Manitoba*: Wildlife Management Bulletin Series 1, No. 17, (Canadian Wildlife Service – reprinted from *Canadian Field-Naturalist* 75: 171-219).

Soper, J. D. 1964. *The mammals of Alberta*: Queen's Printer, Edmonton.

University of Alberta. 1960. *Key to the mammals of Alberta*: Department of Zoology, University of Alberta, Edmonton (multilith).

Animal Tracks

Murie, O. J. 1963. *A field guide to animal tracks*: Peterson Field Guide Series, Houghton Mifflin Company, Boston, Massachusetts.

NON-SPECIALIST JOURNALS

Canadian Field-Naturalist: Ottawa Field-Naturalists' Club, Box 3264, Postal Station C, Ottawa 5, Ontario, (quarterly).

Blue Jay: Saskatchewan Natural History Society, Box 1121, Regina, Saskatchewan (quarterly).

Alberta Bird Report: (annually).

Audubon Field Notes: National Audubon Society, 1130 Fifth Avenue, New York, N.Y., 10028 (bimonthly).

Land, Forest, Wildlife: Department of Lands and Forests, Edmonton, Alberta.

Canadian Audubon: Canadian Audubon Society, 46 St. Clair Avenue East, Toronto 7, Ontario (5 issues per year).

Audubon: National Audubon Society, 1130 Fifth Avenue, New York, N.Y. 10028 (bimonthly).

Animals: Department S, 244 Bay Street, Toronto 1, Ontario (weekly).

Natural History: American Museum of Natural History, Central Park West at 79th Street, New York, N.Y. 10024 (monthly).

Turtox News: General Biological Supply House, Inc., 8200 South Hoyne Avenue, Chicago, Illinois, 60620 U.S. (monthly).

REFERENCE COLLECTIONS

Herbarium, Department of Botany, University of Alberta, Edmonton (plants).

Herbarium, Department of Biology, University of Calgary (plants).

Field Crops Clinic, Field Crops Branch, Dept. of Agriculture, Edmonton (plants and plant diseases).

Forest Disease Survey Herbarium, Canada Dept. of Forestry, Calgary (plants, and plant and tree diseases).

Mycological Herbarium, Canada Dept. of Agriculture, Ottawa (fungi).

Phanerogamic Herbarium, Canada Dept. of Agriculture, Ottawa (higher plants).

Strickland Museum, Dept. of Entomology, University of Alberta, Edmonton (insects).

Insect Collection of the Entomology Section, Research Station, Canada Dept. of Agriculture, Lethbridge (insects).

Forest Insect Survey Museum, Canada Dept. of Forestry, Calgary (insects).

Canadian National Collection, Canada Dept. of Agriculture, K. W. Neatby Building, Ottawa (insects).

University of Alberta Museum of Zoology, Dept. of Zoology, University of Alberta, Edmonton (vertebrate animals).

University of Calgary Museum of Zoology, Department of Biology, University of Calgary (vertebrate animals).

Royal Ontario Museum, Toronto (all animal groups).

National Museum of Canada, Ottawa (all plant and animal groups).

REPRESENTATIVE DEALERS IN BIOLOGICAL SUPPLIES

General Biological Supply House, Inc., 8200 South Hoyne Avenue, Chicago, Illinois, 60620, U.S.A.

Ward's of California, P.O. Box 1749, Monterey, California, 93942, U.S.A.

Northwest Biological Laboratories, 3581 Shelbourne Street, Victoria, British Columbia.

PART III/MAN

MAN

NATURAL HISTORY cannot be divorced from the impact of man on his environment. In Alberta, as elsewhere in North America, he was a comparatively late arrival, but by the time that the mile-deep ice sheet which once sheathed Alberta had begun to melt, he was pressing upon its retreat and has bequeathed to us indubitable evidence of his long-ago presence.

Yet, during the thousands of years that the first people in the interior of western Canada roved its prairies, parklands and forests, they did little to disturb the delicate checks and balances of the natural world. When the white man came, the tides of change began to flow. The first ripples were insidiously gentle. With settlement, however, the flow became first a deepening current and then an upswelling of wave upon wave. Within a century the Indian has been dispossessed, the grasslands have been furrowed by the plough, sawmills have marched into the forests, wells to tap natural gas and oil are dotting a landscape traversed by pipelines, industries have burgeoned and cities sprawl where once moose and elk fed or bison and pronghorn roamed.

The story of man in Alberta is therefore an integral part of this volume. His treatment of his natural environment is part of the ecology of the province.

Title Picture Part III — A Blackfoot Travois in Alberta — by E. S. Curtis.

G.F.

CHAPTER TWELVE

The
First
People

ALAN BRYAN

MEN MAY HAVE WALKED on Alberta soil 30,000 or more years ago. These men would have belonged to the species *Homo sapiens* – the species which today includes all peoples on the earth – and they would have been immigrants. Stone implements and skeletal remains of near-men and early varieties of men, dating back over the last two million or more years, have been unearthed in other continents. No such evidence has been found in either North or South America. In these two continents, man is a late-comer.

Many theories have been advanced about how the first immigrants reached the Americas. The generally accepted belief is that wanderers from northeast Asia crossed from Siberia to Alaska by the Bering land bridge. During the major glaciations of North America, this bridge was up to 1,300 miles wide from north to south. Furthermore, between the glaciations, even when there was no land bridge, groups of people could still have crossed the Bering Strait as Eskimos do today.

Since much of Alaska and the Yukon was never glaciated, men could have lived in those areas as early as 200,000 years ago, but no evidence of their presence this early has been discovered. Very slender evidence does suggest that bands of hunters infiltrated Alaska and the Yukon during the warm interglacial period before the last advance of the ice sheet in North America. At that time it would have been easy for them to spread over the continent. But if, as many scholars think, the first immigrants arrived later during a minor recession (known as an interstadial period) of the last glaciation, their main route southward from Alaska and the Yukon was along an ice-free corridor through Alberta. Later, after the ice had melted further, another route to the south was through British Columbia. We do know that people were already living

Title picture – Petroglyph, Writing-on-Stone Provincial Park.

277

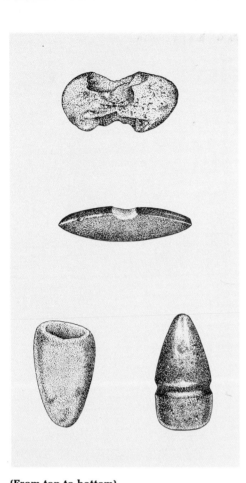

(From top to bottom)
Hafted stone axe, about seven inches long, east-central Alberta.
Ground stone adze, about ten inches long, Peace River area.
Bottom left – **Stone pipe bowl**, about two inches high, southern Alberta.
Bottom right – **Grooved stone maul**, about seven inches long, southern Alberta.

south of the ice mass before it melted. Consequently their ancestors must have arrived in North America before the last glacial advance, or, if they came during its existence, they must have found an ice-free corridor southward.

If the first groups of nomads entered Alaska before about 35,000 years ago, it is unlikely that they had tailored skin clothing. Early people could have survived the bitter temperatures by using fire and wind-breaks, by greasing the body, and by wearing fur robes. We know for instance, that, with only these aids against the cold, the Indians of the Straits of Magellan area at the tip of South America used to exist in mean winter temperatures ranging from zero to four degrees above. Experiments, too, have proved that Australian aborigines are less sensitive to cold than we, and Sherpas tramp barefoot in the snow in the high Himalayas.

We can therefore visualize a group of newcomers drifting gradually through Alaska and the Yukon in the hunt for game, including the mammoth and the giant Alaskan bison, which had a hornspread of up to six feet. Clad in fur robes and huddled behind a wind-break close to leaping tongues of fire, men, women and children would survive the night. In the morning they might wander onward through valleys between ice-capped peaks, searching for food. Finally, as the years went by, they – or, more probably, their descendants – would be moving through Alberta toward the south.

Their kit of tools would be simple. Stone hand-axes and, later on, points and blades of stone were the vogue in Stone Age Europe. In northeast Asia, the original home of these immigrants, the major stone artifacts (a term applied to any object made by man) were flakes used to scrape, cut and punch; and pebble or cobble choppers. A chopper is a stone with a few flakes chipped off one end. These early hunters may well have possessed only stone choppers and perishable weapons, made of wood and bone. We can surmise that large bifacially flaked points (stone tips worked on both sides) were introduced later by new immigrants, or that the idea for them was gradually passed from tribe to tribe across northern Asia and through North America. Eventually groups of nomadic hunters, not through any planned migration, but simply in search of game, reached the richer and warmer land to the south, a land that teemed with animals. Nothing but a speculative trace of the almost certain transit of these nomads through Alberta has as yet been discovered. It is farther south that the antiquity of man in the Americas can be proved.

Antiquity of American man

When groups of people had reached what were at that time the well watered lands south of the ice sheet, some of them gradually spread eastward as far as the Atlantic coast, where their presence 11,000 years ago has been authenticated by radiocarbon dating. Others continued to move southward along the ridges, first those of the Rocky Mountains and the highlands of Mexico and then those of the Andes. By about 9,000 years ago they had reached Fell's Cave in Chile at the southern tip of South America. Here they butchered 20-foot-long ground sloths of a now extinct species. Some scholars think that it took several thousand years for the descendants of the first people in the Americas to drift down the 11,000 miles from the Bering Strait to the tip of South America. The Fell's Cave people, however, are late in American prehistory as compared with the evidence of human habitation found on the Great Plains of the United States. Today much of this area is desert but, in ancient times when the ice sheet was a high mass to the north, it was lake and grassland country.

New Chest, a Piegan.

The first find which proved that man had been in North America earlier than three to five thousand years ago was made in 1927 near Folsom, New Mexico. Here a stone point, lodged between the ribs of a giant bison, was discovered. Further excavations produced 19 points in all and the skeletons of 23 bison. It is believed that these bison had been skinned for their hides since the bones of their tails are missing.

Radiocarbon dating puts this Folsom people at an age of from 10,500 to 11,000 years ago. The stone points they made were light and beautifully shaped, with a long groove or fluting running up each face. These points were probably dart points for spears. It is likely that the spears were used with spear-throwers, which increase the distance and force with which a spear can be flung. Folsom points, up to 9,000 years in age, have been unearthed in the central United States. Two Folsom points have also been found in Alberta and others have been discovered in Saskatchewan. During the time that Folsom points were used, bands of hunters were roaming throughout North America and killing, besides other animals, species of bison now extinct.

The time during which people flourished in North America was pushed still further back when another type of point was found near Clovis, also in New Mexico. This Clovis point has a radiocarbon age of about 11,500 years ago. It is larger and less carefully made than the Folsom point, and is sometimes grooved part way up the face. Quite recently a Clovis site of about 11,000 years ago was unearthed at the head of the Bay of Fundy, close to where the ice mass must have been at that time. The people who used Clovis points hunted along the edges of the ice sheet. They also followed such prehistoric animals as the mastodon, mammoth and giant bison, together with horses and camels, along

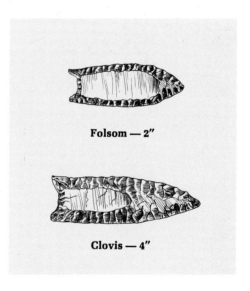

Folsom — 2″

Clovis — 4″

Actual length in inches of the above points and those that follow is given.

the shores of lakes in New Mexico which have since become desert stretches.

Other finds suggest a still older date of possibly 30,000 years ago for man in North America. These finds – such as the charred bones of dwarf mammoths from Santa Rosa Island off California, and charcoal from hearths near Lewisville, Texas – are disputed because no distinctive stone points were found and it cannot be proved that men lit the fires. Indisputable is the fact that Clovis and Folsom man were roving across North America as far north as the edges of the ice mass long before the last ice sheet had melted.

From the Ice Age to Columbus

By about 8,000 years ago the ice sheet had melted, and the mammoth, the horse and the camel had disappeared from North America. But as the ice mass was retreating, and long after it had vanished, very probably new groups of immigrants still made their way across the Bering Strait to mingle with the peoples already in North America. Although in appearance there were obvious differences, all the new-comers belonged to the Mongoloid racial stock.

As the centuries went by, much of North America was occupied. In Central America and Mexico, the Maya, Toltec, Aztec and other civilizations developed. Farther north, differing cultures came into being. Some of them vanished, like that of the Hopewell Mound Builders or the earlier Old Copper Culture in Wisconsin, which flourished between five and three thousand years ago. In other areas some tribes quite early made the beginnings of village life and agriculture; while along the British Columbia coast an elaborate culture based on abundant sea and land food sources came into existence. On the Great Plains of the United States, however, as well as on Canada's prairies and in her woodlands a nomadic way of life was maintained.

And then in 1492, Columbus, in search of a route to India, stumbled upon an island in the blue Caribbean. Obsessed by his search for India he called the people "Indians". This misnomer for all the native peoples of the Americas has persisted. Almost all the Indians of North America share basic similarities such as high cheekbones and dark hair and eyes but other physical features are highly variable in different areas.

Before describing the evidence for the first people in Alberta, we should note that, for convenience, archaeologists divide prehistoric Indians into three groups: Palaeo-Indians, from the time the first immigrants came to about 7,500 years ago; Meso-Indians, from 7,500 years ago to about 600 A.D.; and Neo-Indians, from 600 A.D. to the time of the arrival of the Europeans. These divisions are arbitrary. Periods of history and prehistory cannot be sliced off as with a knife and pigeonholed neatly in separate compartments. But such divisions do make it easier to describe the general development in North America.

The first people in Alberta

It seems almost certain that thousands of years ago groups of the first immigrants into Alaska or their descendants moved southward through Alberta. The chance of finding in this province proof of the presence of the earliest nomadic hunters is very slender, chiefly because the advance of the ice sheet disturbed the surface deposits, and its retreat left behind thick coverings of varied materials. Consequently whatever evidence of their existence preglacial or interstadial man left in Alberta was, almost inevitably, either destroyed or buried. Today, too, the boreal forest makes search in the north difficult, and in the south there are few deep canyons to cut through strata and bring sites of early men into view. As a result, the only likely places in Alberta for the discovery of

Prehistoric fire pit, Cluny site. G.F.

Wolf Child, a Blood.

traces of preglacial man are on the tops of a few unglaciated hills, such as the Cypress Hills, or in those deposits, known as the Saskatchewan Gravels and Sands, which were laid down by preglacial rivers.

These river-channel deposits are easy to identify because they do not contain any igneous rocks, such as granite, schist or gneiss, which were carried over Alberta from the Canadian Shield by the moving ice mass. The exact age of the deposits is not known, although it is certain that they were laid down before the ice had advanced from the east. In them are found the bones of horses, camels and woolly mammoths. The one possible bit of evidence they have yielded so far for the presence of preglacial man is the broken pelvis of a horse from a preglacial sand deposit in Edmonton. The pelvis had been shattered by a heavy blow with a rock or cobble on a naturally concave surface of the bone. Since the pelvis was discovered in a stream-laid deposit of pure sand, in which there were no stones or rocks, it is assumed that it could not have been broken by the action of natural forces. Therefore this pelvis may have been broken by a blow from a preglacial hunter.

The earliest demonstrable evidence for early men in Alberta was found near Taber in southern Alberta by L. A. Bayrock, a geologist of the Research Council of Alberta. Here, while excavating the bones of a now extinct type of bison, he found a cobblestone inside its crushed skull. Since these bones came from a deposit of pure sand laid down by a stream which at that time had been draining the nearby ice sheet, Dr. Bayrock knew that the bison had probably been killed by a hunter. Later, archaeologists recognized the cobble as having been made by man because several flakes had been chipped from one end of it. Radiocarbon dating gives a date to the find of about 11,000 years ago. In 1962 at another site just two miles from the Bayrock discovery, another geologist, A. M. Stalker, came upon the bones of an immature human being. Very few bones of early men have been discovered in North America and this skeleton, dating probably from 11,000 years ago, may be one of the oldest ever found. Thus hunters moving northward into Alberta from the Great Plains of the United States were living at the very edge of the ice sheet as it melted.

The picture of hunting groups moving northward from the Great Plains of the United States into Alberta as the ice cap melted is made more complete by early stone points found in the province. Two fluted Folsom points, as previously mentioned, have been identified – one near Cereal in the south, the other near Stettler in east-central Alberta. Of the three Clovis points discovered in Alberta, one, a complete specimen, was picked out of a trench in Lethbridge; the other two, both only bases of points, were found at Cereal and Edmonton. Several other fluted points, probably in the same time range, have been identified from collections gathered in southern and central Alberta by amateur archaeologists. Since Clovis and Folsom points originated in the south and since fluted points found in Alaska are later in time, once again it seems clear that early hunters from the south, in pursuit of bison, mammoths and other big game animals, ventured into Alberta about 11,000 years ago. These hunters found a bitterly cold land at the edge of the melting ice mass.

There is little doubt that, during the Palaeo-Indian period from 11,000 years ago onward, migration was in general from the south to the north into Canada's three prairie provinces. In addition to the fluted points, like the Folsom and Clovis points, a whole range of carefully flaked and rather large lanceolate points, shaped like spearheads, were made between 9,000 and 8,000 years ago on the Great Plains in the central United States. These points, titled from the sites where they were first found, bear such names as Plainview, Milnesand, Hell Gap, Agate Basin, Scottsbluff and Eden. A lanceolate type pointed at both ends, known as a Lerma point and dated at about 9,000 to 8,500 years ago, has been found in Mexico, in Oregon and Washington States, and, in a related form, near Yale in the Fraser Canyon of British Columbia.

All these Palaeo-Indian points or their very close relatives have been identified in collections made in Alberta. Most of these points have also been collected from sites in the Yukon and the Northwest Territories, but all of these, with the possible exception of leaf-shaped Lerma points, are associated with deposits up to 3,000 years younger than their southern predecessors. This fact suggests a gradual movement northward from the prairie provinces, rather than a migration from Alaska.

By a somewhat curious phenomenon, west of the Rocky Mountains in British Columbia, only one Palaeo-Indian point, exclusive of those near Yale, British Columbia has been found. Instead there are numerous parallel-sided flakes known as blades, like those used in Europe during the last phase of the Old Stone Age and during the Middle Stone Age. True blades are rare on the prairies east of the Rocky Mountains but are common in the Yukon and Alaska. The oldest dated site in western Alaska, Anangula Island in the eastern Aleutians, was occupied about 8,500 years ago by a people who used thousands of blades but had no bifacially flaked projectile points. This evidence suggests that nomads living in unglaciated southwestern Alaska during the latter part of the last glaciation of North America, developed a tool kit based on blades; they then moved south-westward through the northern forests while the big game hunters were advancing from the Great Plains into and through Alberta. In Anangula Island no bone implements have been preserved

Fluted — 2¹/₈"

Plainview — 2¹/₂"

Agate Basin — 4"

E.S.C.

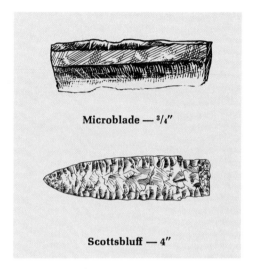

Microblade — ³/₄"

Scottsbluff — 4"

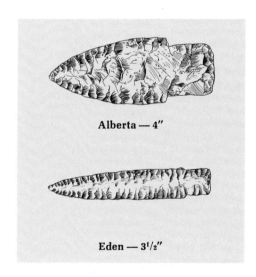

Alberta — 4"

Eden — 3¹/₂"

but in British Columbia, as in Europe, some of the blades were inserted into slots in slender, pointed rods of bone and antler to make long, barbed projectile points.

During the millennia between 11,000 and 7,500 years ago, there were undoubtedly many movements of Palaeo-Indian hunters all over North America. In Alberta, despite the many types of Palaeo-Indian points identified in collections, the only Palaeo-Indian points excavated from actual sites belong to the Scottsbluff type. The major archaeological studies in the province have been directed by Richard G. Forbis, of the Glenbow Foundation and the University of Calgary, by the Department of Anthropology of the University of Alberta, and by the Research Council of Alberta.

It was Dr. Forbis who excavated a large, stemmed Scottsbluff point and a few flake scrapers in a deposit containing hundreds of bison bones near Taber. This deposit lay on top of the stratum where Dr. Bayrock had discovered the crushed bison skull with the cobble inside it. Later, at a site near Skiff, about 20 miles southeast of Taber, Dr. Forbis unearthed seven projectile points mingled with flake tools, knives and hammerstones. The points are classified as either Scottsbluff points or variants. One of the point types is named an Alberta point. It is thought that both these sites were being used by big game hunters about 9,000 years ago.

Dozens of Scottsbluff, Eden and Alberta points are found in collections made from the prairies, the parkland and the Peace River country. In the Peace River region the proportion of early points to later points is greater than it is farther south. Other northern areas of the province have as yet yielded nothing, chiefly because most of the country has not been cleared and ploughed. We expect that Palaeo-Indian points are there, because they are found in the Northwest Territories where big game hunters roamed over country which now is forest. The implication seems

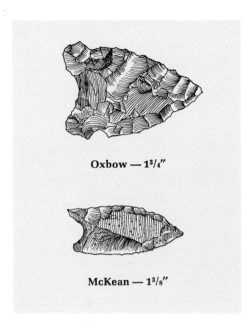

Oxbow — 1¾"

McKean — 1⅜"

Copper crescent — 8¼"

British Block Cairn near Suffield G.F.

to be that at this time, some 9,000 to 7,500 years ago, there were more open prairies amid the now almost continuous northern forest.

Early Meso-Indians in Alberta — 5500-1300 B.C.

No clear division between Palaeo-Indians and Meso-Indians can be made. Furthermore, although Indians dwelt on either side of the Great Plains, no evidence of man for the period between about 7,500 and 4,500 years ago has been found in that area. It is generally believed that the warm and dry climatic phase, known as the Altithermal, made the Great Plains too hot and dry for human habitation; but it may be that further exploration will disprove this theory. Alberta shares in this long hiatus. In this province, as in Saskatchewan and Manitoba, the Meso-Indian phase does not begin until about 4,500 years ago.

The Meso-Indian phase is characterized by various types of side and corner-notched projectile points. Points of this sort were made as early as 10,000 years ago in southern Illinois. Others, found in Iowa, Nebraska, southern Idaho and northern Utah on either side of the Great Plains, are dated as being between 7,000 and 6,500 years old. These particular points, then, belong to the Palaeo-Indian period but persisted into Meso-Indian times.

In Alberta a number of stemmed points with indented or concave bases were fashioned between about 4,500 and 3,300 years ago. The earliest of these is called Oxbow, from a site in southern Saskatchewan. Oxbow points have shallow side or corner notches. In Alberta they were excavated along with a McKean Meso-Indian point, which lacks notches, at the Castor Creek site, about 80 miles east of Red Deer. Nearby was found a copper crescent of a type made between 5,000 and 3,000 years ago by Indians of the western Great Lakes region. We can well imagine what a treasured possession this copper crescent was, possibly for an Indian belle of that ancient time, and how it passed by barter from tribe to tribe until it reached the band living in those days at the Castor Creek site.

Other Oxbow points, associated with an unnamed side-notched type and McKean and Duncan points, were also unearthed from the deeper deposits of a site in the Peace Hills near Wetaskiwin. A Duncan point and a type akin to a Hanna point were excavated from a layer of soil well beneath the surface at a site at Moose Lake near Bonnyville. The early Meso-Indian types, other than the Oxbow, are named from sites in Wyoming. The assumption is that the people who used them in Alberta came from the south. What the countryside was like is not known. Central and northern Alberta may have been covered with timber and the southern part unforested. Farther south, peoples adapted to a desert climate had long been grinding seeds for food, but no seed-grinding tools have been found in this province. Instead the early Meso-Indians of Alberta were efficient hunters of bison.

Later Meso-Indians and early Neo-Indians

There is another gap in our knowledge from about 1300 B.C. to the beginning of the Christian era. At that time two different populations of bison hunters seem to have roamed southern Saskatchewan and Alberta. One group made small, triangular, very thin points with tiny side notches near the straight base. These points, called Avonlea after a site in southern Saskatchewan, are dated at about 1,500 years ago. Avonlea points have been excavated near Lethbridge at a site on the Oldman River, and many have been found as far north as the North Saskatchewan River. The people who used them are classified as Neo-Indians.

The other group of hunters, classified as late Meso-Indians, made corner-notched points, named Besant points, again from a site in Sas

E.S.C.

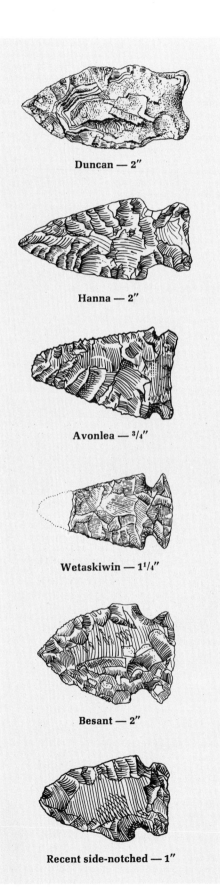

Duncan — 2″

Hanna — 2″

Avonlea — ³/₄″

Wetaskiwin — 1¹/₄″

Besant — 2″

Recent side-notched — 1″

katchewan. Besant points are similar to Oxbow points except that they have straight instead of indented bases. They are often fashioned from Knife River flint, a brown chalcedony obtained from North Dakota. This chalcedony had been used millennia before this time as stone from which to shape Scottsbluff type points.

Avonlea and Besant hunting groups were skilled in killing bison, although they possessed neither horses nor firearms. They drove bison into corrals or stampeded them over cliffs. Besant points have been excavated from the basal deposits of a stratified campsite near Brocket in the Crowsnest Pass area, and also in the lower layers of two important bison jumps. One of these, a few miles west of Fort Macleod, has been excavated by Dr. Forbis. It has yielded Besant points and, in an overlying stratum, Avonlea points. The other, also excavated by Dr. Forbis, is the famed Old Women's Buffalo Jump near Cayley. In both cases we are able to visualize the wildly excited line of beaters, waving their spears and jumping and yelling until the herd of bison was thundering forward. That herd would come suddenly upon a precipitous drop and, unable to check, would plunge by the hundreds over the cliff into a kicking, bellowing, tangled mass at the bottom. Upon them would leap the Indians, to stab and kill with their stone-tipped spears.

These bands seem to have been equally expert in corralling a herd in a coulee, draw or ravine, probably with a barrier set up at one end. Thus at a site near Stettler where, apparently, a herd of bison had been corralled and despatched, Ruth Gruhn of the University of Alberta has excavated the largest number of Besant points found anywhere.

Neo-Indians in Alberta

The so-called Neo-Indian period, beginning about 600 A.D., is characterized by small corner and side-notched points, believed to mark the introduction of the bow and arrow. But since Avonlea points and some of the Besant points were small, the bow and arrow may have come in earlier. In the Neo-Indian period the Plains bison was still the chief game animal. The stratified Old Women's Buffalo Jump has yielded the best evidence in Alberta for the sequence of cultural changes during the last

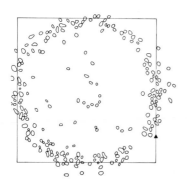

Stone circle about 20 feet in diameter forming a teepee ring, with hearth in the centre.

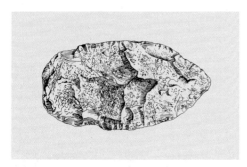

Leaf-shaped point — 4¹/₂"

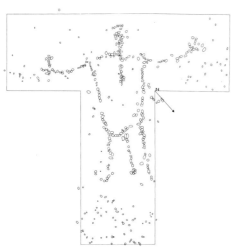

Boulder outline about 40 feet long, from near Steveville, of the figure of a man.

two millennia of our history. After the Besant and other early points went out of style, several different point types were used to despatch the bison at the kill site at the bottom of the cliff. Some types persisted throughout the period. Others tended to be superseded by new styles every few centuries until 1700 A.D. After this date, at the top of the deposits, small, side-notched points became the most common ones.

Neo-Indians and the Blackfoot

Because in historic times the Blackfoot drove bison over the Old Women's Buffalo Jump, and flaked the same type of small, triangular points, it would be tempting to assume that the Blackfoot was the tribe which for more than a thousand years made use of this jump. Unfortunately most other North American Indians used the same type of point, and a sequence of styles similar to that found in the Old Women's Buffalo Jump has been discovered elsewhere. To say therefore that it was the Blackfoot who used these types of points would be the same as stating that the remnants of all model T Fords found anywhere belonged to people who lived in Detroit. To make a proper correlation in Alberta between the historically recorded past and the archaeological past, we need to prove continuity in such things as house types, pottery and art styles in bone and basketry.

Farther south data of this kind are available, as in the Mandan, Arikara and Hidatsa earth-lodge villages, which were still in existence along the middle reaches of the Missouri River when white men arrived. But in Alberta, as in Saskatchewan, Colorado, Wyoming and Montana, there was an almost identical way of life adapted to the nomadic hunting of the bison. Thus over the whole area, most camp sites are marked by teepee (also spelled tipi) rings. These are rings of stones which were used to hold down the ground edges of the skins of the tents. Such sites yield very few artifacts because every few days the people moved on. Kill sites, such as the one at the Old Women's Buffalo Jump, do present the archaeologists with hundreds of artifacts reaching into historic times, but these are almost entirely the stone tools used to slaughter, skin and butcher bison.

A certain amount of evidence of human activities other than those involved in slaughtering bison does exist. A particular kind of pottery known as Ethridge ware is distributed over the territory occupied by the Blackfoot in the historic period. Unfortunately the Blackfoot did not make this pottery in historic times, nor can it be matched with any sites definitely known to have been occupied by them. Furthermore, although most of the evidence suggests that the Blackfoot have ranged over their territory of historic days for a long time, other evidence indicates that they may have moved southward out of the woodlands not very long ago. The Ethridge pottery therefore is of no help in the attempt to link prehistoric remains with the Blackfoot of the historic period.

Of interest is the fact that there is in Alberta one earth-lodge village vaguely similar to those along the middle reaches of the Missouri River. Its site is on the banks of the Bow River near Cluny. Eleven shallow depressions, presumed to be pits for houses, aligned between a semicircular trench and a palisade about 20 feet high, have been found there. The palisade is within the circuit of the trench and possibly the depressions were simply part of a defensive complex.

A number of artifacts, however, were unearthed. These consisted of flaked knives, scrapers, drills, small triangular projectile points, globular pots, abrading stones, grinding slabs, grooved mauls and hammerstones. None of the types is really distinctive, although the simple, unnotched points are found elsewhere only in very late prehistoric contexts. The

Blackfoot chief at the Bow River

Medicine wheel, southern Alberta.

pottery is not the same as the Ethridge ware or any other specific type, but it does appear to have general affinities with Missouri River types. Dr. Forbis, who excavated the site, believes that the occupants were from the Missouri River region. Perhaps they were simply out on a hunting trip or they may have been scouting the possibility of becoming permanent nomadic hunters on the high plains, as did the Crow Indians of southern Montana who broke away from the Hidatsa farmers a few centuries ago.

Another recently occupied site on the Oldman River near its confluence with the Little Bow may very well have been a late prehistoric Blackfoot camp. The small projectile points are the same as those from the top layers at the Old Women's Buffalo Jump, and the pottery is Ethridge ware. Found at this site were tools for working skins, including end-scrapers, knives and awls. Also recovered were shaft straighteners, smoothers, spoke-shaves, stone pipe fragments, bone and shell blades which had been perforated with stone drills, and bone quill flatteners. These last were used to press the porcupine quills which decorated skins before tiny seed beads were introduced from Europe.

Several other features of importance have been found on the prairies of southern Alberta. All of them are believed to be comparatively recent, but only the teepee rings and medicine wheels are known to have been made in both prehistoric and historic times. Teepee rings larger than about 14 feet in diameter, for instance, must have been constructed after the horse was introduced into Alberta between 1730 and 1750 A.D., because no dog and its travois could have hauled so large a tent.

The closely related medicine wheels were also built in both periods as memorials for their war chiefs by the Blackfoot and, presumably, by other prairie tribes. Normally, four or more lines of stones radiate outward from the wheel, usually pointing in the cardinal directions. The main known concentration of teepee rings is in the Neutral Hills near

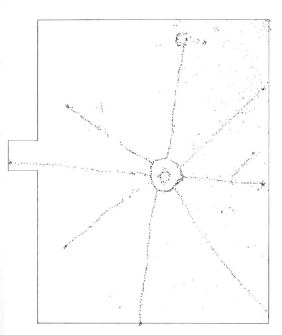

Boulder outline, medicine wheel, recorded in 1967 near Duchess in the Red Deer Valley. Maximum length 200 feet. Two others nearby, 260 feet and 240 feet long are the largest recorded to this date.

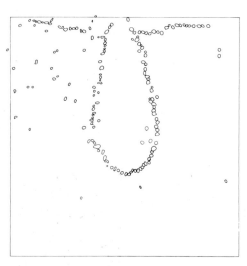

Unusual figure in outline, 28 feet long found near two largest medicine wheels mentioned above.

Consort, recorded by Dr. Bayrock. Many other concentrations of circles have been located. On the shores of Lake Pakowki in southern Alberta, for instance, the boulder outlines of about 150 teepee rings have been discovered. There are also three parallel lines of stones, varying in length from 80 to 300 feet, which end in cairns.

At the Consort site, several effigies outlined by boulders have been mapped. The most interesting of these depict bison, and turtles which appear to be eating snakes. Such Neo-Indian effigies, also found in Saskatchewan, Manitoba, North Dakota and Montana, probably had religious or magical significance. The bison effigies may have been constructed so that the bison spirits might direct the bison to make themselves available for slaughter. Mandan and Hidatsa hunting parties performed magic rites at snake and turtle effigies in North Dakota to make the fog clear so that the bison could be seen.

Several large boulder outlines of human figures of Neo-Indian times have been discovered on the prairies. These may well depict the Blackfoot culture hero, Napi, the Old Man who gave his name to the Oldman River. Napi was supposed to have been the man who first suggested that Blackfoot men live with the women. Having found the women at the Old Women's Buffalo Jump, he dressed in a woman's garb and sneaked into their camp to choose the most beautiful for himself. But when the women selected their male partners, Napi was the only one left unchosen. In anger, he was said to have changed himself into a pine tree, which early in this century still stood by the Old Women's Buffalo Jump.

Stone cairns, such as those on the shores of Pakowki Lake or the massive one in the Medicine Hat area known as the British Block Cairn, which is some 30 feet in diameter and about six feet high, are also Neo-Indian. Apparently they were used for the burial of great chiefs. Some are associated with radiating lines of stones and may be an earlier form of the medicine wheel concept. In some cases, as with the British Block Cairn, these sites have yielded large numbers of artifacts, which were probably offered to the spirit of the buried chief.

Another peculiar type of Neo-Indian boulder figures are the so-called ribstones found on the tops of prominent hills. Hammerstones have been used to peck grooves into large, hard, quartzite boulders. The pattern of grooves apparently depicts a spinal column and branching ribs. According to an old Cree Indian the pecked depressions amongst the ribs depicted bullet or arrow holes. Once again, a form of hunting magic is involved since the stone is the dwelling place of the guardian spirit of the bison. Around the ribstones hunters placed offerings to the bison spirit who would then allow a successful hunt.

It is probable that petroglyphs and pictographs were also connected with ritualistic preparations for hunting bison. Petroglyphs, like rib stones, are designs pecked or scraped on rocks, whereas pictographs are painted on stone. Both petroglyphs and pictographs are found less frequently in Alberta than they are farther west, undoubtedly because of the scarcity of vertical or overhanging cliffs of hard stone in this province. Most of the pictographs at Writing-on-Stone Provincial Park on the Milk River are almost illegible on the soft sandstone cliffs, and many of the petroglyphs are badly weathered in addition to having been damaged by unthinking visitors. A number of the designs are obviously recent because mounted horsemen, some with guns, are depicted. Many of the naturalistic, painted designs of animals are beautiful and very much like designs painted by Blackfoot men on their family teepees. Unfortunately this correlation is not certain, because very similar animals are found painted on wooden objects in the lower Yukon Valley where no Blackfoot

N.Z.

Archaeological "dig", Sutton site at Calling Lake, north of Athabasca.

ever wandered. Yet these varied relics, some Neo-Indian and some belonging to historic Indians, do afford clues to an almost vanished way of life.

Neo-Indians before the white man

Before the Europeans came, increasing numbers of Indians roamed the plains south and north of today's international boundary. The technique of the buffalo jump made their supply of food certain. As a result, in Alberta as elsewhere on the prairies, the population grew larger and the Indians had more leisure time for the decoration of themselves and their clothing, their teepees, and their tools and weapons. It seems likely that their social, ceremonial and religious life became more elaborate. The many war societies of the historic period probably had their roots in the prosperity of late Neo-Indian times.

The Indians of the prairies were still hampered by lack of mobility. Although they had the dog and travois, they were nomads who had to travel on foot. It is likely therefore that numerous small bands were scattered over the countryside, each with its own restricted range and its own communal way of life. At certain seasons the bands might come together, perhaps for some concerted effort such as war.

In the dense forests of the north, other Indians eked out an existence by trapping and fishing. The tribes of the plains looked down upon them. And then came the fur traders. But even before fur-trading forts were established in the interior, firearms and trade goods distributed from the posts on Hudson and James Bays and in Manitoba and Saskatchewan had begun to revolutionize the Indian way of life.

The historic Indians of Alberta

The aboriginal language stocks of the Indians of the historic period in the three prairie provinces include only Algonkian, Athapaskan, Siouan, and the isolated speech of the Kootenai. The first impact of the whites was felt by the Algonkian-speaking Crees of northwestern Ontario and the James Bay region who acquired firearms and trade goods, including metal knives, from the early Hudson's Bay posts, and then rapidly extended their territory westward through the parkland. They pushed the Athapaskan-speaking Beavers, Slaves and Sarcees before them, and were probably in east-central Alberta by 1725. They also moved into the plains but were checked by the Assiniboines and the Blackfoot Confederacy. As time went by they became divided into the Woods Crees and the Plains Crees.

E.S.C.

Piegan teepees by a stream

There was a similar expansion by the Assiniboines. Their name means "people who cook with stones". When translated into English this name was shortened to Stonies. A few centuries ago the Assiniboines split

Painted Blackfoot teepees

E.S.C.

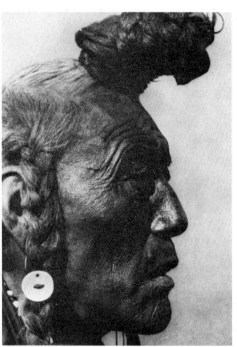

Bear Bull, a Blackfoot.

E.S.C.

from the Yankton Dakotas, a Sioux tribe, to migrate northward toward Winnipeg. They still speak a Siouan language today. Becoming allies of the Crees they, too, moved westward. Although their main territory was in southwestern Manitoba and southern Saskatchewan, a branch of them pushed up the North Saskatchewan River and by 1800 occupied the area around its headwaters. The mysterious Snare Indians in that region were said to have been annihilated by them. These Assiniboines are the Stonies of today's Alberta. Another group of them ranged into Alberta around the Cypress Hills but later migrated into Montana.

Farther north, the most easterly of the Athapaskan-speaking peoples, the Chipewyans, acquired firearms and trade goods from the fur traders' posts. Then they also expanded westward to Great Slave Lake and beyond. Before this time they had probably occupied most of the Lake Athabasca area and the extreme northeast of Alberta. Their fellow Athapaskans—the Beavers, Slaves and Sarcees—were pushed farther into Alberta's northern forest and into the Peace River district. Not long before the arrival of the white men, the Sarcees moved south from Lesser Slave Lake to occupy the upper part of the Athabasca River. They then became allies of the Blackfoot. In these movements, initiated primarily by the introduction of firearms, a number of small tribes probably perished. Indian legends, for example, tell of the "old people" who used to live in central Alberta.

Other Indian tribes had less impact on the Alberta scene. In the north the Saulteaux or Ojibway—from whom comes the name Chippewa – an Algonkian-speaking people – travelled up the North Saskatchewan to trade. One Ojibway band still lives near Hinton. Iroquois from eastern Canada accompanied Canadian voyageurs into Alberta and beyond. These Iroquois became hunters and trappers in the region between Jasper and Edmonton, but most of them lost their language and identity through intermarriage with Crees and the Stonies.

In the west a British Columbia tribe, the Kootenai, who spoke their own peculiar language, used to hunt bison east of the Rocky Mountains until they were driven back by the Blackfoot. At one time the Salish-speaking Shuswap probably made the same sort of sporadic incursions into Alberta. On what is now the Banff golf course, several circular house pits like those in Salishan territory in British Columbia have been discovered. Likewise, the Gros Ventres or Atsina inhabited the southwestern corner of this province briefly before moving into Montana. Part of southwestern Alberta is also said to have been inhabited by the Snake or northern Shoshone Indians who had horses (acquired ultimately from the Spaniards of New Mexico) at a time before the Blackfoot obtained them by raiding. The Blackfoot, allied with Crees, drove them out with the aid of guns.

The Blackfoot Confederacy

In the midst of all this turmoil the powerful Blackfoot Confederacy maintained its range over southern and central Alberta, southwestern Saskatchewan and in territory on the other side of the international boundary. They are called Blackfoot from their own name for themselves, *Siksika* meaning "black feet". Some think this name came from black-dyed moccasins, others from the fact that their moccasins were often black from walking in the ashes of prairie fires. Loosely allied with the Blackfoot were the Bloods and the Piegans, the Sarcees being latecomers into the Confederacy. Except for the Sarcees, the tribes are Algonkian-speaking.

The Blackfoot tribes are the earliest known occupants of the Canadian plains. They may have inhabited them for a thousand years or more

Assiniboine Indian with bow and arrows and dogs carrying packs.

or they may have moved onto the plains from the woodlands but a few centuries ago. In either case, they had achieved an elaborate culture based on hunting the bison, even before they had secured firearms and the horse.

Equestrian culture on the plains

As with all Plains Indians the acquisition of the horse made important changes in the Blackfoot way of life. The southern tribes on the Great Plains were the first to acquire and use the "big Dog". The Blackfoot, despite the ravages of rum and whisky and the diseases of the white man, now rapidly built the apogee of Plains culture on two foundations, the bison and the horse. Since horses were ridden in the hunt for bison and in war, raiding for horses became the accepted way for young braves to prove themselves. Horse-raiding forays ranged as far as Colorado and the Snake River Plains of southern Idaho. Horse-raiding and tribal warfare were often blended, particularly in the struggles between the Blackfoot and the Crees. The Blackfoot became superb cavalrymen.

Other features of equestrian Blackfoot culture obviously had their roots in the social and ceremonial customs of pre-equestrian days. Among these customs were age-group war societies, the competitive giving away of possessions, the sun dance in which young braves proved their courage and endurance of pain, and the value placed on medicine bundles.

Each brave had his own personal fetish, acquired from his guardian spirit, which he took with him for protection on raids or into battle. The more highly valued medicine bundles were supposed to possess special magical powers and were exchanged for robes, weapons, horses and other personal property. Songs and dances accompanying the ritual exchange of such bundles sometimes went on for days. The more important the bundle a man owned, the greater was his status. The last formal transfer of one of the most highly valued of the Blood medicine bundles was to an employee of the Provincial Museum of Alberta in 1965.

The leadership of the Blackfoot was somewhat informal. One of the ablest among the head men of each band came to be regarded as the band chief and acted as spokesman for these head men in the tribal council. There was, however, a talking chief for each of the Blackfoot tribes

Chipewyan Indian and teepee in northern Alberta.

Indians hunting bison. A painting by Nick Eggenhofer.

G.F

Piegan painted lodges

E.S.C.

White Dog, a Blood.

E.S.C.

whose duty it was to summon the tribal council. Thus the tribal councils decided matters, although the advice of a wise and respected chief, – such as Crowfoot at the time of the 1885 Riel rebellion, – was likely to be accepted.

This elaborate culture was destroyed by the advance of the white man and the disappearance of the bison. It was on September 22nd, 1877, that by Treaty Number 7 the Blackfoot Confederacy signed away their lands to the Dominion of Canada and agreed to go on reserves. Soon afterwards the bison all but vanished and the Plains culture disintegrated.

The forest Indians

In northern Alberta the Woods Crees, Beavers, Chipewyans and Slaves – all of them called the Thickwood Indians by the fur traders – also gave up title to their lands. Yet they did not feel the chill of change as keenly as their cousins on the plains. For one thing, most of their subsistence came from the forest animals, which are often difficult to trap or hunt. Consequently they were accustomed to a more meagre and insecure livelihood than the Plains Indians. Secondly, although the trapping of fur-bearing animals for the fur traders had interfered with their pre-historic way of life, as soon as the fur trade diminished, the Thickwood Indians were able to revert to hunting forest animals for food. Their way of life therefore was not much worse than it had been before the white man came.

The importance of trapping as the major means of subsistence in the boreal forest during prehistoric and historic times cannot be over-emphasized. Before the fur traders came, the true trap, which works well for catching most small mammals, was not as important as snares, deadfalls and pitfalls set up on game trails. Projectile points, whether on arrows or spears, were not essential except to despatch trapped animals. It was much easier and more efficient to permit the animal to trap himself.

This is what the Indian hunter did, and still does. Unlike the white man who hunts and kills an animal in order to demonstrate his prowess, today's Indians still believe that to some degree the animal allows itself to be taken so that the hunter and his family will not starve. Hence the Indian hunter of early days felt himself to be an integral part of the natural world and not a subjugator of it.

This belief appears to have been held by most Indians of North America, even though it was recognized that the most skilful hunter would be the most successful. In Alberta, Thickwoods and Plains Indian shared this view. This feeling is still deeply engrained in many of today's Indians. So is the lack of distinction between dreaming and waking.

292

experiences, the refusal to be a slave to calendar time and the strong attachment of each Indian to his own social unit on his reserve. These and other cultural differences perhaps explain why the white man and the Indian often do not understand each other. The Indian cannot comprehend the insistence of the white man on punctuality and lack of absenteeism in a type of work which is often monotonous. The white man, failing to understand the deep roots of the Indian's cultural tradition, is frequently inclined to stigmatize him as lazy and unreliable. Yet, viewed objectively, the fact does remain that white settlement has pushed the descendants of the original inhabitants of Alberta into reserves, while comparatively little has been done either to integrate them into modern society or to comprehend why their attitudes are likely to be different from those of white men. These are difficulties that can scarcely be disregarded today when Indians are the fastest growing ethnic group in Canada.

These matters, however, are problems for the social anthropologist rather than for the archaeologist, just as the story of the Indians in historic times is, pretty largely, the concern of the historian and the cultural anthropologist. The archaeologist may study the cultures of historic Indians in the hope of finding clues to their prehistory. His main preoccupation, however, is in searching for evidence which will throw light on the prehistory of the first peoples on this continent and the varying cultures their descendants developed before the Europeans came. By his researches it is possible that the archaeologist may contribute to the pride of present-day Indians in their past, and to the respect of all of us for that past.

Blackfoot horseman

Pictographs to be seen in Writing-on-Stone Provincial Park.

A treasury of photographic portraits of the primitive North American Indians was captured by the lens of Edward S. Curtis. Curtis left a thriving Pennsylvania law practice in 1832 to go among the western Indians to preserve on film the best types of the many North American tribes. He did nothing else for 25 years and produced thousands of portraits. We are proud to record in this volume reproductions of Curtis' photographs of Indian tribes native to the Western Canadian Plains. These pictures were reproduced from folios owned by the University of Alberta in Edmonton, and are produced herein with the co-operation of the University and the permission of the publishers, Superior Publishing Company.

G.F.

CHAPTER THIRTEEN

Early Natural History Explorations

BRIAN HITCHON

THE FIRST EUROPEANS to venture into the interior of western Canada must have gazed about them with a sense of wonder. Here were vast plains, wide stretches of parkland, broad-flowing rivers, strange beasts and differing types of Indians inhabiting a land that would have remained longer unexplored had it not been for the demands of the fur trade.

The entrance gate into the unknown country was the western shore of Hudson Bay. Although the Indians were intimately familiar with the flora and fauna of the interior, the initial recorded investigations of western Canada were made by mariners searching for the fabled Northwest Passage in the early years of the 17th century, and so were limited to the coastal regions of Hudson Bay. Then in 1670 the "Governor and Company of Adventurers trading into Hudson Bay" were granted a royal charter to trade in Rupert's Land, a vast and unexplored domain which included much of what is now called western Canada. Employees of this company, soon known as the Hudson's Bay Company, established fur-trading posts along the western coastline of Hudson Bay to which the Indians of the interior were to bring their pelts. But the French of Canada were also trying to gain control of this region. Partly because of this competition, the Hudson's Bay Company in 1690 sent Henry Kelsey with a band of friendly Indians on the first great journey inland.

At the time Kelsey was only 20 years of age. With no European companion he travelled across the Canadian Shield as far as the parklands of central Saskatchewan and spent two years in the interior. His journal reveals something of the realization that he was seeing what no European had ever before beheld, and three lines of "his Book" describe the white man's first sight of the bison and the Plains grizzly in these words:

Title picture – The camper, from a painting by Paul Kane.

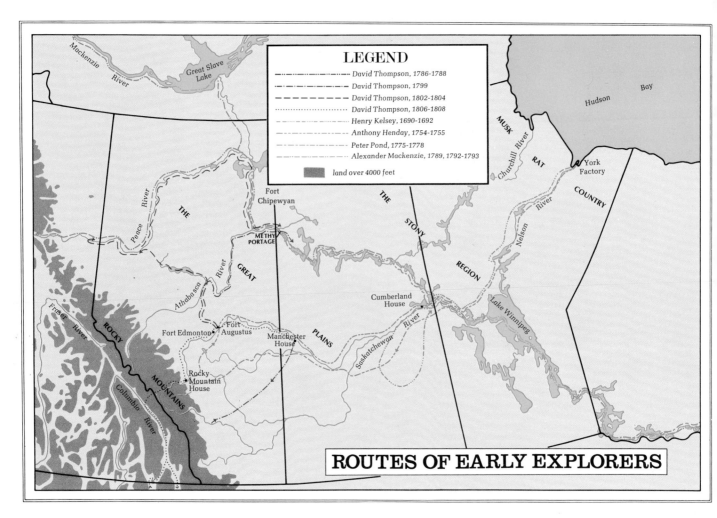

LEGEND

— · — · — David Thompson, 1786-1788
— ·· — ·· — David Thompson, 1799
— — — — David Thompson, 1802-1804
· · · · · · David Thompson, 1806-1808
———— Henry Kelsey, 1690-1692
— — — — Anthony Henday, 1754-1755
—— —— Peter Pond, 1775-1778
— — — Alexander Mackenzie, 1789, 1792-1793

▓ land over 4000 feet

ROUTES OF EARLY EXPLORERS

"And then you have beast of severall kind
The one is a black a Buffillo great
Another is an outgrown Bear w,^{ch} is good meat . . ."

Kelsey also tells of "poplo ridges", of "beavour in abundance", of a "Buffillo" hunt and skirmishes between Indian bands. There was no attempt at this time, however, to classify or synthesize – that is, to put together into a connected whole – the observations which he and other early explorers noted in their accounts; this was to come two centuries later with the development of science in Europe and the arrival of trained observers in western Canada.

In the century following Kelsey's expedition, the impetus for exploration still came from the fur trade. In 1713, by the Treaty of Utrecht, the French were excluded from Hudson Bay but the French fur traders, operating out of Montreal, established a canoe and portage route from Lachine on the St. Lawrence River via the Great Lakes to Lake of the Woods. From this point they founded a group of trading posts in western Canada. Because it had to meet this challenge and also desired to improve its trade, in 1754 the Hudson's Bay Company sent out Anthony Henday to make contact with the Indians of the unexplored interior. In September of that year Henday became the first European to enter what is now Alberta.

The journeys of both Kelsey and Henday stir our imagination. With no other Europeans as companions, they ventured vast distances into the unknown and brought back the first information of those parts of the interior of western Canada through which they travelled. About this time the Sieur de la Vérendrye of Trois Rivières in Quebec travelled west with his four sons and some 40 Frenchmen. During the period from

296

The brothers La Vérendrye in sight of the western mountains. New Year's Day, 1743.

1731 to 1744 he and his sons established trading posts and explored Manitoba, part of southern Saskatchewan and a large tract of the northern United States. It was La Vérendrye who set down the relationships of the Red, Assiniboine and Missouri Rivers, and the geographic position of Lakes Winnipeg, Manitoba and Winnipegosis.

The rivalry between the Hudson's Bay Company and the French was ended in 1763 when, by the Peace of Paris, Canada became a British colony. But then a new challenge came from the North West Company. While in its service, Connecticut-born Peter Pond in 1778 discovered the 13-mile Methy Portage from Methy Lake to the Clearwater River. Following this river to the Athabasca River, he established his first post not far from the present site of Fort Chipewyan on Lake Athabasca. Before his return, he had sent a man to stand on the banks of the Peace River and thus had brought northern Alberta within the knowledge of Europeans. He also drew a few rather crude sketch maps of the area. In one of these Lake Athabasca was placed so far west of Hudson Bay that there was no space for the Rocky Mountains.

About this time the Hudson's Bay Company found that its knowledge and its rough maps of the interior were insufficient for its expansion and hired competent surveyors to gather exact information about Rupert's Land. Of these men the first truly scientific observer was Philip Turnor, who worked in western Canada from 1790 to 1792. Turnor's descriptions from within Alberta are limited to the Peace River region which he noted has "the finest Pine I have seen in the Country". More important, he trained Peter Fidler and David Thompson. The former has provided us with a discerningly descriptive journal of the regions he saw and the latter prepared the first synthesis of the Great Plains, which he defined as extending from the Gulf of Mexico to the 54th Parallel, and which he observed to be bounded by essentially different country.

David Thompson was a quietly courageous man. During the 28 years he served, first with the Hudson's Bay Company and then with its competitor, the North West Company, he made at least four separate journeys into Alberta (1786-88; 1799; 1802-04; and 1806-08). In the first of these he travelled from Manchester House on the North Saskatchewan River near the Alberta-Saskatchewan border as far as the Bow River, southeast of Calgary. In the second, during May, 1799, he became the

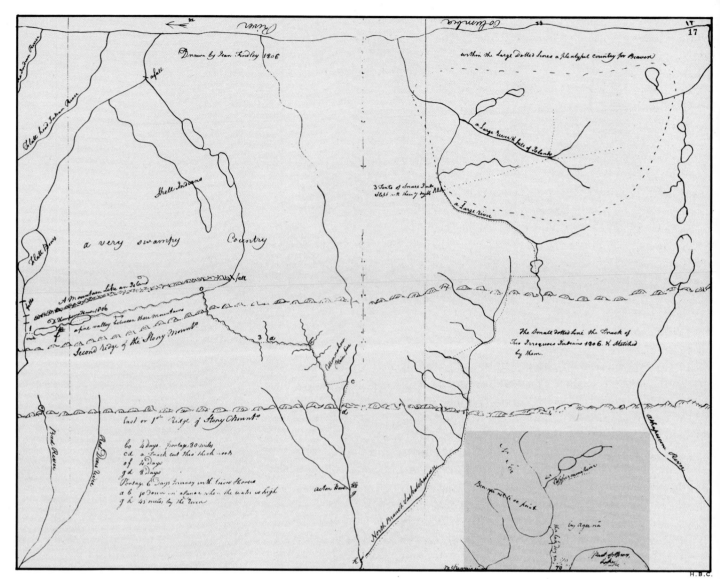

Early map of part of central Alberta and part of British Columbia west to the Columbia River. The original of this map, approximately 20 by 14½ inches, is in the manuscript collection of Peter Fidler, who was a surveyor in the employ of the Hudson's Bay Company. The insert, lower right, is a separate map of a section of the Northwest Territories.

first white man to journey down the Athabasca River from Lesser Slave Lake to McMurray. His third expedition took him along the North Saskatchewan River and to Lesser Slave Lake and the Peace River, returning east by way of the Methy Portage. His most important journey was the fourth in which he discovered the Athabasca Pass, which for many years was the main route to the Pacific coast. He has left us succinct, descriptive pictures of all the main ecological regions of the western interior of Canada, which he charmingly describes as Musk Rat Country, the Stony Region (the Precambrian Shield) and the Great Plains. In recording his first sighting of the Rocky Mountains, he wrote that they were like "shining white clouds in the horizon".

A contemporary of David Thompson and the ablest of all the North West Company's explorers was Alexander Mackenzie. He arrived in the rugged Athabasca country in the winter of 1787, but his journals include only a few descriptions of Alberta along the main canoe routes. In the Peace River country he noted "a succession of the most beautiful scenery I have ever beheld" and wrote of "groves of poplars in every shape — and their intervals are enlivened with vast herds of elks and buffaloes —".

Although Peter Pond showed "tar deposits" in his maps, the first description of the Athabasca oil sands comes from the pen of Alexander Mackenzie. At a point some 24 miles from the junction of the Clearwater and Athabasca Rivers, he records the presence of "some bituminous fountains, into which a pole of twenty feet long may be inserted without the least resistance. The bitumen is in a fluid state, and when mixed with gum, or the resinous substance collected from the spruce fir, serves to gum the canoes. In its heated state it emits a smell like that of sea-coal. The banks of the river, which are there very elevated, discover veins of the same bituminous quality". Yet although Mackenzie was an adventurous and keen-eyed explorer, he seldom attempted to synthesize his observations.

The explorations, then, in the half century that followed Henday's entry into Alberta revealed the broad aspects of the landscape, although only the major rivers and their environs were known in any detail. This period of exciting investigations in unknown country culminated in the first comprehensive and accurate map of western Canada which was produced in 1813-14 by that gifted man, David Thompson. Historically, the era was concluded by the amalgamation in 1821 of the Hudson's Bay and North West Companies. From this time forward, for almost half a century, a vast empire stretching from Hudson Bay to the Pacific Ocean was ruled by one authority, the Hudson's Bay Company. During this period, many of the geographical details of the area were filled in and the first naturalists arrived.

Early naturalists

Prior to 1819 no qualified naturalist had visited Alberta, although essentially descriptive reports of the flora and fauna were known, as well as the most obvious geological features, such as coal and tar sand occurrences. Elements of the climate had been reported and considerable practical knowledge gained concerning the Indians. However, no literature existed dealing primarily with natural history.

In 1819 Dr. John Richardson, a surgeon and naturalist, accompanied Captain John Franklin's Arctic Expedition and reported on the geology, flora and fauna of western Canada. With respect to Alberta, he described again the "pitchy sandstone" at McMurray, the "bed of limestone almost entirely composed of orthoceratites and bivalve shells" lying beneath it, and delineated the boundary of the Precambrian Shield and the sedimentary rocks. It is, however, for his authoritative *Fauna Boreali-Americana* published in 1829 that he is most widely and justifiably remembered. Although Richardson collected some botanical material on his first expedition, most of the botanical observations during the 1825-27 Arctic Expedition were made by his assistant, Thomas Drummond. The plant specimens collected by these two men were sent to England and were augmented by those of David Douglas, a young Scottish botanist after whom the Douglas fir is named. The eminent taxonomist, Dr. W. J. Hooker, then incorporated their findings in his *Flora Boreali-Americana*. Together with Richardson's coloured geological map of northern North America, on a scale of one inch to approximately 230 miles, these publications form the basis of our knowledge of the natural history of this region.

Shortly after the middle of the 19th century, the administration of Rupert's Land came into contention, and this, with the imminent necessity for decisions on transcontinental railway routes, led the British Government to sponsor the scientific exploring expedition of Captain John Palliser from 1857 to 1860. The Canadian Government similarly authorized an expedition under H. Y. Hind and S. J. Dawson in 1857 and 1858, which was to confine its observations to southern Manitoba and southeastern Saskatchewan.

The Palliser Expedition, as it came to be known, was led by Captain John Palliser, an Irish country gentleman, and Dr. James Hector, an Edinburgh medical doctor and geologist. Attached to the group were

W. G.

Bison roamed the western plains by the tens of thousands in the days of the early explorers. The species is now preserved, as seen above, in several of our national parks.

Eugene Bourgeau, a botanist, and Lieutenant Blakiston, whose job it was to conduct a magnetic survey. Hector was the first to identify Cretaceous fossils in the plains, and to discover the Tertiary strata of the Cypress Hills. But probably the most significant scientific achievement of the expedition was the recognition by Hector of the three prairie levels, which are essentially three topographic levels of erosion, and the discernment of the climatic and vegetational contrasts across them. These he defined as the forests, the plains, and an intermediate belt – now recognized as the parklands. Within the Rocky Mountains he described the Carboniferous and Devonian carbonates and the extensive thrusting and folding to which they have been subjected. Indeed, this brilliant geologist has provided us with the elements of the physical background controlling the natural history of the entire western interior of Canada, and these remain valid to this day.

Canadian government surveys

Rupert's Land was transferred to Canada by the Imperial Government in 1870 and ceased to exist as a political entity. Scientific investigations of a reconnaissance nature were now carried out by several government agencies, including the Geological Survey of Canada, the Canadian Pacific Railway Survey, the Land Survey and the Boundary Commission Survey.

The Land Survey began its work in western Canada in 1869 and gradually divided the country into townships and sections. At the same time more exact information concerning the vegetation, soils and major physical features was obtained. The Survey reports form excellent geographies of this part of Canada at that time.

In 1871 the Canadian government made the decision to construct a railway from eastern Canada to the Pacific Ocean, and Sandford Fleming, the engineer-in-chief of the Canadian Pacific Railway, was entrusted with the route survey. Much valuable material was published on a one degree quadrangle basis – that is, an area with one degree of latitude from north to south, and one degree of longitude from east to west until 1880, when the Canadian Pacific Railway Syndicate took over the transcontinental railway project from the government and a rapid decision was made to follow a southern route. The reports of the botanist John Macoun are still of value, although perhaps rather too critical of some of Palliser's reports.

During the period from 1872 to 1874 the North American Boundary Commission was delineating the 49th Parallel from Lake of the Woods to the Pacific Ocean. A young Canadian geologist, George M. Dawson, was attached to the survey and produced a brilliant report. He later rose to become Director of the Geological Survey of Canada and was probably Canada's most distinguished scientist of the 19th century.

In 1873 the first official parties of the Geological and Natural History Survey of Canada entered the field in the western interior of Canada, and the names of the geologists occur repeatedly in the first official reports of this region. They include John Macoun, A. R. C. Selwyn, George M. Dawson, Robert Bell and R. G. McConnell. Their reports almost always included descriptions of the flora and fauna, although a few naturalists, such as R. Kennicott, E. Petitot and J. A. Loring, were also active about this time.

The twentieth century

A tremendous expansion of science and technology took place at the beginning of the 20th century and continues at an increased pace today. This expansion brought to Alberta many professional geologists, botanists and zoologists. Some were attached to the University of Alberta which began its first classes on September 23rd, 1908, with 42 students and four professors. Other scientists were on the staff of the several federal and provincial government agencies operating out of Edmonton and Calgary, or they were employed by the many oil companies which were exploring for gas and oil in the province. Many of those who came during the earlier years of expansion are still alive. Their scientific endeavours and those of their deceased colleagues gave us much of the structure of knowledge on which the naturalists of today are building.

It is a cliché – but a true one – that in the field of knowledge the present stands on the shoulders of the past to reach into the future. The earliest explorers, although their primary task was to extend and improve the fur trade, gathered information about the then unknown interior of western Canada as an integral part of their accounts. In geography, David Thompson, himself an explorer of distinction, synthesized the discoveries up to his time in his map of western Canada. Then after the middle of the 19th century, and especially after the appearance of Darwin's *Origin of Species* in 1859, naturalists and geologists arrived in western Canada from a Europe that was in intellectual ferment. New theories of evolution and geology were being conceived; and here in the almost virgin territory of western Canada was the opportunity to put these theories to the test. In natural history, we of today reap the benefit of their endeavours.

G.F.

CHAPTER FOURTEEN

The Impact of the White Man

JAMES G. MACGREGOR

ON WEDNESDAY, SEPTEMBER 11th, 1754, north of where Chauvin stands today, a band of Crees crossed the eastern boundary of the future Province of Alberta. With them was a lone Englishman, Anthony Henday. Neither the Crees nor any other Indian of that day could possibly have envisioned that this was a day of destiny for Alberta. For thousands of years, tribes had come and gone. In the forests, generation after generation of moose, elk, beaver and a multitude of other animals had flourished. Over the great plains the bison, a seemingly inexhaustible food supply, still roamed in millions. From the native point of view, this was the way it had always been and always would be.

Yet the breezes of change were already touching their lives. Some 80 years before this September of 1754, fur traders had reached Hudson Bay. Since that time, bands of natives had made the long canoe journey to the Hudson's Bay Company's York Factory at the mouth of the Hayes River. There they traded muskrat, otter, marten, fox, mink and beaver pelts for blankets, copper kettles, steel knives, axes, guns and liquor.

The acquisition of firearms led to inter-tribal wars and to the expansion westward of the Crees, Assiniboines, and Chipewyans. Rum and brandy often demoralized the Indians and, to a certain extent, the search for fur-bearing animals disrupted their way of life. Even more shattering were the white man's diseases against which the natives had built no immunity. About 20 years before Henday's journey, for example, a plague of smallpox from far to the south had leaped from tribe to tribe to decimate the inhabitants of the interior of western Canada. From the south, too, came the horse to make the tribes of the plains much more mobile in hunting bison but also, unfortunately, in waging far-ranging warfare. Despite these obvious signs of change, no Alberta

Title Picture — Pioneers and North-West Mounted Police on the southern prairies. A painting by Theodore M. Schintz.

303

Indian could have imagined in 1754 that the tough, black-bearded Henday was the precursor of hordes of white men who, in less than a century and a half, would wrest the Indians' hunting-grounds from them.

Nor did Henday have any foreknowledge. The Hudson's Bay Company had sent him into the interior to persuade the Indians to stop their inter-tribal warfare and to turn instead to the accumulation of more furs. Another purpose was to influence the Blackfoot, the "Tigers of the Plains", to bring pelts to York Factory. Henday did not foresee farms or towns or cities in this land. But although he looked at the countryside with the eyes of a fur trader, he did note a number of its features. On the day he entered the future Alberta he wrote in his diary: "Level land; few woods; & plenty of good water", and added that the "Indians killed eight Waskesew (elk)". He commented on the heat of the golden autumn, but on the next day he complained of the "cold, raw weather which silences the Musketoes". A few days later he went "abuffalo hunting" with the Indians, "all armed with bows and arrows; killed seven, fine sport".

Henday spent the autumn of 1754 and the winter of 1754-55 in Alberta. During those months, according to the generally accepted view, he was the first European to see Canada's Rocky Mountains, and was received by the Blackfoot in their great camp of 322 teepees a few miles west of Pine Lake near where a cairn in Henday's honour now stands. As the squaws giggled and pointed at the lone white man, the sacred pipe was presented to the Heavens, the Four Winds, the Sun and Mother Earth. But to Henday's chagrin the Blackfoot refused to undertake the four-months' return journey to carry pelts to Hudson Bay. The tribes on the north bank of the North Saskatchewan River were more co-operative. On April 29th, 1755 Henday, accompanied by sixty canoes laden with pelts, paddled down the North Saskatchewan River bound for York factory. With him he brought the first eye-witness account of the future Alberta and its Indians. Henday, however, was only the forerunner of several Hudson's Bay Company employees who visited Alberta almost yearly during the next three decades.

The North West Company

As previously noted, for sixty-six years after Henday's return to York Factory a battle for furs raged between the Hudson's Bay Company and its rivals. We have seen that competition from the French was removed in 1763. Shortly thereafter, however, independent fur traders from Montreal, chiefly Scottish-born and known as the "Pedlars", established trading posts in the interior of western Canada. These "Lords of the North" employed mainly Scots for management and French-Canadian voyageurs for the hard, rough work. Packing trade goods in *canots du maître,* which were about 36 feet long and six feet wide amidships, they rendezvoused each June with the men who had spent the previous winter in the interior. At first the meeting was at Grand Portage near the western end of Lake Superior. In 1800, when this place was lost to the United States, their rendezvous was transferred to Kaministiquia, now Fort William. Here the "wintering partners" and their men brought their furs to be loaded in the *canots du maître* and carried back to Montreal; and hence the trade goods in "pieces" of 90 pounds were transported over the Grand Portage, known also as the "Great Carry", to be put into smaller canoes – 24 to 30 feet long and about five feet wide amidships – for shipment to the trading posts. At these rendezvous rum flowed freely – after 1770 brandy was rarely used in the fur trade – and there were

G.F.

Interior of an early Hudson's Bay Company trading post drawn by Frederick Remington in 1888.

fights, dances and general revelry. Then the wintering partners returned to their lonely stations.

Of these "Pedlars" the best organized group and the one which finally brought all the independent fur traders under a single blanket was the North West Company, whose men were often known as the Nor'-westers. It was the quarrelsome but adventurous Nor'wester, Peter Pond, who opened up the rich fur-bearing Athabasca region probably as far as the Peace River. He had planned further explorations, but the death of a fur-trader – apparently Pond's second killing in the district – led to his recall. His successor, Alexander Mackenzie, building on the foundation Pond had laid and imbibing his dream, went on in 1789 to descend the Mackenzie River to the Arctic Ocean. Then, four years later, after establishing a trading post near the site of today's Peace River town, he completed his masterful explorations by ascending the Peace River and crossing the cordillera of British Columbia to salt water – the first white man to cross the continent anywhere north of Mexico.

There were other aggressive Nor'westers in Alberta. In 1789, eleven years after Pond had reached the Athabasca country, Angus Shaw planted a trading post at Moose Lake near modern Bonnyville. Three years later he established Fort George near today's Elk Point, the first station on the Alberta part of the North Saskatchewan River. Next, in 1795 Shaw ordered his men to build Fort Augustus, the precursor of present-day Edmonton, but sited some 20 miles downstream and across the river from today's Fort Saskatchewan. Through the comment of Duncan McGillivray, an associate of Shaw's, we catch a glimpse of the countryside as it was in 1795.

"This is described to be a rich and plentiful Country", he wrote, "abounding in all kinds of animals, especially Beavers & Otters, which are said to be so numerous that the Women and children kill them with Sticks and hatchets".

Counter-campaign

Long before this time, the Hudson's Bay Company had been stung into action. As one part of a counter-campaign they sent out surveyors, such as Peter Fidler and David Thompson, both to contact the Indians and to gain a knowledge of western Canada. Through their accounts we get glimpses of the Alberta of that day. Thus Thompson, on his remarkable

Fort Ethier, built in anticipation of Indian attacks and used as a stopover house on the trail from Edmonton to Calgary. The Fort is seen as it still stands today on the Lucas farm just north of the City of Wetaskiwin.

G.F.

journey into the area around the site of today's Calgary, in 1787 wrote of the Piegans: "They are a fine race of men, tall and muscular, with manly features and intelligent countenances"; while Peter Fidler, when he was crossing the Red Deer River near modern Carbon, said of the bison: "I am sure there were some millions in sight as no ground could be seen for them in a compleat semicircle & extending at least ten miles . . ."

Henday, Pond, Mackenzie, Shaw, McGillivray, Fidler, Thompson and their confrères were the adventurers and explorers who made the general outlines of western Canada, including Alberta, known to the fur traders and to the London map-maker, John Arrowsmith. Their own restless curiosity drove them forward, but it was the struggle between the fur trading companies that made their explorations possible and necessary.

Besides sending out men like Thompson and Fidler, the Hudson's Bay Company established inland posts. The first of these was Cumberland House, founded near The Pas in Manitoba in 1774. The Nor'westers retaliated by founding still more trading stations. From 1774 to 1821 a feverish competition stretched as far as the Pacific coast. By 1821 the Hudson's Bay Company had built 76 trading posts as compared to 97 held by the North West Company.

In Alberta, when the Nor'westers built Fort George in 1792, in the same year the Hudson's Bay Company placed Buckingham House right beside it. In 1795, matching stride with stride, Edmonton House was planted almost next door to the Nor'westers' Fort Augustus, which had just been opened. While the two companies watched each other like jealous dogs with a single bone between them, the two forts were transferred three times up and down the North Saskatchewan River. Then, in 1812 both posts were sited on the flat which is now occupied by the Edmonton power house. Later, after a great flood in 1820, both forts were moved to the hill just below today's Legislative Building of the Province

York boats, such as the one in this early photograph, plied the North Saskatchewan River transporting men and supplies. A remnant of one such boat is on display at a museum site in Edmonton.

of Alberta. Similarly, when in 1799 Duncan McGillivray of the Nor'westers put up Rocky Mountain House, in that same year the Hudson's Bay Company set up Acton House beside it. Except for the Blackfoot country to the south, where only the short-lived Bow Fort was planted, trading stations multiplied within Alberta. To supply these posts and to take back pelts, canoe brigades made the long journey up and down the North Saskatchewan River. Later the Hudson's Bay Company used York boats, a special craft suited to the river, or brigades of horses or of squealing Red River carts to carry their goods. In the period of the canoe brigades the rivalry between the two companies was intense and often violent. At times each company ambushed the other's brigades, seizing their furs and occasionally imprisoning the men. At other times, the men of the two companies met in mutual festivities. But always the traders of each company would resort to almost any measures to lure hunters and their furs away from the other's posts.

The effect on the Indians

With trading posts established in the interior of western Canada, an inevitable result was the intermingling of Scots and French-Canadians with dusky Indian belles, unions which often resulted in marriages *à la façon du Nord.* Hence came the proud Métis. Other effects were almost entirely for the worse. As early as 1794 the Nor'wester, Duncan McGillivray, wrote of the Indian hunters: "The love of rum is their first inducement to industry". Now, under the stress of competition, rum, diluted according to the degree of sophistication of the hunters, was poured like cups of coffee today. To get rum, the hunters would trade not only their hard-won pelts but their guns and their women. When the canoe brigades reached the forts, the voyageurs were just as thirsty. There were indescribable orgies around the posts, and scenes of violence were so ordinary that the fur traders merely noted them and passed on to more important

The Red River cart, which brought settlers from Winnipeg west in the late 1800's.

Reverend Father Albert Lacombe   E.B.C.

Reverend Robert T. Rundle   G.F.

Reverend Jean Baptiste Thibault   G.F.

concerns. Thus Alexander Henry the Younger, who traded for the Nor'-westers from 1799 to 1814, when the Indians asked for liquor, promising to hunt well afterward, wrote in his journal: "I gave them some. Grand Gueule stabbed Capot Rouge, Le Boeuf stabbed his young wife in the arm, Little Shell almost beat his old mother's brains out with a club. I sowed garden seeds".

Through rum, whole tribes were debauched and became dependent upon the traders. Meanwhile the fur-bearing animals were depleted, fierce Indian wars blazed and measles, tuberculosis, venereal disease and, above all, the dreaded smallpox took their toll. During this period of intense rivalry, the two companies were destroying the two primary resources of the fur trade, fur-bearing animals and the hunters who trapped them.

The zenith of the fur trade

By 1821 unbridled competition had brought the North West Company to virtual bankruptcy and the Hudson's Bay Company to the verge of it. The two rivals therefore amalgamated under the name of the Hudson's Bay Company. Now came the peak days of the fur trade. From Hudson Bay to the Pacific Ocean, except for the Blackfoot Confederacy, only one writ ran – that of the Company. With the monopoly of the fur trade in its hands, the Company could begin to conserve both fur-bearing animals and the hunters. It could not stop fierce inter-tribal wars, but it did its best to discourage them. The Company could and did diminish the use of rum in trade until, finally, the practice was almost abolished. It could and did reorganize the fur trade to show a profit, and it even fed the Indians whenever there was a bad season for furs. Moreover, its chief factors meted out a stern but impartial justice to Indians, whites and Métis. In the United States liquor and warfare – between tribe and tribe or between Indians and the competing fur traders or advancing settlers – led to anarchy, injustice and massacres. In Canada there was comparative order and peace. It was largely because of the régime of the Hudson's Bay Company that, ultimately, there was a reasonably tranquil take-over of the Canadian West in contrast to the savage Indian wars south of the international boundary.

One factor the Company could not control – the mortality due to the white man's diseases. It is estimated that from 1801 to 1858 the population of the Blackfoot tribes decreased from 9,000 to 7,600. This decline in numbers may be assumed to have applied proportionately to all Alberta Indians.

Despite the Company's monopoly, change was knocking at its door. For one thing, the churches were now sending missionaries to the Canadian West. Thus, in 1840, the Reverend Robert Terrell Rundle, a Wesleyan, became the first resident cleric in what is now Alberta. In 1842 and 1852 respectively, Roman Catholic missionaries, Father Thibault and the famed "black-robe voyageur", Father Lacombe, arrived. The equally noted Methodist missionary, the Reverend George McDougall, settled in the province in 1863. These and other missionaries, whom Sir John A. Macdonald, Canada's first Prime Minister, called "the finest moral police force in the world", preached Christianity to the Indians and the Métis. They established missions. They travelled from north to south and east to west over the lonely land under summer heat and through biting cold. Often the sky was their night-time roof and the howling blizzard their daytime companion. Their sincerity and devotion, which won the respect of the Indians, contributed greatly to the comparatively peaceful transition from the fur empire to the Dominion of Canada.

The coming of the missionaries was only one of the signs of change.

Settlement was beginning, and small plots of garden vegetables and grain could be seen around the Company's posts and the Christian missions. In eastern Canada and even in England, interest in the Canadian West was growing. In the United States, men looked northward with covetous eyes to the vast domain held by the Company. The fur empire had reached its zenith. At that moment the marching forces of history were preparing its overthrow.

The end of the fur empire

Besides adding greatly to the knowledge of the geology and natural history of the interior of western Canada, the reports published by the members of the Palliser and Hind-Dawson expeditions also made it clear that much of the Northwest was suitable for agricultural settlement – and the fur empire was doomed. Meanwhile, except in the territory affected by the formation of British Columbia as a Crown Colony in 1858, the Hudson's Bay Company continued to govern its domain. In Alberta settlement increased slightly, chiefly because gold had been found in the North Saskatchewan River near Fort Edmonton. For half a century enough gold was reclaimed to keep about 50 itinerant miners on the razor-edge of hope but no one ever found a fortune. And then in 1869, like a thunderbolt from a clear sky, came the news that the just-formed Dominion of Canada had purchased Rupert's Land from the Hudson's Bay Company. The actual transfer was not completed until the next year.

Years of transition

The take-over of Rupert's Land was marred by the Red River revolt of 1869-70, but in 1870 Manitoba became a province. A year later the Dominion was able to shepherd British Columbia into its fold. The rest of western Canada was supposed to be ruled by the Lieutenant-Governor of Manitoba, assisted at first by a council of three and later by a council of not more than fifteen and not less than seven members. Inevitably, for a time, the men of the Hudson's Bay Company still traded for furs and maintained what law there was.

It was during this era of transition from 1870 onward that several score of Métis hunters and fishermen left Manitoba for Alberta. Most of them settled at St. Albert, Lac Ste. Anne, Lac La Biche, Buffalo Lake and a few other spots where fishing was good, and they were within striking distances of the millions of bison which still roamed the prairies. Some of these people, like the personnel of the forts, planted small patches of oats

Reverend George MacDougall

Pioneer log cabin and buildings are seen in this photograph of early Alberta life.

A contingent of North-West Mounted Police in parade dress cross the prairies to Shaganappi Point, Calgary, in 1901.

G.F.

and vegetables. On the whole, though, the future province was still hunter's land and Indian land.

Then smallpox struck again. Lieutenant W. F. Butler reported that up to the time he left Edmonton near Christmas, 1870, of 900 Indians and Métis congregated around the Roman Catholic mission at St. Albert, 600 had caught the disease and 311 had died. He estimated that of the Indians scattered through the countryside 600 to 800 Crees had perished, that the proportion of dead to living was about the same among the Blackfoot, and that the small tribe of the Sarcees was reduced from 50 lodges to 12, that is, from perhaps 300 persons to 70.

During this period, up from Fort Benton on the Missouri River into southern Alberta swarmed the American free traders. Their most notable post was at Fort Whoop-Up, about seven miles south of today's Lethbridge. These men, with regard for nothing but profit, peddled whisky and repeating rifles in exchange for pelts and bison hides. The proud Blackfoot, among whom no mission or trader's post had survived for long, succumbed to whisky. Thus Colonel Robertson-Ross, sent out by the Dominion government to observe conditions, reported in 1872 that "last year eighty-eight of the Blackfoot Indians were murdered in drunken brawls amongst themselves".

The free traders' lawlessness brought its own destruction. In 1873, the formation of the North-West Mounted Police – a name changed to the Royal Canadian Mounted Police in 1920 – was authorized. In the autumn of 1874 a detachment of this force reached Edmonton, while the main body established itself in the south at Fort Macleod. From this post the "Force" stamped out the illicit whisky traffic. Other posts in Alberta were built at Calgary and at Fort Saskatchewan. From this time forward, the North-West Mounted Police, although at first composed of fewer than 300 men, upheld justice in what was to become Saskatchewan and Alberta.

The coming of the North-West Mounted Police did not end the misfortunes of the Indians. The bison were fading from the prairies, and a

few whites were already settling around the police posts at Fort Macleod and Fort Calgary. Meanwhile, from Qu'Appelle in Saskatchewan up through the Touchwood Hills to the North Saskatchewan River, and along it as far as Edmonton, stretched a belt of scattered settlements. The shape of the future was slowly emerging, and the strength and spirit of the Indians had been sapped by the white man's disease. In treaties made in 1876 and 1877 the Crees, Stonies and the Blackfoot Confederacy, including the Sarcees, signed away their heritage of parkland, plains and foothills. In exchange, they were to receive treaty money, live on reserves and try somehow to farm instead of hunt.

By an almost terrifying coincidence the bison then disappeared from the Canadian prairies. In the years around 1879 hunger stalked the teepees. The police and government authorities could do little. Some 600 of the once proud Blackfoot died of starvation.

Other treaties extinguished the Indian title over the whole of the Northwest. With the bison gone and the Indians being herded onto reserves, Alberta was now open for settlement. At first growth was slow. In the south a few sturdy souls tried their luck at ranching. In the northern forest only the occasional sod-roofed shanty squatted. Elsewhere, North-West Mounted Police posts at Fort Macleod and Fort Saskatchewan, log dwellings clustered around Fort Calgary and the much older Edmonton settlement were practically the only pockets of white men. In 1881 Calgary housed only 75 people, and Edmonton, along with Fort Saskatchewan, St. Albert, Lac Ste. Anne and Lac La Biche, boasted in all 766 white and Métis adults. In 1881, in the whole of what is now Alberta, according to a figure based on the Dominion census of that year, there were only 18,072 Métis and whites. Meantime the whole country was astir in expectation of the long-awaited transcontinental railroad and the settlers it might bring.

The transcontinental

To induce British Columbia to join the Dominion of Canada in 1871, John A. Macdonald had promised a railroad. Soon, throughout the Canadian

In 1881 Fort Calgary nestled between the Bow and Elbow Rivers, a cluster of buildings surrounded by a log palisade.

View of Fort Edmonton in 1845 showing the southwest stockade from inside the fort. This fort was located below the present parliament buildings.

Steel rails opened the west. Pictured above is a section of the Grand Trunk Pacific Railroad being built near Wainwright in 1909.

G.F.

Buffalo bones were shipped east from the prairies to be made into fertilizer.

West, a horde of surveyors and scientists was unleashed. In Alberta these men reported on routes for railroads, fertility of soils and prospects for coal and minerals. They even began to track down the courses of long-vanished glaciers. As a result of these studies Alberta's potentialities for settlement came into clearer focus, particularly in eastern Canada and the mid-western United States.

About the same time, particularly from 1871 onward, Dominion land surveyors fanned out over the countryside. During the next few years thousands of square miles of prairie and parkland were divided into neat square parcels of 160 acres each. And then in 1881, after a long period of travail, the sweating track-layers of the Canadian Pacific Railway Company entered the prairies in Manitoba. By August 10th, 1883 they reached Calgary. By the end of the year newly laid rails gleamed at what is now Lake Louise Station. On the 7th of November, 1885 the last spike was driven home. Canada had its first transcontinental railway.

The railroad brought settlers to Alberta. In the south, Calgary – incorporated in 1884 as a bustling frontier town – was the hub of a burgeoning ranching industry. In Edmonton, by 1883, 35 to 40 houses straggled along a somewhat ramshackle main street, and a weekly stage-coach carried mail and passengers to and from Calgary. Between Edmonton and Calgary the only nucleus of whites was at Red Deer River Crossing. In the extreme south a coal seam had brought Lethbridge into being. By 1886, it boasted a thousand inhabitants.

In the midst of this slow development the 1885 Riel rebellion blazed. Alberta trembled with fear and excitement. But except for one or two sporadic incidents, Alberta's Métis and Indians took no part in the uprising. The revolt was crushed, chiefly by troops from eastern Canada. Yet the new railroad and the offer of free land brought only a trickle of settlers into Alberta. Most of her soils still awaited the plough.

The great influx

Alberta's hour of destiny did not strike until a group of factors finally converged. The first of these factors was the discovery in Ontario around

G.F.

The settlers seen in this photograph arrived in Bassano by special train, March 1914, and settled at Gem.

G.F.

Settlers arriving by horse-drawn wagons. This cavalcade was photographed near Wainwright about 1911.

1842 of a hard spring wheat which ripened ten to twelve days earlier than any other variety of that time. This wheat, called Red Fife, was the obvious answer to the danger of early autumn frosts in the Canadian West. Red Fife wheat was taken to Minnesota by emigrants from Ontario. From Minnesota by a happy accident it reached Manitoba in 1868, and thence spread over the Canadian prairies. Then, in 1904 a father-and-son team of cereal scientists, William and Charles Saunders, developed Marquis wheat which ripened eight days earlier than Red Fife.

Hard wheat, though excellent for bread, needs the roller-milling technique to process it into flour. In 1878 this technique was invented. In addition, before 1896, new types of ploughs and binders suitable for large-scale farming had been developed along with a one-crop, mass-production method.

Except for Marquis wheat, these factors were waiting in the wings for the Alberta of 1896. Yet profitable wheat production requires a market. Toward the close of the 19th century a long economic depression had begun to lift, much of Europe and the United States had been industrialized and urbanized, and factory workers and city-dwellers were clamouring for bread. And then in 1896, when a gaping-mouthed market for wheat was assured, Canada found a dynamic Minister of the Interior in Sir Clifford Sifton. His cry was for settlers and yet more settlers.

And settlers came. They moved in from eastern Canada and the United States by train and paddle-wheeler, by ox-cart and covered wagon. They crossed the ocean from the British Isles to Halifax and

Passengers and freight ready to float down the North Saskatchewan by raft from Edmonton to Lloydminster. A ferry and Walter's mill are seen in this 1903 photograph.

In 1888 this stagecoach carried passengers, mail and freight over this muddy trail between Edmonton and Calgary.

Quebec City, there to be crowded onto the wooden-slatted seats of colonists' cars for the long journey west. Packed in the steerage of ship after ship, immigrants poured in from a Europe that Sifton saturated with agents and with advertisements of free land for the asking. There were Germans and Scandinavians. There were Poles, Russians and Ukrainians, often called "Sifton's sheepskins", from the coats they wore. Canadians, Americans, Europeans, Irish, Scots and English flooded into the Canadian West. And they kept coming.

As one result of the influx Alberta became a province in 1905 with Edmonton as its capital city. As another effect its population doubled and redoubled. From 1901 to 1906 the population rose from 73,022 to 185,412. By 1911 the total had reached 374,663. Furthermore, by 1921, about twenty-nine million acres of land, or 45,000 square miles, had been claimed by some 83,000 farmers who had cultivated nearly 18,700 square miles. Every foot was cleared by axe and grubhoe, and nearly every yard was broken with oxen or horses. From this land in 1921 the farmers produced 131 million bushels of wheat, oats, and barley and marketed livestock valued at about 20 million dollars. In the southern part of the province, many miles of irrigation canals had been built and 217,000 acres were "under the ditch". All of this had been accomplished in 30 years. All this was the work of a single generation.

While farms were being carved out of the bush, Alberta's principal cities were developing. In 1921 the four main service and supply centres for the farming industry were Edmonton, Calgary, Lethbridge and Medicine Hat. The capital city had over 58,000 inhabitants, Calgary had some 5,000 more and Lethbridge and Medicine Hat combined, totalled 20,000. Meanwhile villages and towns had mushroomed everywhere.

The breaking of the soil and the growth of villages, towns and cities were only part of this first burst of development. A growing demand for houses spawned scores of small sawmills which ate their way into the foothills and the northern forests. To heat homes in the cities and towns, and to counteract the bitter winds that swept across the land, everyone needed coal. The first coal mine had been started near Lethbridge in 1869 by Nicholas Sheran. By 1921 coal was mined all over southwestern Alberta. As far back as 1885, natural gas had been discovered near Medicine Hat, and by 1890 the people of that city, which Rudyard Kipling described as having "all hell for a basement", were heating their homes

G.F.

Farming was the principal industry on the prairies in the early 1900's. This threshing scene was a familiar sight throughout Alberta and Saskatchewan.

offices, schools and churches with it. Just before World War I, natural gas was discovered at Bow Island and piped to Lethbridge and Calgary. Another of Alberta's resources had begun to play its part.

Using the abundance of natural gas in the south, and of coal all over the western part of the province, steam power plants began to supply the larger cities and towns with electricity. In Calgary, situated on the Bow River, coal-fired electricity found a competitor in hydro power when Calgary Power's Horseshoe Canyon plant came into operation in 1911. In 1914, to add yet another source of energy to the growing list, the Turner Valley oil field was discovered.

All these relatively new resource industries – agriculture, forestry, coal, natural gas and oil production, and water power development – required large initial amounts of capital. So did the 5,000 miles of railway lines that soon formed a network criss-crossing the country south of the North Saskatchewan River and even flinging out 400-mile arms to the traditional gateways to the Northwest Territories, Peace River Crossing and Fort McMurray. As well as an influx of people, Alberta enjoyed an imposing flow of capital from eastern Canada, the United States, Great Britain and France. The province prospered and, when war came in 1914, it was able to make a significant contribution.

The depression and World War II

After the war, prosperity continued for a while. By 1930 registration at the province's 22-year-old university at Edmonton approached the three thousand mark. Schools, hospitals, and churches had been established. More timber was being cut, more coal produced and more oil discovered. The extensive Viking gas field was developed, and its fuel was piped west to Edmonton in 1923. The area occupied by farms increased by one-third. Much more land was cultivated, but now tractors and other modern machinery were taking the drudgery out of working the soil. During the decade ending in 1929 the province's population jumped 24 per cent.

Then almost overnight, Alberta and the rest of the continent were plunged into economic depression. The "Hungry Thirties" brought drought and dust to the farms, and bread lines and soup kitchens to the cities. On the prairies, the soil drifted. In the foothills, hydro plants and coal mines stood idle. In the parklands, the wheat withered. Throughout the great boreal forests, fires burned unchecked. Nothing flourished but

315

Drilling rig in the lesser Slave Lake area in northern Alberta in the 1920's.

G.F.

"gophers" and tumbleweed. Over half of Alberta's production came from agriculture. When rains failed and markets fell, farming became a nightmare of fruitless effort.

Eventually, as out of a lingering fever, the economy of the world began to recover, and Alberta, sitting on the edge of its sick-bed, began to look ahead. Like the rest of the world, it also looked back to see what had put it there.

Of the many voices offering explanations, several were heeded as never before. Among these was the voice of the conservationist. Meanwhile, in a worried mood, Alberta staggered along the road to recovery until the outbreak of World War II in 1939. The exigencies of war created jobs and along with them scarcities of lumber, coal, water power, natural gas and oil. Even the roaring flames of Turner Valley's "Hell's Half Acre", burning waste gases, had to be curbed, for they consumed precious petroleum products. As a consequence of war, conservation began to become important.

War brought a feeling of prosperity, but in fact the economy of Alberta remained static. During the period from 1941 to 1946 its population increased only marginally, and in 1946 agriculture was still the dominant industry, accounting for over 50 per cent of all production. Small manufacturing ventures had started, and some diversification was evident, but the economy of the province was still relatively simple in structure. No one seemed interested in Alberta's 25,000 million tons of mineable coal or its 171,000 square miles of forests. In spite of their several million horsepower of potential hydro power, its great rivers slipped, unexploited, to Hudson Bay and the Arctic Sea. Sealed within the Athabasca oil sands were an estimated 625 billion barrels of oil, of which at least 300 billion barrels were recoverable. But,although before and during World War II experiments and discoveries toward unsealing the oil were made, after the war these projects faltered. Meanwhile, for decades throughout the province venturesome drillers had probed the underlying rocks, searching for another Turner Valley, but gas and oil continued to elude them. It appeared that Alberta would have to make do with an economy based on agriculture.

Oil, natural gas and prosperity

Then, just to the south of Edmonton, in February 1947 a black smoke ring belched from the flare line of Imperial Leduc Number One. It floated off into the wintry sky, an amazing portent of the province's future. Alberta's "Dynamic Decade" had begun.

During the ensuing year, near Leduc, 131 more oil wells came into production. Other fields followed in rapid succession, such as Woodbend, Redwater, far larger than Leduc, with 888 wells and the Pembina field, bigger than the sum of all previous discoveries. Although about three-quarters of Alberta's oil fields were within a hundred miles of Edmonton, it turned out that almost any part of Alberta was likely to have oil under it.

Meanwhile natural gas, once regarded as a by-product of oil production that had limited domestic use, began to be recognized as an exportable product, and to be sought for its own sake. It, too, was found, and in tremendous quantities. Oil and gas wells by the thousands soon tapped scores of fields. Gathering lines and transmission lines began to stretch across the province to feed raw material to refineries and petrochemical plants. Then, since Alberta had now become the fountain-head of Canada's reserves of energy, gas and oil lines up to three feet in diameter

Discovery well, Imperial Oil Leduc No. 1.

I.O.

317

began carrying Alberta's surplus fuel east to Ontario and the midwestern United States, west to British Columbia and south to California. During the "Dynamic Decade" of 1946-56, the province's population increased by 40 per cent from 803,000 to 1,123,000. Only once before had there been such a compounding of population – between 1901 and 1906 when knowledge and demand had made possible the utilization of Alberta's soil.

The next decade from 1956 to 1966 brought similar progress, with the population approaching the 1,500,000 mark. In 20 years the population had almost doubled. As oil and gas wells roared into production, attracting a variety of allied industries, the other resources of the province, coal excepted, were called into play. With increased demand for timber, the forests were turning out lumber as never before, and were supporting a large pulp industry. Power plants, both hydro and steam, regularly doubled their output every seven years. On farms, more production was being achieved with less manpower. Yet agriculture, though turning out more food than ever, now accounted for less than one-fifth of the province's production, and manufacturing, construction and mining produced well over one-fifth each. The fluctuation from prosperity to despair inherent in an economy based almost solely on agriculture had given way to a prosperous mixed economy. Thanks to the finds of oil and gas, a year of drought or frost, or one of low wheat prices, could no longer cripple Alberta.

Most of the province's increase in population was concentrated in the urban centres. Edmonton grew until by the mid-sixties it housed more than 375,000 people. Calgary had over 310,000. Alberta's six other cities shared in the prosperity. The universities in Edmonton and Calgary now enrolled more than 14,000 full-time students. Modern hospitals and other institutions served the province, and consolidated schools brought urban standards of education to rural areas. School buses in their daily trips used most of Alberta's 93,000 miles of roads, of which 50,000 were gravelled, and over 4,000 hard-surfaced. Alberta, which once had been one of the "have-not" provinces, now took its place as fourth largest both in population and production. Endowed with more than 80 per cent of all Canada's fossil fuel energy, it could confidently face the future.

Effects, past, present and future

In retrospect – but also with a thought for the future – the impact of the white man on Alberta can be viewed both from the debit and the credit side.

No credit can be taken for the treatment of the Indians, or for the virtual elimination of a number of species of birds and animals. Agriculture, ranching, lumbering, and the oil and natural gas industry inevitably altered large tracts of land and drove out or depleted its wildlife. Partial amends, however, have been made through government-established parks and wildlife preserves.

Against our rivers and sources of water, so far we have committed little crime. Through ignorance, however, we have abused our soil, both by breaking thousands of acres that should have been left in grass, and by irrigating land without providing proper drainage.

The forests, perhaps, have fared worse than our other natural resources. The great forest fires of the past, although most were started by natural causes, wrought havoc. In the period from 1941 to 1957 alone, fires in northern Alberta destroyed more than 15 billion board feet of lumber stock, or twelve times as much as was cut annually ten years later. They also burnt 27 million cords of pulp wood. Fortunately, this danger is being recognized.

In the development of natural gas and oil resources we have not been overly wasteful. When the Turner Valley field was the only significant oil and gas field in Alberta, knowledge of the petroleum business was elementary compared to what it is today. Now, well spacing, proration and gas conservation are given high priority. For the most part, the damage we have done to our resources has come from lack of knowledge and from indifference.

On the credit side, what can we show? We can point to over a million and a half people, most of them living in comfort, health and relative affluence, where formerly some ten thousand Indians eked out a strenuous and often hungry life. The primitive prairies that once supported millions of bison, though utterly transformed, are no less beautiful today as field flows into field and farm merges into farm over the vast area of rolling countryside. Having been blessed with rich resources, we have become a wealthy province and we are spending a great deal of this wealth on education and on scientific studies. One of the first things we ought to emphasize is conservation.

The incidence of conservation first reached modern Alberta in the practice of irrigation. This led to the conception of multiple-use watershed development, and to the Prairie Farm Rehabilitation Act, dealing mainly with soil conservation and restoration. About the same time, the Eastern Rockies Conservation Board was set up to remedy previous damage and to prevent further deterioration of the upper watersheds of our rivers. Soon great emphasis was being placed on wildlife conservation and on saving the forests.

Much has been done and yet the battle is by no means over, for the white man's imperious demands on his natural environment are bound to continue. If to support his children he needs pulp mills, then the beauty of the forest and some of the wildlife will be sacrificed. If he needs more power, reservoirs with fluctuating levels will be built at the possible sacrifice of spawning beds. Yet the mistakes of the past are there to remember, and perhaps man will finally come to recognize more fully the limits beyond which he may not go in defiance of sound conservation practices. Meanwhile, to ensure that nature itself shall survive, parks and wildlife preserves must continue as in the past to be created and protected.

ILLUSTRATION CREDITS

PHOTOGRAPHERS

Photographer or source of photograph is indicated below each picture according to the following initials:

A.B.	Alan Bryan, *Edmonton*
A.G.	Alberta Government, *Edmonton*
A.J.	Alexander Johnston, *Lethbridge*
A.K.	Albert Karvonen, *Edmonton*
B.F.	Benson Fogle, *College, Alaska*
C.D.B.	C. D. Bird, *Calgary*
C.D.F.	Canada Dept. of Forestry, *Calgary*
C.G.	Christopher Gibson, *Lethbridge*
C.H.	Cy Hampson, *Edmonton*
C.T.	California Institute of Technology and Carnegie Institute (copyright 1959)
D.A.B.	David A. Boag, *Edmonton*
D.N.	D. Nieman, *Medicine Hat*
D.N.D.	Department of National Defence, *Ottawa*
E.B.	Eugene Bozniak, *Edmonton*
E.B.C.	Ernest Brown Collection, *Edmonton*
E.S.C.	Edward S. Curtis
G.F.	Glenbow Foundation, *Calgary*
G.H.	George Hunter, *Toronto*
G.N.H.	G. N. Haugen, *Edmonton*
H.B.C.	Hudson's Bay Co., *London, England*
H.R.	Harry Rowed, *Jasper*
I.O.	Imperial Oil Ltd., *Edmonton*
I.R.H.	Ian A. R. Halladay, *Calgary*
J.M.	J. MacKenzie, *Calgary*
J.M.G.	J. M. Grant, *Calgary*
M.B.	Michael Burn, *Calgary*
McD.	McDermid Studios, *Edmonton*
M.H.	Mary Hampson, *Edmonton*
M.W.P.O.	Mt. Wilson and Palomar Observatories, *California*
N.R.C.	National Research Council, *Ottawa*
N.W.P.	North Western Pulp and Power Ltd., *Hinton*
N.Z.	Norman Zierhut, *Edmonton*
P.S.	Peter Summers, *Edmonton*
R.C.T.	R. C. Thomas, *Victoria*
R.D.B.	R. D. Bird, *Winnipeg*
R.G.	Robert Green, *St. Albert*
R.H.-R.	R. Hartland-Rowe, *Calgary*
R.J.P.	R. J. Paterson, *Edmonton*
R.M.	Ron Mackay, *Edmonton*
R.Mc.	Rae McIntyre, *Edmonton*
R.N.S.	R. N. Smith, *Seebe*
S.D.M.	S. D. MacDonald, *Ottawa*
S.P.S.	Shipley Photo Service Limited, *for Calgary Aquarium*
T.E.B.	Thomas E. Berg, *St. Albert*
W.A.L.	W. A. Lea, *Edmonton*
W.D.	Wayne Dwernychuk, *Smoky Lake*
W.G.	W. J. L. Gibbons, *Vancouver*
W.J.H.	W. J. Hackett, *Calgary*

ARTISTS, ILLUSTRATORS AND CARTOGRAPHERS

Frank M. Ludtke, *Edmonton, Art Co-ordinator*
Jan Vandenberg, *Edmonton, Illustrator*
Man Mohan, *Edmonton, Chief Cartographer*
Allison Cherniawski, *Edmonton, Cartographer*
F. L. Copeland, *Edmonton, Cartographer*
James W. Godwin, *Edmonton, Cartographer*
Helen Luteyn, *Glenevis, Illustrator*
E. Harrison, *Vancouver, Book Design*

SPECIAL CREDITS

William John Cable, *Edmonton for researching and compiling material appearing in Chapter I.*
Dr. D. R. Crosby, *Edmonton, for technical advice and assistance.*
Governor and Committee of the Hudson's Bay Company, *for permission to publish map on page 298.*

BIOGRAPHICAL SKETCHES

Charles D. Bird, M.Sc., Ph.D., is Administrative Officer of the Department of Biology at the University of Calgary and Curator of its Lower Plant Herbarium to which, in 1962, he donated his own personal herbarium. In addition to being on the Advisory Committee of the Systematics and Phytogeography Section of the Canadian Botanical Association, he is a member of 14 technical and professional societies and is the author of 27 publications. Service with the Northern Insect Survey, the Forest Entomology Branch of the Northern Affairs and National Resources Department of Canada, and the Canadian Wildlife Service has supplemented his special floristic and ecological investigations of the vegetation of the three prairie provinces.

Ralph D. Bird, M.Sc., Ph.D., born in Arrow River, Manitoba, and father of Charles D. Bird, has had a distinguished career as Research Officer and Head of Entomology Section for the Department of Agriculture of Canada, Research Station, Winnipeg. Author of a number of publications, his special field is the ecology of the aspen parkland of the prairie provinces.

David A. Boag, M.Sc., Ph.D., is Assistant Professor of Zoology at the University of Alberta. A member of a number of professional societies, including the Canadian Society of Wildlife and Fishery Biologists and the American Ornithologists' Union, he is a Past President of the Edmonton Bird Club, the Natural History Club and the Alberta Chapter of the Canadian Society of Zoologists. His special interest is bird ecology, a field in which he has published a number of articles.

Alan Lyle Bryan, M.A., Ph.D., is Associate Professor in the Department of Anthropology of the University of Alberta. His publications include a work on Palaeo-American History and many papers on field work in Western North America, Brazil and England. A member of the Society for American Archaeology, and of the American Anthropological Association, he is a Past President of the Edmonton Centre of the Archaeological Society of Alberta.

William John Cable, born in Lethbridge, Alberta. He is Director of the Queen Elizabeth Planetarium in Edmonton. Long active in astronomical observations, he is a Past President of the Royal Astronomical Society of Canada, Edmonton Centre.

William George Evans, M.Sc., Ph.D., born in Swansea, Wales, is Associate Professor of Entomology at the University of Alberta. A Past President of the Entomological Society of Alberta and a member of the Ecological Society of America, the Entomological Society of Canada and the Entomological Society of America, he has specialized in insect ecology. His publications include papers on insects associated with forest fires in Alberta.

William A. Fuller, M.Sc., Ph.D., is Associate Professor of Zoology at the University of Alberta. His previous experience includes 12 years in the Canadian Wildlife Service in the Northwest Territories and the Yukon. The author of a number of technical articles and a member of numerous professional societies, he is also a member of the boards of several national and international conservation societies and a Past President of the Natural History Club. His particular interests are the winter ecology of Alberta's northern forests and the conservation of wild nature.

Robert Green, B.Sc., Ph.D., a native of Northumberland, England, is Chief of the Earth Sciences Branch of the Research Council of Alberta. During his ten years' service with that organization, he has published a number of articles on the geology of Alberta.

Ian A. R. Halladay, B.Sc., born at Hamilton in Ontario, is an exploration geologist with Pan American Petroleum Corporation in Calgary. Vice President of the Calgary Bird Club in 1966 and a member of American and Alberta societies of Petroleum Geologists as well as of the Saskatchewan Natural History Society and the Calgary Zoological Society, he has published an outstanding work on the Cypress Hills Plateau.

Cyril G. Hampson, B.A., Ph.D., a native of Lacombe, Alberta, is Professor of Biological Sciences in the Faculty of Education of the University of Alberta. A member of several professional societies, a co-founder of the Alberta Wildlife Foundation and the author of numerous articles, particularly on the birds of Alberta, he is internationally known for his striking photographic studies of wildlife.

Mary G. Hampson, born in Scotland, an expert in photography and a keen naturalist, has been of constant assistance to her husband, Dr. Hampson, in all phases of his interest in photography and wildlife.

William George Hardy, C.M., M.A., Ph.D., F.I.A.L., L.L.D., is Professor Emeritus and former head of the Department of Classics, University of Alberta Among the positions he has held are the presidency of the *Ligue Internationale de Hockey sur Glace,* the Edmonton Little Theatre, and the Canadian Authors' Association. Besides academic articles, his publications include six novels, five histories, a considerable number of short stories, and addresses and lectures on radio and television. Elected a Life Fellow of the International Society of Arts and Letters in 1960, in 1962 he received the University of Alberta National Award in Letters. His most recent book is entitled *The Origins and Ordeals of Western Civilization.*

Richard C. B. Hartland-Rowe, B.Sc., Ph.D., born in Bristol, England, is Associate Professor of Zoology in the Department of Biology of the University of Calgary. He has been President of the Entomological Society of Alberta and is a member of a number of professional societies, including a fellowship in the Royal Entomological Society of London. Before coming to Alberta, he taught for seven years at Makerere College in the University of East Africa. His special interest is freshwater ecology, a field in which he has published a number of articles.

Brian Hitchon, B.Sc., Ph.D., is Associate Research Officer of the Research Council of Alberta. A Past President of the Archaeological Society of Alberta and of the Natural History Club and a Past Vice President of the Edmonton Geological Society, he is a member of a number of professional societies, including a fellowship in the Geological Society of London. Widely travelled in Mexico, Europe, the Middle and Far East and Central and East Africa, and with two years' professional work in Zambia, he is the author of over twenty technical papers. His special field is geochemistry.

Margaret Coleman Johnson has travelled widely in Europe and North America. A Past President of the Edmonton Branch, Canadian Authors' Association, she is the author of numerous articles and short stories and of one book. As a teacher of Creative Writing for nine and a half years and as a judge of Literary Awards Contests, she has had a long experience in literary criticism. In 1954-55 she was Executive Secretary of the Alberta Golden Jubilee Anthology and is Articles Editor of the Alberta Centennial Anthology.

Alexander Johnston, B.S.A., M.S., is a Research Officer in re-grassing and range management for the Canada Department of Agriculture. Born at Webb in Saskatchewan he has spent twenty-five years in Alberta and is now stationed at Lethbridge where he is Provincial Executive Member and Chairman of the Leth-bridge Branch of the Historical Society of Alberta. He was one of the founding committee of the Lethbridge Branch of the Archaeological Society of Alberta. A member of numerous pro-fessional societies, he has published almost 40 papers. In 1962 he spent a year with the Food and Agricultural Organization of the United Nations as a range management adviser to the Government of West Pakistan.

Lorene L. Kennedy, M.Sc., Ph.D., a native Edmontonian, is Pro-fessor of Botany at the University of Alberta. A member of sev-eral professional societies, including the Canadian Botanical Society and the Phycological Society of America, she is well known for her specialized field studies of seasonal succession of algae in lakes of the Edmonton region and in some of the running water habitats of the Province of Alberta.

George Henri La Roi, M.A., Ph.D., born in Chicago, is Assistant Professor of Botany at the University of Alberta. His field of specialization is boreal and mountain forest ecology. A member of the Ecological Society of America and the Canadian Botanical Association, he is also a Past President of the Natural History Club.

Arleigh Howard Laycock, M.Sc., Ph.D., is Professor of Geography at the University of Alberta. He is a Director of the Canadian Association of Geography, served for three years as Hydrologist of the Eastern Rockies Forest Conservation Board and for one summer on the Prairie Provinces Water Board, is in charge of the field excursions of the Alberta Geographical Society, and is a member of a number of professional societies. He is the author of many technical papers, including a number relating to Alberta.

Franklin C. Loehde, B.Sc., B.Ed., is a high school teacher in his native Edmonton. A Past President and long-term Council Mem-ber of the Royal Astronomical Society of Canada, Edmonton Centre, he has specialized for sixteen years in astronomy and for two years was a professional astronomer at the Dominion Astrophysical Observatory in Victoria, British Columbia.

Richmond W. Longley, B.Sc., M.A., a native of Nova Scotia, is Associate Professor in the Department of Geography at the Uni-versity of Alberta and for a year was also Acting Head of that Department. Before coming to the University of Alberta he spent nineteen years in forecasting and in research with the Meteorolog-ical Services of Canada. A member of several professional soci-eties, and the author of many articles and a textbook on meteorology, his research has been in various aspects of dynamic climatology, as, for example, the causes of hail.

Ian C. MacDonald, B.Ed., M.Ed., formerly editorial writer with the *Edmonton Journal* and now Publisher of the *Medicine Hat News*, has also written on the educational impact of the growth of learn-ing. His Master's thesis dealt with the meaning of the growth of scientific information for education for the advancement of scientific knowledge. A Past President of the Edmonton Zoologi-cal Society, he was for six years a member of the Zoo Advisory Board of the City of Edmonton.

James G. MacGregor, B.A., B.Sc., a native of Scotland, is Chair-man of the Power Commission of the Government of Alberta, and in 1957 was Chairman of the Royal Commission on the Devel-opment of Northern Alberta. A Past President of the Historical Society of Alberta, an honorary member of the Archaeological Society of Alberta and a member of the Canadian Authors' Asso-ciation, he is the author of six books on the history of Alberta.

He has been honoured with an award by the Canadian History Association for outstanding achievement in regional history.

Miles Timothy Myres, M.A., Ph.D., born in London, England, is Assistant Professor of Zoology at the University of Calgary. He was educated at Cambridge University and the University of British Columbia. During the last eight years he has been en-gaged in the study of bird migration by means of radar. Dr. Myres is Editor of the Calgary Bird Club *Bulletin* and the *Alberta Bird Report,* and Assistant Editor of the Canadian Wildlife and Fisheries *Newsletter.* He was President of the Calgary Bird Club in 1965-67, and is a Director of the Alberta Field Studies Council and of the Saskatchewan Natural History Society. One of his major interests is the promotion of co-operation between natu-ralists and field biologists.

Edo Nyland, B.S.F., a native of Amsterdam, Holland, is Divisional Forester in the Alberta Forest Service. His specialized field is forest management and he is a member of the Canadian Institute of Forestry. His publications include an article on forestry in Indonesia.

Martin J. Paetz, B.Sc., M.Sc., is Chief Fishery Biologist of the Fish and Wildlife Division of the Department of Lands and Forests of the Government of Alberta. His specialized field is freshwater fishery biology and he is a Director of the Canadian Society of Wildlife and Fishery Biologists. His published work includes articles on the watersheds and sport fisheries of Alberta.

Rodney G. Paterson, B.A., born in Surrey, England, is Fishery Biologist in the Fish and Wildlife Division of the Department of Lands and Forests of the Government of Alberta, and has had eight years' experience working as a biologist in various parts of the province. He is a member of the Canadian Society of Wild-life and Fishery Biologists, the Edmonton Bird Club and the American Fisheries Society. His field of specialization is Lim-nology and Fisheries Management.

J. Dewey Soper, LL.D., recognized as the senior authority on mammals in Canada, is also an authority on birds. In June of 1929 during an eight-year federal appointment as naturalist to Arctic expeditions, he discovered the breeding grounds of the blue goose along the west coast of Baffin Island and was hon-oured by the Canadian Government establishing the Dewey Soper Bird Sanctuary in this area. During his long career he has discovered several races of mammals and birds new to science, most of which have been named after him. A member of a num-ber of professional societies and Honorary Research Zoologist at the University of Alberta, Dr. Soper has published thirty-one articles and brochures on the mammals and birds of Alberta. His best known work is his definitive book, "The Mammals of Alberta". In addition, he has published eighty-four popular and scientific works on mammals and birds in various parts of Can-ada, together with track surveys and articles on general explora-tions in Canada's eastern Arctic regions.

Charles R. Stelck, M.Sc., Ph.D., F.R.S.C., is Professor of Geology at the University of Alberta. For the last quarter of a century his field of research has been the Stratigraphy and Palaeontology of Western Canada. Much of his work has been done in Alberta where he has also done research in Oil Geology. Dr. Stelck is a Fellow of the Royal Society of Canada and has published twenty articles on the Micropalaeontology, Palaeontology and Stratig-raphy of Alberta.

Robert Webb, B.Sc., born in Saskatchewan, is District Wildlife Biologist at Calgary in the Fish and Wildlife Division of the De-partment of Lands and Forests of the Government of Alberta. He has had twelve years' experience as biologist in various parts of the province. Apart from membership in societies such as the Wildlife Society, the American Society of Mammalogists and the Canadian Society of Wildlife and Fishery Biologists, he is a member of the Calgary Zoological Society. His published works include a number of articles on the wildlife of Alberta.

FURTHER READING

NIGHT SKIES OVER ALBERTA

Baker, R. H. 1961. *An introduction to astronomy*: 6th ed., Van Nostrand, New York.

Barbeau, M. 1960. *Indian days on the western prairies*: National Museum of Canada, Bulletin 163.

Barnett, L. K. 1955. *The starry universe*: Part 13 of *The World We Live In*, by Barnett and the editorial staff of Life. Time Incorporated, New York.

Bernhard, H. J. 1956. *New handbook of the heavens*: McGraw-Hill, New York.

Clarke, A. C. 1964. *Man and space*: by Clarke and the editorial staff of Life. Time Incorporated, New York.

Currie, B. W. 1961. *The need for observations of the noctilucent clouds*: Journal Royal Astronomical Society of Canada, Vol. 55.

Ernst, B. 1961. *Atlas of the universe*: Thomas Nelson and Sons, Toronto. Edited by H. E. Butler, translated by D. R. Welsh.

Folinsbee, R. E. and Bayrock, L. A. 1961. *The Bruderheim meteorite – fall and recovery*: Journal Royal Astronomical Society of Canada, Vol. 55, No. 5, p. 218-228.

Gamow, G. 1961. *The creation of the universe*: Macmillan, Toronto.

Hoyle, F. 1957. *Frontiers of astronomy*: Grosset and Dunlap, New York.

Moore, P. 1961. *The picture history of astronomy*: Grosset and Dunlap, New York.

Murchie, G. 1961. *Music of the spheres*: Houghton Mifflin, Boston.

Northcott, R. J. (editor). 1966. *The observer's handbook*: Royal Astronomical Society of Canada, Toronto.

Norton, A. P. 1950. *A star atlas and reference handbook*: Gall and Inglis, London.

Taylor, H. W. 1962. *A study of the radioactivity of the Peace River meteorite*: Journal Royal Astronomical Society of Canada, Vol. 56.

THE RECORD OF THE ROCKS

Alberta Society of Petroleum Geologists. 1954. *Lexicon of geologic names in Alberta and adjacent portions of British Columbia and Northwest Territories*: Alberta Society of Petroleum Geologists, Calgary.

Baird, D. M. 1963. *Jasper National Park*: Geological Survey of Canada, Miscellaneous Report No. 6.

Baird, D. M. 1964. *Waterton Lakes National Park*: Geological Survey of Canada, Miscellaneous Report No. 9.

Belyea, H. R. 1960. *The story of the mountains in Banff National Park*: Geological Survey of Canada, Miscellaneous Report No. 1.

McCrossan, R. C. (editor). 1958. *Annotated bibliography of geology of the sedimentary basin of Alberta and of adjacent parts of British Columbia and Northwest Territories, 1845-1955*: Alberta Society of Petroleum Geologists, Calgary.

McCrossan, R. C., and Glaister, R. P. (editors). 1964. *Geological history of western Canada*: Alberta Society of Petroleum Geologists, Calgary.

Nelson, S. J. 1965. *Field methods in palaeontology*: Bulletin Canadian Petroleum Geology, Vol. 13, p. 1-138.

Sabina, A. P. 1964. *Rock and mineral collecting in Canada, Vol. 1, Yukon, Northwest Territories, British Columbia, Alberta, Saskatchewan, Manitoba*: Geological Survey of Canada, Miscellaneous Report No. 8.

Stockwell, C. H. (editor). 1957. *Geology and economic minerals of Canada*: Geological Survey of Canada, Economic Geology Series No. 1.

Swinton, W. E. 1961. *Instructions to young naturalists No. 4, Fossils*: Burns and MacEachern, Don Mills, Ontario.

White, R. J. (editor). 1960. *Oil fields of Alberta*: Alberta Society of Petroleum Geologists, Calgary.

The Alberta Society of Petroleum Geologists publishes a quarterly, the *Bulletin of Canadian Petroleum Geology,* and annually, a guidebook for their summer field conference. The Geological Survey of Canada and the Research Council of Alberta publish occasional reports of their geological research.

CLIMATE AND WEATHER PATTERNS

Carder, A. C., 1965. *Climate of the upper Peace River region*: Canada Department of Agriculture, Publ. 1224.

Kendrew, W. G., and Currie, B. W. 1955. *The climate of central Canada*: Queen's Printer, Ottawa.

Thomas, M. K. 1953. *Climatological atlas of Canada*: National Research Council, Publ. No. 3151.

Thomas, M. K. 1957. *The climate of Canada*: Encyclopedia Canadiana, Vol. 2, p. 407-412.

The Meteorological Branch of the Department of Transport publishes *Monthly Record of Meteorological Observations.* Also available are *Climatic Summaries,* volumes I, II, and III, giving temperature, humidity, sunshine and precipitation, winds and humidity, and frost data, respectively, for selected stations. Various other summary data have been published by the Meteorological Branch.

MOUNTAINS AND PLAINS

Alberta, Department of Lands and Forests. 1960. First and Second Alberta Resources Conferences, Edmonton, 1959 and 1960. (Transcripts, collected papers).

Alberta, Department of Lands and Forests, Forest Surveys Branch. 1961. *Alberta Forest Inventory.* Edmonton, 40 p.

Alberta, Department of Lands and Forests, and Department of Geography, University of Alberta, Edmonton. *Atlas of Alberta*: Atlas of Alberta Committee, (in preparation).

Bostock, H. S. 1948. *Physiography of the Canadian Cordillera with special reference to the area north of the 55th parallel*:

Geological Survey of Canada, Memoir 247.

Butzer, K. W. 1964. *Environment and archeology*: Aldine Publishing Company, Chicago, 524 p.

Donald, J. T. and Company, Ltd. 1958. *Alberta, Province of opportunity*: Calgary Power, Ltd., Calgary.

Ehrlich, W. A. and Odynsky, W. 1960. *Soils developed under forest in the Great Plains region*: Agricultural Institute Review, p. 29-32.

Gravenor, C. P., and Bayrock, L. A. 1961. *Glacial deposits of Alberta*: in *Soils in Canada*, edited by R. F. Legget: Royal Society of Canada, Special Publ. No. 3, p. 33-50.

Gravenor, C. P., Green, R., and Godfrey, J. D. 1960. *Air photographs of Alberta*: Research Council of Alberta, Bulletin 5, Edmonton.

Laycock, A. H. 1961. *Precipitation and streamflow in the mountain and foothill region of the Saskatchewan River Basin*: Prairie Provinces Water Board, Report No. 6, Edmonton.

Laycock, A. H. 1964. *Water deficiency patterns in the Prairie Provinces*: Prairie Provinces Water Board, Report No. 8, Regina.

McCrossan, R. G., and Glaister, R. P. (editors). 1964. *Geological history of western Canada*: Alberta Society of Petroleum Geologists, Calgary.

Moss, E. H. 1955. *The vegetation of Alberta*: Botanical Review, Vol. 21, p. 493-567.

North, F. K., and Henderson, G. G. L. 1954. *Summary of the geology of the southern Rocky Mountains of Canada*: Alberta Society of Petroleum Geologists, Guidebook 4th Annual Field Conference, p. 15-81.

Stockwell, C. H. (editor). 1957. *Geology and economic minerals of Canada*: Geological Survey of Canada, Economic Geology Series No. 1.

Toogood, J. A., and Newton, J. D. 1955. *Water erosion in Alberta*: Faculty of Agriculture, University of Alberta, Edmonton, Bulletin No. 56.

Williams, M. Y. 1929. *The physiography of the southwestern plains of Canada*: Transactions, Royal Society of Canada, Vol. 23, p. 61-79.

Reports of the Alberta Soil Survey, geological reports of the Research Council of Alberta and Geological Survey of Canada, papers and articles in the Geographical Bulletin of the Geographical Branch, Department of Energy, Mines and Resources, Ottawa.

THE PRAIRIE WORLD

Allee, W. C., et al. 1959. *Principles of animal ecology*: W. P. Saunders Company, Philadelphia.

Alberta, Department of Industry and Development. 1964. *Alberta industry and resources*: Edmonton, 183 p.

Brown, A. 1954. *Old man's garden*: J. M. Dent and Sons, Toronto and Vancouver.

Budd, A. C. 1952. *A key to plants of the farming and ranching areas of the Canadian prairies*: Canada Department of Agriculture, Experimental Farms Service, Ottawa.

Cormack, R. G. H. 1964. *Trees and shrubs of Alberta*: Alberta Department of Lands and Forests, Edmonton.

Coupland, R. T. 1950. *Ecology of mixed prairie in Canada*: Ecological Monographs, Vol. 20, p. 271-315.

Coupland, R. T. 1958. *The effects of fluctuations in weather upon the grasslands of the Great Plains*: Botanical Review, Vol. 24, p. 273-317.

Coupland, R. T. 1961. *A reconsideration of grassland classification in the northern Great Plains of North America*: Journal of Ecology, Vol. 49, p. 135-167.

Denney, C. E. 1904. *The riders of the plains*: Original manuscript in Alberta Provincial Library, Edmonton.

Dice, L. R. 1952. *Natural communities*: University of Michigan Press, Ann Arbor.

Flint, R. F. 1957. *Glacial and pleistocene geology*: Wiley, New York.

Hornaday, W. T. 1887. *The extermination of the American bison, with a sketch of its discovery and life-history*: Smithsonian Reports, part 2, p. 367-548.

Hubbs, C. (editor). 1958. *Zoogeography*: American Association for the Advancement of Science, Publ. No. 51, Washington, D.C.

Kristjanson, B. H. (collator). 1961. *Resources for tomorrow*: Conference background papers. Vols. 1 and 2. Canada Department of Northern Affairs and National Resources, Queen's Printer, Ottawa.

Lewin, V. 1963. *The herpetofauna of southeastern Alberta*: Canadian Field-Naturalist, Vol. 77, p. 203-214.

Linduska, J. P. (editor). 1964. *Waterfowl tomorrow*: U.S. Department of Interior, Bureau of Sports Fisheries and Wildlife, Washington, D.C.

Logier, E. B. S., and Torer, G. C. 1955. *Check-list of the amphibians and reptiles of Canada and Alaska*: Contributions of Royal Ontario Museum of Zoology and Paleontology, No. 41.

Macoun, J. 1882. *Manitoba and the great north west*: World Publishing Company, Guelph, Ontario.

McClintock, W. 1910. *The old north trail or life, legends, and religion of the Blackfeet Indians*: Macmillan, London.

Metcalf, C. L., Flint, W. R., and Metcalf, R. L. 1951. *Destructive and useful insects*: McGraw-Hill, New York.

Morton, A. S., and Martin, C. 1938. *History of prairie settlement and "Dominion Lands" policy*: Macmillan, Toronto.

Morton, A. S. 1957. *A history of the Canadian west to 1870-71*: Thomas Nelson and Sons, Toronto and New York.

Moss, E. H. 1955. *The vegetation of Alberta*: Botanical Review, Vol. 21, p. 493-567.

Myres, M. T. (compiler). 1964. *The widespread pollution of soil, water and living things by toxic chemicals used in insect control programmes. An introduction to the subject through direct quotations from published reports*: Department of Biology, University of Calgary (Mimeographed).

Palliser, J. 1863. *The journals, detailed reports, and observations relative to the exploration by Captain Palliser of that portion of British North America which in latitude lies between the British Boundary line and the height of land or the watershed of the northern or frozen ocean, respectively, and in longitude, between the western shores of Lake Superior and the Pacific Ocean, during the years 1857, 1858, 1859, and 1860*: Eyre and Spottiswoode, London.

Rand, A. L. 1954. *The ice age and mammal speciation in North America*: Arctic, Vol. 7, p. 31-35.

Roe, F. G. 1951. *The North American buffalo: A critical study of the species in its wild state*: University of Toronto Press, Toronto.

Rudd, R. L., and Genelly, R. E. 1956. *Pesticides: their use and toxicity in relation to wildlife*: State of California, Department of Fish and Game, Game Bulletin No. 7.

Salt, W. R., and Wilk, A. L. 1958. *The birds of Alberta*: Queen's Printer, Edmonton.

Schultz, C. B. and Stout, T. M. 1948. *Pleistocene mammals and terraces in the Great Plains*: Bulletin Geological Society of America, Vol. 59, p. 553-588.

Scott, W. B. 1913. *A history of the land mammals of the western hemisphere*: Macmillan, New York.

Simpson, G. G. 1953. *Evolution and geography*: Gordon Lectures, Oregon State System of Higher Education, Eugene, Oregon.

Soper, J. D. 1964. *The mammals of Alberta*: Queen's Printer, Edmonton.

Thomas, W. L., Jr. (editor). 1956. *Man's role in changing the face of the earth*: University of Chicago Press, Chicago.

Warkentin, J. 1964. *The western interior of Canada*: McClelland and Stewart, Toronto.

Weaver, J. E., and Albertson, F. W. 1956. *Grasslands of the Great Plains: Their nature and use*: Johnson Publishing Company, Lincoln, Nebraska.

Wormington, H. M., and Forbis, R. G. 1965. *An introduction to the archaeology of Alberta, Canada*: Denver Museum of Natural History, Proceedings, No. 11.

Land, Forest, Wildlife: Department of Lands and Forests, Edmonton.

THE CYPRESS HILLS

Alberta Society of Petroleum Geologists. 1965. *Guidebook, Cypress Hills Plateau, Alberta and Saskatchewan*: 15th Annual Field Conference.

Bird, C. D. 1962. *Bryophytes of the Cypress Hills Provincial Parks, Alberta and Saskatchewan*: Canadian Journal of Botany, Vol. 40, p. 573-587.

Breitung, A. J. 1954. *A botanical survey of the Cypress Hills*: Canadian Field-Naturalist, Vol. 68, p. 55-92.

Cormack, R. G. H. 1945. *Botanical survey, Cypress Hills forest*: Unpublished Manuscript, Alberta Department of Natural Resources.

Cormack, R. G. H. 1948. *The orchids of the Cypress Hills*: Canadian Field-Naturalist, Vol. 62, p. 155-156.

Gravenor, C. P. and Bayrock, L. A. 1961. *Glacial deposits of Alberta*: in *Soils in Canada*, edited by R. F. Legget: Royal Society of Canada, Special Publ. No. 3, p. 33-50.

Furnival, G. M. 1946. *Cypress Lake map-area, Saskatchewan*: Geological Survey of Canada, Memoir 242.

Godfrey, W. E. 1950. *Birds of the Cypress Hills and Flotten Lake regions, Saskatchewan*: National Museum of Canada, Bulletin 120.

Kendrew, W. G., and Currie, B. W. 1955. *The climate of central Canada*: Queen's Printer, Ottawa.

Macoun, J. 1882. *Manitoba and the great north west*: World Publishing Company, Guelph, Ontario.

Macoun, J. 1883-1909. *Catalogue of Canadian plants*: Dawson Brothers, Montreal.

McConnell, R. G. 1885. *Report on the Cypress Hills, Wood Mountain and adjacent country*: Geological Survey of Canada, Annual Report, Vol. 1, Part C.

Moss, E. H., and Campbell, J. A. 1947. *The fescue grassland of Alberta*: Canadian Journal of Research, C. 25: p. 209-227.

Moss, E. H. 1959. *Flora of Alberta*: University of Toronto Press, Toronto.

Rand, A. L. 1948. *Mammals of the eastern Rockies and western plains of Canada*: National Museum of Canada, Bulletin 108.

Russell, L. S. 1951. *Land snails of the Cypress Hills and their significance*: Canadian Field-Naturalist, Vol. 65, p. 174-175.

Russell, L. S., and Landes, R. W. 1940. *Geology of the southern Alberta plains*: Geological Survey of Canada, Memoir 221.

Salt, W. R., and Wilk, A. L. 1958. *The birds of Alberta*: Queen's Printer, Edmonton.

Saskatchewan Department of Natural Resources. *Birds of the Cypress Hills Provincial Park*: Regina.

Saskatchewan Department of Natural Resources. *Mammals of Cypress Hills Provincial Park*: Regina.

Soper, J. D. 1961. *Field data on the mammals of southern Saskatchewan*: Canadian Field-Naturalist, Vol. 75, p. 23-41.

Soper, J. D. 1964. *The mammals of Alberta*: Queen's Printer, Edmonton.

de Vries, B., and Bird, C. D. 1966. *Additions to the vascular flora of the Cypress Hills*: Canadian Field-Naturalist (in preparation).

Westgate, J. A. 1965. *Surficial geology of the Cypress Hills area, Alberta*: Research Council of Alberta, Preliminary Report 65-2.

Williams, M. Y. 1946. *Notes on the vertebrates of the southern plains of Canada*: Canadian Field-Naturalist, Vol. 60, p. 47-60.

Williams, M. Y., and Dyer, W. S. 1930. *Geology of southern Alberta and southwestern Saskatchewan*: Geological Survey of Canada, Memoir 163.

Wyatt, F. A., Newton, J. D., Bowser, W. E., and Odynsky, W. 1941. *Soil survey of Milk River sheet*: University of Alberta, Bulletin 36, Edmonton.

THE ASPEN PARKLAND

American Ornithologists' Union. 1957. *Check-list of North American birds*: Ithaca, N.Y.

Bird, C. D. *Phytogeography and ecology of the bryophytes of the aspen parkland of west-central Canada*: (in preparation).

Bird, R. D. 1930. *Biotic communities of the aspen parkland of central Canada*: Ecology, Vol. 11, p. 356-442.

Bird, R. D. 1961. *Ecology of the aspen parkland of western Canada in relation to land use*: Canada Department of Agriculture, Publ. 1066.

Bowman, K. 1951. *An annotated list of the Lepidoptera of Alberta*: Canadian Journal of Zoology, Vol. 29, p. 121-165.

Bowser, W. E. 1961. *Genesis and characteristics of solonetzic soils; with particular reference to those in Alberta, Canada*: in *Soils in Canada*, edited by R. F. Legget: Royal Society of Canada, Special Publ. No. 3, p. 165-173.

Brooks, A. R. 1958. *Acridoidea of Southern Alberta, Saskatchewan and Manitoba, (Coleoptera)*: Canadian Entomologist, Supplement 20.

Clark, S. E., Campbell, J. A., and Campbell, J. B. 1942. *An ecological and grazing capacity study of the native grass pastures in southern Alberta, Saskatchewan and Manitoba*: Canadian Department of Agriculture, Publ. 738.

Coupland, R. T. 1950. *Ecology of mixed prairie in Canada*: Ecological Monographs, Vol. 20, p. 271-315.

Farley, F. L. 1932. *Birds of the Battle River region of central Alberta*: Institute of Applied Art, Edmonton.

Frankton, C. 1955. *Weeds of Canada*: Canada Department of Agriculture, Publ. 948.

Godfrey, W. E. 1966. *The birds of Canada*: National Museum of Canada, Bulletin 203.

Graham, S. A., Harrison, R. P., Jr., and Westell, C. E., Jr. 1963. *Aspens, phoenix trees of the Great Lakes region*: University of Michigan Press, Ann Arbor.

Gravenor, C. P., and Bayrock, L. A. 1961. *Glacial deposits of Alberta*: in *Soils in Canada*, edited by R. F. Legget: Royal Society of Canada, Special Publ. No. 3, p. 33-50.

Hind, H. Y. 1859. *A preliminary and general report on the Assiniboine and Saskatchewan exploring expedition*: Queen's Printer, Toronto.

Keith, L. B. 1964. *Early notes on wildlife from New Sarepta, Alberta*: Canadian Field-Naturalist, Vol. 79, p. 29-34.

Macoun, J. 1882. *Manitoba and the great north west*: World Publishing Company, Guelph, Ontario.

Moss, E. H. 1932. *The vegetation of Alberta. IV. The poplar association and related vegetation of central Alberta*: Journal of Ecology, Vol. 20, p. 380-415.

Moss, E. H. 1938. *Longevity of seed and establishment of seedlings in species of Populus*: Botanical Gazette, Vol. 99, p. 529-542.

Moss, E. H. 1952. *Grassland of the Peace River region, western Canada*: Canadian Journal of Botany, Vol. 30, p. 98-124.

Moss, E. H. 1955. *The vegetation of Alberta*: Botanical Review, Vol. 21, p. 493-567.

Moss, E. H., and Campbell, J. A., 1947. *The fescue grassland of Alberta*: Canadian Journal of Research, C, Vol. 25, p. 209-227.

Mozley, A. 1937. *A biological study of the sub-arctic mollusca*: Proceedings of the American Philosophical Society, Vol. 78, p. 147-189.

Mozley, A. 1938. *The fresh-water mollusca of sub-arctic Canada*: Canadian Journal of Research, D, Vol. 16, p. 93-138.

Palliser, J. 1863. *Exploration — British North America*: Eyre and Spottiswoode, for H. M. Stationery Office, London.

Rowan, W. 1952. *Some effects of settlement on wildlife in Alberta*: Transactions of the Canadian Conservation Association, p. 31-39.

Salt, W. R., and Wilk, A. L. 1958. *The birds of Alberta*: Queen's Printer, Edmonton.

Seton, E. T. 1909. *Life-histories of northern animals*: Scribner's, New York.

Soper, J. D. 1964. *The mammals of Alberta*: Queen's Printer, Edmonton.

Stewart, O. C. 1956. *Fire as the first great force employed by man*: in *Man's role in changing the face of the earth*, edited by W. L. Thomas, Jr.: University of Chicago Press, Chicago, p. 115-133.

Strickland, E. H. 1938. *An annotated list of the Diptera (flies) of Alberta*: Canadian Journal of Research, D, Vol. 16, p. 175-219.

THE BOREAL FOREST

Alberta, Department of Lands and Forests. *Annual Reports*: Queen's Printer, Edmonton.

Alberta, Department of Lands and Forests. 1960. *Conference on Land, Forest, Wildlife*: Transcripts, Queen's Printer, Edmonton.

Canada Department of Forestry. 1961. *Native trees of Canada*: Bulletin 61, Queen's Printer, Ottawa.

Chitty, D. 1960. *Population processes in the vole and their relevance to general theory*: Canadian Journal of Zoology, Vol. 38, p. 99-113.

Day, J. A. 1962. *Wintry art in snows*: Natural History, Vol. 71, p. 24-31.

Elton, C. S. 1924. *Periodic fluctuations in the numbers of animals; their causes and effects*: British Journal of Experimental Biology, Vol. 2, p. 119-163.

Formozov, A. N. 1964. *Snow cover as an integral factor of the environment and its importance in the ecology of mammals and birds*: Moscow Society of Naturalists. (English translation in Boreal Institute of the University of Alberta, Occasional Paper No. 1).

Hare, F. K. 1954. *The boreal conifer zone*: Geographical Studies 1, p. 4-18.

Hultén, E. 1937. *Outline of the history of arctic and boreal biota during the Quaternary Period*: Stockholm.

Keith, L. B. 1963. *Wildlife's ten-year cycle*: University of Wisconsin Press, Madison, Wisconsin.

Lutz, H. J. 1956. *Ecological effects of forest fires in the interior of Alaska*: U.S. Department of Agriculture, Technical Bulletin 1133.

MacKay, A. A. 1962. *An easy method of trapping small taiga mammals in winter*: Journal of Mammalogy, Vol. 43, p. 556-557.

Macoun, J. 1877. *Geological and topographical notes on the lower Peace and Athabaska Rivers*: Geological Survey of Canada, Report of Progress for 1875-76, p. 87-95.

Mason, B. J. 1963. *Ice*: in *The art and science of growing crystals*, edited by J. J. Gilman: Wiley, New York, p. 119-150.

Moss, E. H. 1955. *The vegetation of Alberta*: Botanical Review, Vol. 21, p. 493-567.

Moss, E. H. 1959. *Flora of Alberta*: University of Toronto Press, Toronto.

Preble, E. A. 1908. *A biological investigation of the Athabaska-Mackenzie region*: U.S. Department of Agriculture, Bureau of the Biological Survey, North American Fauna No. 27.

Pruitt, W. O., Jr. 1957. *Observations on the bioclimate of some taiga mammals*: Arctic, Vol. 10, p. 131-138.

Pruitt, W. O., Jr. 1960. *Animals in the snow*: Scientific American, Vol. 202, p. 61-68.

Pruitt, W. O., Jr., and Lucier, C. V. 1958. *Winter activity of red squirrels in interior Alaska*: Journal of Mammalogy, Vol. 39, p. 443-444.

Raup, H. M. 1935. *Botanical investigations in Wood Buffalo Park*: National Museum of Canada, Bulletin 74.

Rowe, J. S. 1959. *Forest regions of Canada*: Canada Department of Northern Affairs and National Resources, Forestry Branch Bulletin 123.

Seligman, G. 1936. *Snow structure and ski fields*: Macmillan, London.

Siivonen, L. 1956. *The correlation between the fluctuation of partridge and European hare populations and the climatic conditions of winters in S.W. Finland during the last 30 years*: Papers on Game Research, Vol. 17, p. 1-30.

Tiffany, L. H. 1958. *Algae, the grass of many waters*: Charles C. Thomas, Springfield, Illinois.

Toogood, J. A., and Newton, J. D. 1955. *Water erosion in Alberta*: Faculty of Agriculture, University of Alberta, Edmonton, Bulletin 56.

Research Council of Alberta. 1958-1965. *Preliminary Soil Survey Reports on Exploratory Soil Surveys of northern Alberta*.

MOUNTAIN HABITATS

Barrows, J. S. 1951. *Fire behavior in northern Rocky Mountain forests*: Northern Rocky Mountain Forest and Range Experiment Station, U.S. Department of Agriculture, Forest Service, Station Paper No. 29.

Chapman, J. A. 1954. *Studies on summit-frequenting insects in western Montana*: Ecology, Vol. 35, p. 41-49.

Craighead, F. C. 1949. *Insect enemies of eastern forests*: U.S. Department of Agriculture, Miscellaneous Publication 657.

Godfrey, W. E. 1966. *The birds of Canada*: National Museum of Canada, Bulletin 203.

Hardy, G. A. and Hardy, W. V. 1949. *Wild flowers in the Rockies*: H. R. Larson, Saskatoon.

Kamp, J. W. 1963. *Descriptions of two new species of Grylloblattidae and of the adult of Grylloblatta barberi, with an interpretation of their geographical distribution*: Annals Entomological Society of America, Vol. 56, p. 53-68.

Keen, F. P. 1938. *Insect enemies of western forests*: U.S. Department of Agriculture, Miscellaneous Publication 273.

Moss, E. H. 1959. *The flora of Alberta*: University of Toronto Press, Toronto.

Rand, A. L. 1948. *Mammals of the eastern Rockies and western plains of Canada*: National Museum of Canada, Bulletin 108.

Salt, W. R. and Wilk, A. L. 1958. *The birds of Alberta*: Queen's Printer, Edmonton.

Soper, J. D. 1964. *The mammals of Alberta*: Queen's Printer, Edmonton.

AQUATIC LIFE

Anonymous. 1965. *Erosion, a blessing and a curse*: Land, Forest, Wildlife, Vol. 8, p. 3-15.

Bartsch, A. F., and Ingram, W. M. *Stream life and the pollution environment*: Public Works publications, Ridgewood, New Jersey. Reprinted by Public Health Service, U.S. Department of Health, Education and Welfare.

Carl, G. C., Clemens, W. A., and Lindsey, C. C. 1959. *The freshwater fishes of British Columbia*: British Columbia Provincial Museum, Handbook No. 5.

Carson, R. 1962. *Silent spring*: Houghton Mifflin, Boston.

Coker, R. E. 1954. *Streams, lakes, ponds*: The University of North Carolina Press, Chapel Hill, North Carolina.

Cordone, A. J. and Kelley, D. W. 1961. *The influences of inorganic sediment on the aquatic life of streams*: California Fish and Game, Vol. 47, p. 189-228.

Cunningham, E. B. 1964. *Trout and the land*: Land, Forest, Wildlife, Vol. 7, p. 22-24.

Davis, H. S. 1953. *Culture and diseases of game fishes*: University of California Press, Berkeley and Los Angeles.

Dymond, J. R. (editor). 1964. *Fish and wildlife*: Longmans, Toronto.

Eddy, S. 1957. *How to know the freshwater fishes*: Pictured-key nature series, Wm. C. Brown Company, Dubuque, Iowa.

Erickson Jones, J. R. 1964. *Fish and river pollution*: Butterworth, London.

Hubbs, C. L., and Lagler, K. F. 1958. *Fishes of the Great Lakes region*: Cranbrook Institute of Science, Bloomfield Hills, Michigan.

Hynes, H. B. N. 1960. *The biology of polluted waters*: Liverpool University Press, Liverpool.

Ingram, W. M. and Towne, W. W. *Effects of industrial wastes on stream life*: Engineering Bulletin, Purdue University, Vol. 44, p. 678-710. Reprinted by U.S. Department of Health, Education and Welfare, Public Health Service.

Jackson, D. F. (editor). 1964. *Algae and man*: Plenum Press, New York.

Jones, J. R. E. 1964. *Fish and river pollution*: Butterworth, London.

Lindsey, C. C. 1964. *Problems in zoogeography of the lake trout, Salvelinus namaycush*: Journal Fisheries Research Board of Canada, Vol. 21.

Lowdermilk, W. C. 1953. *Conquest of the land through 7,000 years*: U.S. Department of Agriculture, Agricultural Information Bulletin 99.

Macan, T. T. 1963. *Freshwater ecology*: Longmans, Green, London.

Macan, T. T., and Worthington, E. B. 1951. *Life in lakes and rivers*: Collins, London.

McClane, A. J. (editor). 1965. *McClane's standard fishing encyclopedia and international angling guide*: Holt, Rinehart and Winston, New York.

Mackay, H. H. 1963. *The fishes of Ontario*: Department of Lands and Forests of Ontario, Toronto. Bryant Press, Toronto.

Mackenthum, K. M., and Ingram, W. M. 1964. *Limnological aspects of recreational lakes*: U.S. Department of Health, Education and Welfare, Public Health Service Publication No. 1167.

Miller, R. B. 1958. *Inventory of fisheries research in Alberta*: Alberta Resources Conference, Queen's Printer, Edmonton.

Miller, R. B. 1962. *A cool curving world*: Longmans, Toronto.

Miller, R. B., and MacDonald, W. H. 1949. *Preliminary biological surveys of Alberta watersheds, 1947-1949*: Alberta Department of Lands and Forests, Edmonton.

Miller, R. B., and Paetz, M. J. 1952. *Preliminary biological surveys of Alberta watersheds, 1950-1952*: Alberta Department of Lands and Forests, Edmonton.

Miller, R. B., and Paetz, M. J. 1959. *The effects of power, irrigation and stock water developments on the fisheries of the South Saskatchewan River*: Canadian Fish Culturist, No. 25, p. 1-14.

Morgan, A. H. 1930. *Field book of ponds and streams*: Putnam, New York.

Needham, J. G., and Needham, P. R. 1962. *A guide to the study of freshwater biology*: Holden-Day, San Francisco.

Nelson, J. S. 1965. *Effects of fish introductions and hydroelectric development on fishes in the Kananaskis River system, Alberta*: Journal Fisheries Research Board of Canada, Vol. 22, p. 721-753.

Paetz, M. J. 1958. *An inventory of the stream sport fisheries of Alberta*: Alberta Resources Conference, Queen's Printer, Edmonton.

Palmer, C. M. 1959. *Algae in water supplies*: U.S. Department of Health, Education and Welfare, Public Health Service Publ. No. 657.

Pennak, R. W. 1953. *Fresh-water invertebrates of the United*

States: Ronald Press, New York.

Prescott, G. W. 1954. *How to know the freshwater algae:*
Pictured-key nature series, Wm. C. Brown Company,
Dubuque, Iowa.

Rounsefell, G. A., and Everhart, W. H. 1953. *Fishery science, its*
methods and applications: Wiley, New York.

Rudd, R. L. 1964. *Pesticides and the living landscape:*
University of Wisconsin Press, Madison, Wisconsin.

Saskatchewan Department of Natural Resources. 1959. *The fish*
of Saskatchewan: Conservation Bulletin No. 7.

Smith, G. M. 1950. *The fresh-water algae of the United States:*
McGraw-Hill Book Company, New York.

Thomas, R. C. 1958. *Alberta lake fisheries:* Alberta Resources
Conference, Queen's Printer, Edmonton.

Tiffany, L. H. 1958. *Algae. The grass of many waters:*
C. C. Thomas, Springfield, Illinois.

Toogood, J. A., and Newton, J. D. 1955. *Water erosion in Alberta:*
Faculty of Agriculture, University of Alberta, Edmonton,
Bulletin 56.

THE STUDY OF NATURAL HISTORY

Further reading to chapter 11 is to be found on page 271.

THE FIRST PEOPLE

Curtis, Edward S. 1908-28. *The North American Indian:*
Vols. 3, 6, 18, Norwood, Massachusetts.

Ewers, J. C. 1955. *The horse in Blackfoot Indian culture:*
Bureau of American Ethnology, Bulletin 159, Washington.

Ewers, J. C. 1958. *The Blackfeet:* University of Oklahoma Press,
Norman, Oklahoma.

Forbis, R. G. 1960. *The Old Women's Buffalo Jump, Alberta:*
National Museum of Canada, Bulletin 180, p. 57-123.

Forbis, R. G. 1963. *The direct historical approach in the Prairie*
Provinces of Canada: Great Plains Journal, Vol 3, Lawton.

Goddard, Pliny E. 1916. *The Beaver Indians:* American Museum
of Natural History, Anthropological Papers, Vol. 10, Part 4,
New York.

Hector, J., and Vaux, W. S. W. 1861. *Notice of the Indians seen by*
the exploring expedition under the command of Captain
Palliser: Ethnological Society of London, Transactions,
Vol. 1, p. 245-261.

Hlady, Walter M. 1960. *Indian migrations in Manitoba and the*
west: Historical and Scientific Society of Manitoba, Series III,
Nos. 17-18, Winnipeg.

Jenness, D. 1938. *The Sarcee Indians of Alberta:* National
Museum of Canada, Bulletin 90, Ottawa.

Jenness, D. 1955. *The Indians of Canada:* National Museum of
Canada, Bulletin 65, Third edition.

Lowie, Robert H. 1910. *The Assiniboine:* American Museum of
Natural History, Anthropological Papers, Vol. 4, Part 1,
New York.

Mandelbaum, D. G. 1940. *The Plains Cree:* American Museum of
Natural History, Anthropological Papers, Vol. 37, Part 2,
New York.

Murdock, George P. 1960. *Ethnographic bibliography of North*
America: Human Relations Area Files, Third edition,
New Haven.

Wormington, H. M., and Forbis, R. G. 1965. *An introduction to*
the archaeology of Alberta, Canada: Denver Museum of
Natural History, Proceedings, No. 11, Denver.

EARLY NATURAL HISTORY EXPLORATIONS

Alcock, F. J. 1947. *A century in the history of the Geological*
Survey of Canada: National Museum of Canada, Special
Contribution No. 47-1.

Coues, E. 1897. *New light on the early history of the Greater*
Northwest, the manuscript journals of Alexander Henry and
of David Thompson, 1799-1814: Frances P. Harper, New York.

Dawson, G. M. 1875. *Report on the geology and resources of the*
region in the vicinity of the forty-ninth parallel from Lake
of the Woods to the Rocky Mountains: British North American
Boundary Commission, Montreal.

Glover, R. 1962. *David Thompson's narrative 1784-1812:* The
Champlain Society, Toronto.

Harmon, D. W. 1820. *A journal of voyages and travels in the*
interior of North America: Flagg and Gould, Andover.

Hector, J. On the geology of the country between Lake Superior
and the Pacific Ocean — between the 48th and 54th parallels
of latitude: Quarterly Journal Geological Society of London,
Vol. 17, p. 388-445.

Hooker, Sir W. J. 1840. *Flora Boreali-Americana; or the botany of*
the northern parts of British America: 2 vols., London.

Innis, H. A. 1962. *The fur trade in Canada; an introduction to*
Canadian economic history: Yale University Press, New Haven.

Mackenzie, Sir A. 1801. *Voyages from Montreal, on the River*
St. Laurence, through the continent of North America to the
Frozen and Pacific Oceans in the years 1789 and 1793 with a
preliminary account of the rise, progress, and present state
of the fur trade of that country: T. Cadell, London.

Macoun, J. 1882. *Manitoba and the great north west:*
World Publishing Company, Guelph, Ontario.

Morton, A. S. (editor) 1929. *The journal of Duncan McGillivray*
of the North West Company at Fort George on the
Saskatchewan, 1794-5: Macmillan, Toronto.

Palliser, J. 1863. *Exploration — British North America:*
Eyre and Spottiswoode, for H.M. Stationery Office, London.

Rich, R. E. (editor). 1951. *Cumberland House Journals and*
Inland Journals, 1775-82: Hudson's Bay Record Society, London.

Rich, R. E. 1958. *The history of the Hudson's Bay Company,*
1670-1870: Hudson's Bay Record Society, London.

Richardson, Sir J. 1829. *Fauna Boreali-Americana:*
John Murray, London.

Spry, I. M. 1963. *The Palliser Expedition: An Account of*
John Palliser's British North American Expedition 1857-1860:
The Macmillan Company of Canada, Toronto

Thompson, D. 1916. *Narrative of his explorations in western*
America, 1784-1812: (edited by J. B. Tyrrell)
Champlain Society, Toronto.

Wagner, H. R. 1955. *Peter Pond, fur trader and explorer:*
Yale University Press, New Haven.

Warkentin, J. 1964. *The western interior of Canada:*
a record of geographical discovery 1612-1917:
The Carleton Library No. 15, McClelland and Stewart, Toronto.

THE IMPACT OF THE WHITE MAN

Butler, Sir W. F. 1910. *The Great Lone Land; a tale of travel and*
adventure in the north-west of America: Macmillan, Toronto.

Glover, R. 1962. *David Thompson's narrative 1784-1812:*
Champlain Society, Toronto.

Hanson, E. J. 1958. *Dynamic Decade:* McClelland and Stewart,
Toronto.

Hardy, W. G. 1960. *From sea unto sea: Canada 1850 to 1910;*
the road to nationhood: Doubleday, Toronto and New York.

Hughes, K. 1920. *Father Lacombe, the black-robe voyageur:*
McClelland, Toronto.

Kane, P. 1925. *Wanderings of an artist among the Indians of*
North America: Radisson Society of Canada Ltd., Toronto.

MacGregor, J. G. 1949. *Blankets and beads; a history of the*
Saskatchewan River: The Institute of Applied Arts, Edmonton.

MacGregor, J. G. 1954. *Behold the shining mountains; being an*
account of the travels of Anthony Henday, 1754-55, the first
white man to enter Alberta: Allied Art Products, Edmonton.

Mackay, O. 1939. *The Honourable Company: a history of the*
Hudson's Bay Company: Cassell, London.

Morton, A. S. (editor). 1929. *The Journal of Duncan McGillivray*
of the North West Company at Fort George on the
Saskatchewan, 1794-5: Macmillan, Toronto.

Morton, A. S. 1957. *A history of the Canadian West to 1870-71:*
Thomas Nelson and Sons, Toronto.

Morton, A. S., and Martin, C. 1938. *History of prairie settlement*
and "Dominion Lands" policy: Macmillan, Toronto.

Nix, J. E. 1960. *Mission among the buffalo:* Ryerson, Toronto.

Rich, R. E. 1958. *The history of the Hudson's Bay Company,*
1670-1870: Hudson's Bay Record Society, London.

Soper, J. D. 1964. *The mammals of Alberta:* Queen's Printer,
Edmonton.

Stanley, G. F. G. 1936. *The birth of western Canada: a history of*
the Riel rebellions: Longmans, Green, London.

Turner, J. P. 1950. *The North-West Mounted Police, 1873-1893:*
2 vols. E. Cloutier, King's Printer, Ottawa.

Wagner, H. R. 1955. *Peter Pond, fur trader and explorer:*
Yale University Press, New Haven.

Warkentin, J. 1964. *The western interior of Canada; a record of*
geographical discovery 1612-1917: The Carleton Library No. 15,
McClelland and Stewart, Toronto.

INDEX

1. Numbers in bold face type refer to illustrations of textual material.

2. Animals will be found under the headings of Amphibians, Birds, Fish, Invertebrates, Mammals and Reptiles.

3. All forms of vegetation will be found under the heading of Vegetation.

4. Major Maps.

The Bedrock Geology of Alberta, p. 25

Late Devonian Seas and Coral Reefs, p. 32

Preglacial River Valleys, p. 72

Surface Deposits, p. 80

Hills, Rivers and Lakes, p. 86

Major Soil Zones, p. 88

Alberta Place Names, p. 94

A

Aeolian plains, 82

Agriculture, effect on streams, 257

Alaska, 277-82, 253-54

Alberta Bird Report, 268, 273

Alberta Forest Service, 187

Alberta Provincial Museum, 291

Albireo, 14

Alcock, F. J., 122

Aldebaran, 10

Algae, 23, 31, 33, 222-23
    Benthic forms, 229-39
    control of, 259
    diatoms, 230-37
    limnetic zone, 231
    littoral zone, 229
    phytoplankton, 231, 240
    seasonal cycles, 233
    species: (see Vegetation, algae)

Algol, 16

Allan, J. A., 41

Alliance, 139, 146

Alluvial plains, **83**

Alpha Centauri, 18

Altair, 13

Altithermal:
    climate, 96, 98
    period, 284

Amateur naturalists, 265-70

Amphibians:
    Frog:
        Boreal chorus, *Pseudacris triseriata maculata,* 127, 131
        Leopard, *Rana pipiens,* 111, 127, 131, **147**, 149
        Wood, *R. sylvatica,* 229
    Salamander:
        Blotched tiger, *Ambystoma tigrinum melanostictum,* **111**, 131

Anangula Island, Alaska, 282

Andromeda, 15
    Galaxy, **5**, 15, 19

Animals:
    census of, 270
    keeping animals, 266
    population cycles, 181
    species: (see above, note 2)

Anthracite, 60

Antiquity of man, 278

Aquatic plant life, 227-38

Aquila, 13

Archaeological "dig," **289**

Arctic:
    air, 55, 59, 61, 66
    winds, 54

Arctic embayment, **40**

Arctic region, 50

Arcturus, 12

Arrowsmith, John, 306

Arthropods, 24

Asia, 277-78

Aspen (bluffs, groves, parkland, stands, woodland) 96, 98, 100, 107, 125, 128, **135**-37, **138**-39, 141-42, 145, 147-49, 158-69, 206

Astronomical distances, 18-19

Astronomical studies in Alberta, 5-6, 8-9

Astronomy, foundations of, 16, 17

Athabasca, 62, 73-75, 78, 84, 305

Athabasca oil sands, 39, 298-99, 316

Athabasca Pass, 298

Atlee, 45

Audubon Field Notes, 268, 273

Aurora borealis, **7**-8
    origin, 8

B

Bacteria, 233, 236

Badlands, **44**-45, 99, 107

Baker-Nunn Satellite Tracking Camera, **9**

Banff, 37, 47-48, 51, 54, 58, 60, 70-71, 73

Banff Cosmic Ray Station, 9

Banff Shale, 34

Bark removal, **180**

Barrhead, 83

Basement, Precambrian, **22**-24, 27, 49, 69
    depth to, **22**

Bassano, 85

Batholiths, 47, **48**

Bay of Fundy, 279

Bayrock, L. A., 5, 281, 288

Beaver Creek, 254

Beirne, B. P., 267

Bell, Robert, 301

Benthic fauna (see Invertebrates), 239, 241

Bering Strait, 277-78, 280
    land bridge, 48, 50, 151, 277

Betelgeuse, 10-11

Biological Supply Houses, 266, 273

Biologists, 265, 268, 270

Bird, C. D., 124

Birds:
    banding of, 267
    collecting of, 267
    distribution of:
        dry years, 269-70
        wet years, 269-70
    eggs, 267
    of prey, 270
    water birds, 270
    species:
        Avocet, *Recurvirostra americana,* **109**, 111, 148
        Bittern, *Botaurus lentiginosus,* 148
        Blackbird:
            Brewer's, *Euphagus cyanocephalus,* 115, 126

Birds (Continued)

    Red-winged, *Agelaius phoeniceus*, 112, 115, 130, 133, 148, 169

    Rusty, *Euphagus carolinus*, 169, 200

    Yellow-headed, *Xanthocephalus xanthocephalus*, 112, 115, 148

Bluebird, Mountain, *Sialia currucoides*, **109**, 128

Bunting:

    Lark, *Calamospiza melanocorys*, 111

    Lazuli, *Passerina amoena*, 206

Catbird, *Dumetella carolinensis*, 128, **137**

Chat, Yellow-breasted, *Icteria virens*, 128

Chickadee, Black-capped, *Parus atricapillus*, 128, 144, 169, 170, 176, **178**, 179-80

Chicken, Prairie, *Tympanuchus cupido*, 113

Coot, *Fulica americana*, 112, 148

Cowbird, Brown-headed, *Molothrus ater*, 126, 128, 140-41

Crane:

    Sandhill, *Grus canadensis*, 112, **171**

    Whooping, *G. americana*, 107, 171, **173**

Creeper, Brown, *Certhia familiaris*, 180

Crossbill, Red, *Loxia curvirostra*, 128, 131, 180

Crow, Common, *Corvus brachyrhynchos*, 128, 133

Curlew, Long-billed, *Numenius americanus*, 111, **112**

Dipper (Water ouzel), *Cinclus mexicanus*, **197**

Dove, Mourning, *Zenaidura macroura*, **121**, 128, 133

Duck:

    Baldpate or Widgeon, *Mareca americana*, **109**, 130, 148

    Barrow's Goldeneye, *Bucephala islandica*, 206-**07**

    Blue-winged Teal, *Anas discors*, 148

    Canvasback, *Aythya valisineria*, 148

    Gadwall, *Anas strepera*, 148

    Green-winged Teal, *A. carolinensis*, 130, 148, 169

    Harlequin, *Histrionicus histrionicus*, **196**

Lesser Scaup, *Aythya affinis*, **130**, 148

Mallard, *Anas platyrhynchos*, 130, 148, 169

Pintail, *A. acuta*, 111, 148

Redhead, *Aythya americana*, 148

Ruddy, *Oxyura jamaicensis*, 148

Shoveler, *Spatula clypeata*, 148

Eagle, Golden, *Aquila chrysaetos*, 107-08, 111, 202-**03**

Egret, Cattle, *Bubulcus ibis*, 114

Falcon:

    Prairie, *Falco mexicanus*, **107**

    Peregrine, *F. peregrinus*, **169**

Finch:

    Purple, *Carpodacus purpureus*, 169

    Rosy, *Leucosticte tephrocotis*, 218

Flicker, Red-shafted, *Colaptes cafer*, 206

Flycatcher:

    Dusky, *Empidonax oberholseri*, 131, 212

    Least, *E. minimus*, 128, 144

Godwit, Marbled, *Limosa fedoa*, 111, **112**

Goldfinch, *Spinus tristis*, 141

Goshawk, *Accipiter gentilis*, 144-45, 170, **173**

Goose:

    Canada, *Branta canadensis*, 112, 115, 148, **236**

    Snow, *Chen hyperborea*, 112, 148

    Ross's, *C. rossii*, 112

    White-fronted, *Anser albifrons*, 112, 148

Grackle, Bronzed, *Quiscalus quiscula*, 115

Grebe, 169

    Horned, *Podiceps auritus*, **137**

    Pied-billed, *Podilymbus podiceps*, 148

Grosbeak:

    Pine, *Pinicola enucleator*, 180

    Rose-breasted, *Pheucticus ludovicianus*, 169, **173**

Grouse:

    Blue, *Dendragopus obscurus*, **211**, 214, **216**

    Franklin's, *Canachites canadensis franklinii*, **211**

    Ruffed, *Bonasa umbellus*, 128, 144-45, 163, 170, **178**, 182, **184**, **219**

Sage, *Centrocercus urophasianus*, 107, 120

Sharp-tailed, *Pedioecetes phasianellus*, 107, 114, 127, 140, **145**, 182

Spruce, *Canachites canadensis*, 170, 180, 182, 210, **211**-12

Gull:

    Bonaparte's, *Larus philadelphia*, 169, **173**

    Franklin's, *L. pipixcan*, **109**, **149**

Hawk:

    Ferruginous Rough-legged, *Buteo regalis*, 107

    Pigeon, *Falco columbarius*, **144**-45

    Sparrow, *F. sparverius*, **173**

Heron:

    Black-crowned Night, *Nycticorax nycticorax*, 114, 149

    Great Blue, *Ardea herodias*, 130, 148, 169

Hummingbird, Rufous, *Selasphorus rufus*, 197-**98**

Jay:

    Blue, *Cyanocitta cristata*, 170

    Canada, *Perisoreus canadensis*, 170, **211**

Junco, Oregon, *Junco oregonus mearnsi*, 128, 131

Killdeer, *Charadrius vociferus*, 130, 148

Kingbird:

    Eastern, *Tyrannus tyrannus*, 126

    Western, *T. verticalis*, 126, 149

Kingfisher, Belted, *Megaceryle alcyon*, 130, 146

Kinglet, Ruby-crowned, *Regulus calendula*, 169, 180, 209

Lark, Horned, *Eremophila alpestris*, 111, 126, 141

Longspur:

    Chestnut-collared, *Calcarius ornatus*, 111

    McCown's, *Rhyncophanes mccownii*, 111, 120

Loon, Common, *Gavia immer*, 169

Magpie, Black-billed, *Pica pica*, 115, 128, **145**

Martin, Purple, *Progne subis*, 115, 149

Meadowlark, *Sturnella neglecta*, 111, 126, 141

Nighthawk, *Chordeiles minor*, 127, 169

Nutcracker, Clark's, *Nucifraga columbiana*, **216**

Birds (Continued)

Nuthatch, Red-breasted, *Sitta canadensis*, 169, 179-**80**

Oriole, Baltimore, *Icterus galbula*, 144

Osprey, *Pandion haliaetus*, 169

Ovenbird, *Seiurus aurocapillus*, 169

Owl:

Great Horned, *Bubo virginianus*, 128, 144, 176, **179**

Hawk, *Surnia ulula*, 170, **181**

Long-eared, *Asio otus*, **121**

Richardson's (Boreal), *Aegolius funereus*, **170**

Snowy, *Nyctea scandiaca*, **172**

Partridge, Hungarian (Gray or European), *Perdix perdix*, **113**-14, 127, 133, 149, 178

Peewee, Western Wood, *Contopus sordidulus*, 128

Pelican, White, *Pelecanus erythrorhynchus*, 112

Pheasant, Ring-necked, *Phasianus colchicus*, **114**, 127, 133, 149

Pigeon, Domestic (Rock Dove), *Columba livia*, 114

Plover:

Piping, *Charadrius melodus*, 148

Upland, *Bartramia longicauda*, 111

Poor-will, *Phalaenoptilis nuttallii*, 128

Ptarmigan:

Rock, *Lagopus mutus*, 178, 218

White-tailed, *L. leucurus*, **211**, 218

Willow, *L. lagopus*, 172, 178, 180, **182**

Raven, Common, *Corvus corax*, 169

Robin, *Turdus migratorius*, 128, 169, 200

Sandpiper:

Solitary, *Tringa solitaria*, 169, 199, **211**

Spotted, *Actitis macularia*, 130, 148

Shrike:

Northern, *Lanius excubitor*, 169

Siskin, Pine, *Spinus pinus*, 128

Snipe, Common or Wilson's, *Capella gallinago*, **121**, 148

Solitaire, Townsend's, *Myadestes townsendi*, 216

Sora Rail, *Porzana carolina*, 112, 148, 199-200

Sparrow:

Brewer's, *Spizella breweri*, 218

Clay-coloured, *S. pallida*, 126

English or House, *Passer domesticus*, 133, 149

Savannah, *Passerculus sandwichensis*, 126

Song, *Melospiza melodia*, 128, 141

Vesper, *Pooecetes gramineus*, 111, **126**, 141

White-crowned, *Zonotrichia leucophrys*, **121**, 128, 131, 195

Starling, European, *Sturnus vulgaris*, 114, 133, 149

Swallow:

Bank, *Riparia riparia*, 130, 146

Barn,*Hirundo rustica*, 115, 130

Cliff, *Petrochelidon pyrrhonota*, 115, 130

Swan:

Trumpeter, *Olor buccinator*, 107, **122**, 133

Whistling, *O. columbianus*, 112

Tern:

Black, *Chlidonias niger*, 130, 149

Common, *Sterna hirundo*, 149

Thrasher, Brown, *Toxostoma rufum*, **121**, 128

Thrush, Swainson's, *Hylocichla ustulata*, 128, 169

Towhee, Rufous-sided, *Pipilo erythrophthalmus*, 128

Veery, *Hylocichla fuscescens*, 128, 145

Vireo, Red-eyed, *Vireo olivaceus*, 141, 144

Vulture, Turkey, *Cathartes aura*, 128

Waxwing, Cedar, *Bombycilla cedrorum*, **137**

Warbler:

Audubon's, *Dendroica auduboni*, **124**, 125, 128, 131

MacGillivray's, *Oporornis tolmiei*, 128, **212**

Myrtle, *Dendroica coronata*, 169

Orange-crowned, *Vermivora celata*, 128, 131

Yellow, *Dendroica petechia*, 128, **137**, 141

Willet, *Catoptrophorus semipalmatus*, **109**, 111, 148

Woodpecker, 108

Downy, *Dendrocopus pubescens*, 128, 144

Hairy, *D. villosus*, 128, 144

Pileated, *D. pileatus*, 206

Wren:

House, *Troglodytes aedon*, 128, 197

Long-billed Marsh, *Telmatodytes palustris*, 112, 148

Winter, *Troglodytes troglodytes*, 209

Yellowlegs:

Lesser, *Totanus flavipes*, 169

Blades, stone, 282-86

Blairmore, 75

Blakiston, Lieut., 300

Blizzards, 58

Blue Jay, 268, 273

Bonnyville, 284, 305

Boreal forest, 135, **151**-92, economic aspects, 186 erosion problems, 187-88 pipelines, 188 road building, 188-**89** seismic lines, 188 water storage, 189 wood harvesting, 190-**91**

Boreal mixedwood section, 156, **162**

Boreal-subarctic mixedwood section, **155**, 156

Boreal-subarctic alluvial lowlands section, **152**, 157

Boreal-subarctic jackpine sand plain section, 157

Bottom-dwelling animals (*see* Benthic fauna), 241

Bourgeau, Eugene, 300

Bow Island, 82

Brachiopods, 28, 34, 36, 38

Breitung, A. J., 124

Bridal Veil Falls, 75

British Columbia, 23, 38-39, 41, 43-45, 47-48, 50, 277, 280, 283, 305, 309, 318

British North American Boundary Commission, 122

Brocket, 285

Brooks, 62, 106

Buffalo bones, **312**

Butler, Lieut. W. F., 310

C

Cadomin, 39

Cairns, **284**

Calgary, 8, 9, 18-19, 34, 49, 55-58, 60-63, 67, 78, 250, 254, 261, 297, 301, 306, 310, 312, 314-15, 318

Calgary Bird Club, 268

Cambrian Period, 24, 28 sea life, 24, 26 seas, **26**, 27

Campbell, J. W., 8

Camrose, 139

Canadian Pacific Railway, 112, 300-01, 311-12

Canadian Field-Naturalist, 268, 273

Canadian Shield, 21, **22**, 51, 69, 83, **158**

Canadian Wildlife Service, 267

Canis Major, 11

Carbon dioxide, in decaying matter, 222, 232, 235-36, 238

Carboniferous Period, **33**
    animal life 35-36
    oil producing, 34

Cardium Sand, 43

Cardston, 67

Carway, 57

Cassiopeia, 13, 15

Castle Mountain Thrust (Lewis Fault), 71

Castor Creek site, 284

Cayley, 285

Cenozoic Era, 46

Cereal, 282

Cetus, 15

Chant Medal, 8

Chemical insecticides, 260

Chemicals, 265, 270

Chinook, 54-55
    arch, **55**
    winds, 58-59, 125

Churchillian rocks, 23

Clear cutting, 189-**90**

Climate, 124
    changes in, 53, **59**
    definition, 53
    effect of altitude on, **54**, 65
    effect of latitude on, 53
    effect of mountains on, 53-55, 58-60
    effect of topography on, 56, 60, 62
    factors of, 53
    prairie, 99-100

Climatic zones, **54**, **66**, 67

Climax cover, 100-01

Cloudburst, 64

Clouds, 55, 58, **63**, 66
    cumulus, 62-63

Clovis man, 280

Cluny, 286

Coal, 38-40, 312, 314-16

Cold Lake, 67

Cold Lake Satellite Tracking Station, 9

Coleman, 42

Collecting and equipment, 266-**67**, **269**, 271

Columbia Icefields, 84

Columbus, 280

Comet Mrkos, **17**

Conrad, 81

Conservation, 270, 319

Consort, 288

Continental Divide, 73

Conversion of food, 239

Copernicus, Nicolaus, 17

Copper crescent, **284**

Coral reefs, 28, 30-31
    Devonian, **32**

Corals, 28, 34, 36

Cormack, R. G. H., 124

Coronation, 61, 78

Coulees, 81, **99**

Cretaceous Period, 38-48, 119, 138
    animals, 45-46
    fish, 40-41, 43-44
    forests, 39, 42-43, 45
    shales, 76, 79

Crowsnest Pass, 38, 42-43, 55, 58, 60, 66, 75, 285

Crowsnest volcano and volcanics, **42**

Curtis, Edward S., 293

Cygnus, 13, 14

Cypress Hills, 61, 98, 111, **117**, 121, 281, 300

D

Dawson Creek, 27, 29

Dawson, George Mercer, 41, 122, 301

Dawson, S. J., 299

Delburne, 111

Deltas:
    Belly River, **45**
    Dunvegan, **42**, 43
    Edmonton, 45

Deneb, 14

Denebola, 12

Dermatitis, Schistosome ("swimmer's itch"), 242, 258-59

Devon, 83, 85

Devonian Period, 29
    animals, 29
    aquatic life, 29, 33
    plants, 29, 33
    salt deposits, 29, **30**

De Vries, B., 124

Dinosaurs, 38, 43-**46**

Dipper (*see* Ursa Major; Ursa Minor)

Distribution of species, changes in, 268-70

Douglas, David, 299

Dowling, D. B., 41

Drainage, **85**
    preglacial, **72**

Drought, 60, 62, 66

Drumheller, 30, 39, 44-45, 56, 63, 67

Drummond, Thomas, 299

Dun, 243

Dunes, **82**, 83, 98

Dyer, W.S., 124

E

Earth-lodge villages, 286, 288

Eastend, Saskatchewan, 117

Ecologists, 265, 270

Edmonton, 7-9, 18-19, 54, 56, 59-63, 82, 85, 89, 136, 281-82, 290, 301, 305, 310-14, 318

Edmonton Bird Club, 268

Edson, 34

Effluents:
    gravel, **259**, 261
    pulp-mill, 260
    refinery, **256**

Embarras, 59, 65

Empress, 58, 83, 85

Engelmann spruce-subalpine fir forest, 154

Entrance, 60, 77

Entwistle, 82

Erosion, 187-88, 256-58
    impact of, 258
    of streams, **256**

Eskimos, 7

Esker, **100**

Expeditions, 295, 299-301, 309

Exploration of Western Canada, 295-301, 306, 309
    routes, **296**

Exshaw, 60

F

Fairview, 84

Faults, 70-71

Federal Department of Mines and Technical Surveys, 6

Fernie Shale, 37

Fidler, Peter, 297-**98**, 305-06

Field:
    guides, 266, 271-73
    notes, 266
    trips, 268

Fires, 166, 168, 184, 193, **194**, 209-10
  controlled, 188
  crown, 166, 168, **185**
  forest, 318
  prairie, **101**
  prevention, 188
Fish:
  collecting of, 267
  culture of, 253
  distribution of, 253
  lateral line system, 248
  trade, 252
  families and species:
  Family Acipenseridae:
    Sturgeon, *Acipenser fulvescens*, 248-49
  Family Catostomidae:
    Longnose sucker, *Catostomus catostomus*, 252, **255**
    Northern mountain sucker, *Pantosteus jordani*, 251
    Quillback sucker, *Carpiodes cyprinus*, 252
    Redhorse sucker, *Moxostoma aureolum*, 249, 252
    White sucker, *Catostomus commersoni*, 146, 252
  Family Coregonidae:
    Lake whitefish, *Coregonus clupeaformis*, 250-**51**, 263
    Mountain whitefish, *Prosopium williamsoni*, 250-**51**
    Round whitefish, *P. cylindraceum*, 250-51
    Tullibee or cisco, *Leucichthys* sp., 249-51
  Family Cottidae:
    Deepwater sculpin, *Triglopsis thompsoni*, 253
    Slimy sculpin or Miller's thumb, *Cottus cognatus*, 253
    Spoonhead sculpin, *C. ricei*, 253
  Family Cyprinidae:
    Carp, *Cyprinus carpio*, 253, 263
    Fathead minnow, *Pimephales promelas*, **255**
    Flathead chub, *Hybopsis gracilis*, 249
    Goldfish, *Carassius auratus*, 253-54
    Lake chub, *Hybopsis plumbea*, **255**
    Northern squawfish, *Ptychocheilus oregonense*, 253, 263
    Redbelly dace, *Chrosomus eos*, 253
    Redside shiner, *Richardsonius balteatus*, 253

Family Esocidae:
  Northern pike, *Esox lucius*, 146, **251**, **255**, 263
Family Gadidae:
  Burbot, *Lota lota*, 253
Family Gasterosteidae:
  Brook or fivespine stickleback, *Eucalia inconstans*, 252, **255**
  Ninespine stickleback, *Pungitius pungitius*, 252
Family Hiodontidae:
  Goldeye, *Hiodon alisoides*, **251**
Family Ictaluridae:
  Stonecat, *Noturus flavus*, 253-54
Family Percidae:
  Iowa darter, *Etheostoma exile*, 251
  Johnny darter, *E. nigrum*, 251
  Sauger, *Stizostedion canadense*, **251**
  Walleye, *S. vitreum*, 146, **251**-52
  Yellow perch, *Perca flavescens*, 249, **251**
Family Percopsidae:
  Troutperch, *Percopsis omiscomaycus*, 253
Family Petromyzonidae:
  Lamprey, *Petromyzon* sp., 248-49
Family Salmonidae:
  Brook trout, *Salvelinus fontinalis*, **250**, 254
  Brown trout, *Salmo trutta*, **250**, 254
  Cutthroat trout, *Salmo clarki*, **250**
  Dolly Varden trout, *Salvelinus malma*, **250**
  Golden trout, *Salmo aquabonita*, **250**
  Kokanee, *Oncorhynchus nerka*, 249, 254
  Lake trout, *Salvelinus namaycush*, **250**, 254
  Rainbow trout, *Salmo gairdneri*, **250**, 254
Family Thymallidae:
  Arctic grayling, *Thymallus arcticus*, **251**, 254
Fish and Wildlife Division, 267
Fishing, sport, 258
Fleming, Sandford, 300
Folsom man, 280
Food chain, 241
Foothills, 39, 48, 50, 59, 63, **69**, 76-77, 135, 315
Forbis, R. G., 283, 285

Forest, **186-87**
  boreal, 135, **151**
  climax, 194
  coniferous, **194**, 207, **208**-09
  Engelmann spruce-subalpine fir, 154
  environment, 161
  fires, 193-**94**, 209-10, 318
  floor, **164**
  foothill, 135
  management, 184-86, 256
  mixedwood, boreal, **159**, **160**, **162**, **164**, 202-06
  mountain, 208-09
  reserve, **186**, 258
  sequence, 165-69
  service, 188, 258
  winter in northern, 172-84
Forest or Thickwood Indians, 292
Forestry operations, 256
Fort Macleod, 64, 285
Fort McMurray, 59, 61-62, 78, 84-85
Fort Smith, 57, 61-62
Fort Vermilion, 59, 65
Forts:
  Acton House, 307
  Augustus, 305-06
  Bow, 307
  Buckingham House, 306
  Calgary, 310-**11**
  Chipewyan, 297
  Cumberland House, 306
  Edmonton, 309, **311**
  Edmonton House, 306
  Ethier, **306**
  George, 305-06
  Macleod, 310-11
  Manchester House, 297
  Rocky Mountain House, 307
  Saskatchewan, 85, 305, 310-11
  Whoop-Up, 103, 310
Fossils:
  Ammonites, 33, 36-38, 41-42, 44
    Baculites, 44
    Gastroplites, **39**
    Placenticeras, 44
    Scaphites, **44**
  Amphipora, **31**, 33
  belemnite, **38**
  brachiopods, 28, 38
    Orthis, **28**
  Brontotherium, **48**
  bryozoa, 28, 34
  Cladopora, **31**
  coelocanth fish, Triassic Period, **37**
  Collenia, **23**

Fossils (Continued)
  crinoid columnals, **34**
  Dinichthys, 31
  dinosaurs:
    Brontosaurus, 38
    Gorgosaurus, 45, 46
    hadrosaur, 45
    Monoclonius, 45
    Stegoceras, 45
    Triceratops, **46**
    Tyrannosaurus, **45**, 46
  figs, **43**
  fusulinids, **36**
  Ginkgo, 38
  Globigerina, 44
  graptolites, 27
  Halysites, **28**
  Heliocoprion, 36
  Ichthyosaurus, **37**
  Metasequoia, 45
  microfossils, 28
  Monograptus, **29**
  Ordovician, 28
  ostracode, 31, 40
  ostracoderm, 31
  placoderm, **31**
  plesiosaur, 41
  Psilophyton, **29**
  Sapindopsis, 43
  Scenella, **24**
  Stephen Shale, **27**
  sycamore leaf, **42**
  Titanotherium, 48
  trilobites, 24, 28, 33, 36
    Olenellus, **24**
Frank Slide, **75**
Franklin Arctic Expedition, 299
Freshfield Glacier, **2**
Frog (*see* Amphibians)
Frost-free period, 59-**60**, 65
Frost, 59, 61
  autumn, **65**
  hollows, 56, 59, 61
  spring, **59-60**
Fungi, 163, 165, 179, 208, 233, 236
Fur trade, 303-09
Fur traders, 103, 112-13, 136, 289,
  292, 296
Furnival, G. M., 124

G

Galileo, 17
Galls, **204**
Gas conservation, 319

Geological time chart, **24**
Geology, bedrock, map, **25**
Glacial:
  deposits, 75-77, 79-**80**
  erosion, **73**-75, 83
  erratics, **79**
  melt-waters, 73, 81-85
  valleys, **73**
Glaciation, 45, 50,**51**, 70, 79, 83, 96,
  118-120,131, 138, 277, 280, 282
Gleichen, 61, 82
Glenbow Foundation, 283
Gold Creek, 33
Gondwanaland, 34-35
Grand Portage, 304
Grand Trunk Pacific Railroad, **312**
Grande Prairie, 67, 83
Granite Wash sands, 29
Grasslands, 93-99
Grasses (*see* Vegetation, grasses)
Great Plains, 93, 96, 103, 135, 278, 280,
  282, 284, 291, 297, 298
Grimshaw, 84
Gruhn, Ruth, 285

H

Habitat:
  destruction of, 270
  hybridization of, 163-65
  mountain, 193-99
Hail, 60-**64**
Hardisty, 139
Hector, Dr. James, 103, 122, 299-300
Henday, Anthony, 296, 303-04, 306
Henry, Alexander, the younger, 308
Herbicides, 138
  aquatic, 258
High River, 62
Highwood Pass, 73
Hill:
  lands, 77, **86**
  montane elements, 131
  remnants, 78
Hills:
  Buffalo Head, 49, 78-79
  Chinchaga, 79, 84
  Clear, 49, 79, 84
  Crawford Plateau, 50
  Cypress, 46-51, 61, 77-78, 98, 111,
    117-33, 281, 300
  Hand, 49, 78, 138
  Hawk, 79
  Middle Sand, 83

Naylor, 79
Neutral, 78, 287
Nose Hill, 78
Peace, 284
Pine, 117
Porcupine, 46-51, **78**
Saddle, 49
Swan, 30, 78, 122
Sweetgrass, 49
Thickwood, 78
Virginia, 30
Wintering, 49, 78
Hind, Henry Youle, 135, 141, 299
Hind-Dawson Expedition, 309
Hinton, 84, 290
Hooker, W. J., 299
Hopewell Mound Builders, 280
Horses, 48, 50, 95, 279-81, 291, 303
  Merychippus, 96
Hoyle, Fred, 19
Hudson Bay, 119, 295, 297, 299, 303,
  308, 316
Hudson's Bay Company, 136, 295-97,
  299, 303, **305**, 308,
Hume, C. S., 41
Humidity, 61
Hydrogen sulphide, 222, 225
Hydrograph, **87**
Hypolimnion, 222

I

Ice-cap zone, 67
Idaho, 284, 290
Identification keys, 266, 268, 271-73
Indian:
  cairns, **284**, 288
  effigies, **286**
  Ethridge ware, 286-87
  legends, 10-16
  medicine bundles, **291**
  tools, 278
  treaties, 311
  wheels, **287**
Indian Summer, 67
Indians, 103, 280-293, 303-12, 318
  Assiniboine, 122, **283**, 289-**291**, 303,
  Beaver, 289-90, 292
  Blackfoot Confederacy, 104, 117,
    122, 136, **274**, 280-87, 288-**93**, **290**,
    304, 308, 310-11
  Blood, **281**, 290-**92**
  Treaty No. 7, 292
  Chipewyan, 290-**91**-92, 303
  Cree, 122, **285**, 288-90, 292, 303, 310-11

Indians (Continued)
  Crow, 287
  Gros Ventres, 290
  Hidatsa, 286-88
  Iroquois, 290
  Kootenai, 290
  Language stocks:
    Algonkian, 289-90
    Athapaskan, 289-90
    Kootenai, 289-90
    Salishan, 290
    Siouan, 289-90
  Meso-Indians, 280, 284
  Neo-Indians, 280, 284-89
  Ojibway, 290
  Palaeo-Indians, 280, 282-84
  Piegan, **279**, 288-**89**-90, 306
  Plains, 122, 290-92
  Salteaux, 290
  Sarcee, 289-90, 310-11
  Shoshone, 290
  Shuswap, 290
  Sioux, 290
  Slave, 289-90, 292
  Snare, 290
  Stoney, 103, 289-90, 311
Insect Collector's Guide, The, 267, 271
Insecticides, 260
Insects (*see* Invertebrates)
  life cycle of, 244
Invertebrates:
  Annelids (*see* Worm, segmented)
  Ant, Order Hymenoptera, 141, 209
  Aphid, Order Hemiptera,
    Spruce gall, *Adelges cooleyi*, **204**
  Backswimmer, Order Hemiptera,
    Notonecta sp., 200, **246**
  Beetle, Order Coleoptera,
    Ambrosia, Family Scolytidae,
      *Trypodendron bivittatum, T.
      borealis* and *T. retusus*, 208
    Bark, Family Scolytidae,
      Dendroctonus spp., 204, 207-**09**
    Boring, Family Buprestidae, 210
    Diving, Family Dytiscidae, 200
    Dung, Family Scarabaeidae, 209
    Engraver, Family Buprestidae, 207
    Fire, Family Buprestidae,
      Melanophila acuminata, 210
    Ground, Family Carabidae, 209-**10**
    Long-horned, Family
      Cerambycidae, *Ropalopus
      sanguinicallis*, 194-**95**, 210
    Metallic wood-boring,
      Family Buprestidae, 209-10

Poplar-borer, Family
    Cerambycidae, *Saperda
    calcarata*, **145**
  Stack, Family Buprestidae, 209
  Water, Families Dytiscidae and
    Hydrophilidae, 245-**46**
  Water scavenger, Family
    Hydrophilidae, 200, 245-46
  Whirligig, Family Gyrinidae, 200
  Wood-boring:
  Flatheaded, Family Buprestidae,
    204
  Round-headed,
    Family Cerambycidae, 204
Bug, Order Hemiptera,
  Flat, *Aradus* sp., 210
Bumblebee, Order Hymenoptera, 209
Butterfly, Order Lepidoptera,
  Parnassius smintheus, 209
  Silverspot, *Argynnis* sp., **147**
  Swallowtail, *Papilio* sp., **129**, 209
Caddisfly, Order Trichoptera, 146,
  195, 200, 242, **244**
Caterpillar, Order Lepidoptera,
  Eastern tent, *Malacosoma
  americanum*, 204
  Forest tent, *M. disstria*, 145, **203**
  Ugly-nest, *Archips cerasivorana*,
    204
  Western tent, *M. pluvialis*, 204
Centipede, Order Chilopoda, 145
Corixidae (*see* Waterboatman)
Cutworm, Order Lepidoptera,
  141, 149
  Red-backed, *Euxoa ochrogaster*,
    142
  Striped, *E. tessellata*, 142
Damselfly, Order Odonata, 149, **245**
Dobsonfly, Order Neuroptera, 243
Dragonfly, Order Odonata, 149, 200,
  245-46
Fly, Order Diptera,
  Black, *Simulium arcticum,
  S. venustum*, 146, 172, 245
  Bluebottle, Family Calliphoridae,
    208
  Crane, Family Tipulidae, *Chionea
  alexandriana*, 200, 208, 214
  Deer, Family Tabanidae,
    Hormopeza sp., 208
  Empidid, *Hormopeza* sp., 210
  Hessian, *Phytophaga destructor*,
  Horse, Family Tabanidae, 172, 208
  Hover, Family Syrphidae, 208
Gerridae (*see* Waterstrider)

Grasshopper, Order Orthoptera,
  Clear-winged, *Camnula pellucida*,
    141-42
  Migratory, *Melanoplus bilituratus*
    var. *mexicanus*, **113**, 141-42
  Rocky Mountain, *M. spretus*, 141
  Two-striped, *M. bivittatus*, **141**
  Wingless, *Asemoplus* sp., 219
Grylloblattidae (*see* Iceworm)
Hellgrammites (*see* Dobsonfly)
Hemiptera (*see* Bug)
Hydra, Class Hydrozoa,
  Hydra spp., **240**
Iceworm, Order Orthoptera,
  Family Grylloblattidae, *Grylloblatta
  campo dei formis, G. barberi*,
  212, 214
Leaf miner, Order Lepidoptera, 204
  Aspen, *Phyllocnistis populiella*,
    194, 204, **206**
Leech, **241**
Lymnaeidae (*see* Snail)
Mayfly, Order Ephemeroptera,
  195, 200, **242, 243**-44
  Rhithrogena doddsi, 243
Midge, Order Diptera, 208
  Phantom, Family Chironomidae,
    Chaoborus sp., 241
  Gall, Family Cecidomyiidae, 204
Mite, Order Acarina, 145
Mosquito, Order Diptera, 111, 149,
  172, 209, **245**
  Family Culicidae,
    Aedes sp., 245
Physidae (*see* Snail)
Planorbidae (*see* Snail)
Pondskater (*see* Waterstrider)
Roundworm, Class Nematoda,
  141, 145
Sawfly, Order Hymenoptera,
  Wheatstem, *Cephus cinctus*,
  113-14, 142
Scale insect, Order Hemiptera, 194
Scorpion fly, Order Mecoptera,
  Boreus californicus fuscus, 120, 214
Shrimp, Class Crustacea,
  Fairy, *Branchinecta gigas*, **241**
  Freshwater, *Gammarus* sp., **241**
  Relict, *Mysis relicta*, 241
Snail, Class Gastropoda, 131, 145
  Families Lymnaeidae, Planorbidae,
  · Physidae, **242**
Snow fleas, Order Collembola, 214
Snow insects (*see* Scorpion fly and
  Cranefly)

Invertebrates (Continued)
  Spider, Order Araneida, 145
  Spittlebug, Order Hemiptera,
      Aphrophora permutata, **206**
      Western pine, Family Cercopidae,
      206
  Sponge, Phylum Porifera,
      Spongilla sp., 239-40
  Springtail (see Snow fleas)
  Stonefly, Order Plecoptera, 242-**43-44**
  Tapeworm, Class Cestoda,
      Bladder, *Muticeps* spp., 144
  Tubificidae (see Worm, segmented)
  Wasp, Order Hymenoptera, 209
      Gall, Family Cynipidae, **204**
  Water boatman, Order Hemiptera,
      Family Corixidae, 200, **246**
  Waterbug, Order Hemiptera, 246
      Giant, *Lethocerus americanus*, **246**
  Water-flea, Class Crustacea,
      Order Cladocera, *Daphnia* spp.,
      241, 251
      Order Copepoda, *Cyclops* spp., 240
      Diaptomus spp., **241**
  Waterstrider, Order Hemiptera,
      Family Gerridae, **200**, 239-**40**, 246
  Webworm, Order Lepidoptera,
      Beet, *Loxostega sticticalis*, 114
  Wireworm, Order Coleoptera,
      Prairie grain, *Ctenicera æripennis
      destructor*, 141-42, 149
  Worm,
      Flat,
          Fluke, Class Trematoda, 242
          Rhadocoel, *Mesostomum*, 246
          Planarian, *Polycelis coronata*,
          242, 246
      Horsehair, *Gordius* sp., 246
      Segmented,
          Families Annelidae, Tubificidae,
          145, **241**, 242
Iron deposits, 23
Irrigation, (see reservoirs), 262-63

J

Jasper, 24, 37, 47-48, 54, 60, 69-71,
    74-75, 84, 290
Johnson's Canyon, 74-75
Jonas Creek, 75
Jurassic Period, 37-38, 43
    plant life, 38

K

Kaministiquia, 304
Kananaskis Valley, 70-73
Keewatin ice sheet, 157
Kepler, Johannes, 17
Killing bottles, dangers of, 267
Koeppen, W., 67

L

Lac La Biche, 62-63, 67, 309, 311
Lac Ste. Anne, 311
Lacombe, 60
Lake deposits, 82
Lake plains, 81
Lakes:
    eutrophic, 224
    food in, 224
    in winter, **235**
    limnetic zone, 223, 227, 235
    littoral zone, **223**, 225, 227-**28**, 235
    oligotrophic, 224, 253
    overturn, 222
    oxygen demand in, 222
    plant life in, 227-35
    productivity, 223-25
    profundal zone, 227
    temperatures in, **222**
Lakes, **86**
    Athabasca, 23, 58, 83-84, 155, 157,
        170, 249, 252, 290, 297
    Battle, 138
    Beaverhill, 139, 149
    Bow, **53**, 74
    Brulé, 84
    Buck, 224
    Buffalo, 139, 309
    Claire, 78, 252
    Cold, 29, 241, 250-51, 253
    Cooking, 81
    Crowsnest, 74
    Dowling, 139
    Eaglenest, 79
    Edmonton, 81
    Egypt, 74, 81
    Elkwater, 129
    Eva, 79
    Great Slave, 29, 44, 155, 290
    Hay, 83
    Hector, **70**

Jasper, 84
Kananaskis, 262
Kehiwin, 251
Lake of the Woods, 296, 301
Legend, 79
Lesser Slave, 28, 35, 57-58, *78*,
    83, 190, 290, 298
Louise, 26, 51, 58-60, **62**, 71, 74, 224
Maligne, 74
Manitoba, 297
Mann, 128
Many Islands, 98
Margaret, 79
Medicine, 75
Methy, 297
Minnewanka, 74
Moose, 284, 305
Moraine, 74-75, **224**
Namur, 79
Pakowki, 98, 288
Peyto, 74
Pigeon, 138
Pine, 224, 304
Pitchimi, 79
Pyramid, 224
Reesor, 129
Rock, 253
Spray, 74, 262
Sullivan, 139
Superior, 22-23, 304
Wabamun, 224, 227, **228**
Wadlin, 79
Waterton, 74, 224, 241
Winnipeg, 297
Landes, R. W., 124
La Vérendrye, 296-**97**
Leo, 12
Lethbridge, 29, 45, 54, 58, 60-63,
    81-82, 88, 282, 284
Lewis Fault (see Castle Mountain
    Thrust), 71
Lichens (see Vegetation, lichens)
Light-year, 18
Limestones, 23, 48, 70
    Minnewanka, 34
    Rundle, 34
    Tyndall, 28
Lizard (Horned Toad) (see Reptiles)
Lloydminster, 58-59
Loess, 99
Logan's Sea, 37
Loring, J. A., 301
Lowell, Percival, 9
Lyra, 13-14

M

Mackenzie, Alexander, 298-99, 305-06
Mackenzie Lowlands, 77
Macoun, John, 124, 301
Maligne Canyon, 74-75
Mammals:
  grass eating, 95
  prehistoric, 26, **48**, **50**, 95-96, 98-99,
    278-82
  species:
  Antelope (see Pronghorn),
  Badger, Silver, *Taxidea taxus*, 108,
    110, 115, 133, 140
  Bat:
    Big-eared, *Myotis evotis*, 111
    Hoary, *Lasiurus cinereus*, 111
    Little brown, *M. lucifugus*, 111
    Red, *L. borealis*, 111
    Say, masked, *M. subulatus*, 111
  Bear:
    Black, *Ursus americanus*, 107, 146,
      170, **183**, 212
    Grizzly, *U. arctos*, 96, 98, 106,
      122, **219**
  Beaver, *Castor canadensis*, 107-08,
    131, 133, 146, 171, 178, 198-99,
    226, 242
  Bison, *Bison bison*, 100, 103-04, 106,
    112, 122, 135-36, 140-41, 149,
    170-71, 178-79, 280-94, **300**, 303,
    306, 309-11
  Bobcat, Barred, *Lynx rufus*, **108**
  Caribou, *Rangifer tarandus*, 171-72,
    175, 178-80
  Chipmunk:
    Buff-bellied, *Eutamias amoenus*,
      206
    Least, *E. minimus*, 128, 145, **177**
  Cougar, Rocky Mountain,
    Felis concolor, 108
  Coyote, *Canis latrans*, 108, 110, 115,
    127, 128, 144, 146-**47**, 171, **177**, 179
  Deer:
    Mule, *Dama hemionus*, 107, 115,
      128, 133, 149, **170**-71, **179**, 201
    White-tailed, *D. virginianus*,
      106-07, 115, 128, 133, 149, 181
Elk (see Wapiti)
  Fisher, *Martes pennanti*, 171, 179
  Fox:
    Arctic, *Alopex lagopus*, 172
    Kit, *Vulpes velox*, 106, 122, **129**
    Red, *V. vulpes*, 115, 127, 128, 144,
      179, 182, 184
  Goat, Mountain, *Oreamnus*
    americanus, **215**, 218

Gopher, Anderson's Pocket,
  Thomomys talpoides andersoni,
  107, 127, 140
"Gopher" (see Richardson's ground
  squirrel)
Groundhog (see Marmot)
Hare:
  White-tailed Prairie (Jack Rabbit),
    Lepus townsendii, 111, 115, 127,
    147
  Varying (Snowshoe hare or
    "rabbit"), *L. americanus*, 128,
    144, 176-**77**, 178, 180, 182, 184
Jack Rabbit (see Hare, White-tailed
  Prairie)
Lemming, Bog, *Synaptomys borealis*,
  178
Lynx, *Lynx canadensis*, 108, 128, 144,
  146, 171, **178**, 182, 184
Marmot:
  Hoary, *Marmota caligata*, **215**, 219
  Woodchuck, *M. monax*, 170
Marten, *Martes americana*, 171, 179,
  182, 184, 209
Mouse, **108**, 144-46, 176, **180**-81
  Deer, *Peromyscus maniculatus*,
    107, **179**
  Grasshopper, *Onychomys*
    leucogaster, 107
  House, *Mus musculus*, 114, 133
  Maximilian Pocket, *Perognathus*
    fasciatus, 107
  White-footed, *Peromyscus*
    leucopus, 107, 128
Mink, *Mustela vison*, 131, 133, 146,
  171, 178, 182
Moose, *Alces alces*, 96, 107, 133, 149,
  164, 171, 176, 178, **181**, 212
Muskrat, *Ondatra zibethica*, 131, 133,
  147, 170, 171, 178, **183**
Otter, *Lutra canadensis*, 146, 171, 178
Pika, *Ochotona princeps*, **217**
Porcupine, *Erethizon dorsatum*,
  97, 108, 170-71
Pronghorn, *Antilocapra americana*,
  100, **104**, 106-07, 122, 127-**29**, 133
Rabbit, Cottontail, *Sylvilagus*
  nuttallii, **111**, 115, 123, 127
Raccoon, *Procyon lotor*, 110, 125
Rat:
  Kangaroo, *Dipodomys ordii*,
    98, 107, 120
  Norway, *Rattus norvegicus*,
    114, 133
  Gray Bushy-tailed Wood (Pack or
    Trader), *Neotoma cinerea*, 217

"Rock Rabbit" (see Pika),
Shrew, 176, 179, 180-81
  Cinereous, *Sorex cinereus*, 110, **183**
  Mountain Water, *S. palustris*, **196**
  Prairie Dusky, *S. obscurus*, 110
Sheep, Mountain, *Ovis canadensis*,
  198, 201, **215**, 218
Skunk, *Mephitis mephitis*, 110, 115,
  127-28, **176**
Squirrel:
  Columbian Ground, *Spermophilus*
    columbianus, 201-02, **215**
  Flying, *Glaucomys sabrinus*,
    170, 175, 179
  Golden-mantled Ground, *S.*
    lateralis, **215**-16, 219
  Red or Tree, *Tamiasciurus*
    hudsonicus, 128, 160, 170, 176-**77**,
    209
  Richardson's Ground,
    S. richardsonii, **97**, 108, 115,
    127, 140
  Thirteen-lined, *S. tridecemlineatus*,
    97, 108, 127, 140
Vole, **108**, 144-46, 176, 179-80, 182
  Badlands, *Microtus pennsylvanicus*
    insperatus, 108
  Meadow, *M. pennsylvanicus*,
    107, 130, 178
  Pallid or Sagebrush, *Lemmiscus*
    curtatus, 107, 120
  Phenacomys, *Phenacomys*
    intermedius, 178
  Red-backed, *Clethrionomys*
    gapperi, 108, 178, **183**
Weasel, 115, 144, 171, **177**
  Ferret, Blackfooted, *Mustela*
    nigripes, 110
  Least, *M. rixosa*, 110
  Long-tailed, *M. frenata*, 110, 127, **177**
  Short-tailed, *M. erminea*, 110, 126, **180**
Wapiti (see Elk), *Cervus canadensis*,
  96, 107, **129**, 149, 170-**71**, 178,
  201, 218
Wolverine, *Gulo luscus*, 171
Wolf:
  Great Plains or "Lobo," *Canis*
    lupus nubilus, 96, 106, 122,
    144, 146
  Timber, *C. lupus*, 171, **179**
Manitoba, 136, 141, 262, 297, 299, 309,
  312-13
Manyberries, 117
Manyberries Experimental Range
  Station, 100

Maya, 280

Mayerthorpe, 6

McConnell, R. G., 41, 122, 301

McGillivray, Duncan, 305-07

McLearn, F. H., 41

McMurray, 298-99

McMurray Sands (*see* Athabasca
  Oil Sands)

Meadow Lake Escarpment, 28

Meanook Meteor Station, 6, 8-9

Medicine Hat, 44, 54, 60, 65, 124,
  288, 314

Melt-water channels, 73-81, 85
  coulees, 81

Mesozoic Era, 36, 46, 48, 50
  Cretaceous, 38-43
  Jurassic, 37-38, 43
  Triassic, 36-37

Mesozoic foliage, 43

Meteorites, 5-6
  Bruderheim, 5-**6**
  carbonaceous, 6
  importance of quick recovery, 6-7
  Orgueil, 6
  Peace River, 6

Meteors, 5-6, 10
  Perseid, **6**

Methy Portage, 297-98

Métis, 307-12

Microblade, **283**

Miette, 24

Miocene Epoch, 95-96

Migration, 269

Migratory Birds Convention Act, 267

Milky Way, 12-16, 18-**19**

Mining, 258

Missionaries, 136, 308-09
  Lacombe, Father, **308**
  McDougall, Rev. George, 308-**09**
  Rundle, Rev. Robert Terrell, **308**
  Thibault, Father, **308**

Mississippi drainage system, 51, 253-54

Mistaya Canyon, 75

Montagne de Cyprès, 117

Montana, 22-31, 39, 43, 49, 124, 258

Montane elements (*see* Cypress Hills),
  131

Montania, 27

Moraines, 51, **89**

Morley, 76-77

Morningside, 83

Mosses (*see* Vegetation, mosses)

Mount Palomar Observatory, 18

Mountains:
  Mt. Assiniboine, 48

Birch, 59, 78-79

Brazeau Range, 76

Caribou, 49, 79, 84

Cascade, 48

Mt. Edith Cavell, 26

Chief, 47

Churchillian, 23-24

Coast Range, 35, 38, 41

Colin Range, **71**

Crowsnest, **47**, 71

Deer, 78

Mt. Eisenhower, **26**, 48, 71

Fiddle Range, 48

Folding, **49**

House, 49, 78

Livingstone Range, 73

Mackenzie, 37, 41

Moose, 76

Muskeg, 78

Nose, 49

Omineca, 38, 43

Pelican, 78

Pyramid, 24

Mt. Robson, 48

Roche Miette, 48, **217**

Rocky, **21**-51, 53-54, 58-60, 70-76, 95,
  119-20, 193, 278, 282, 297-98, 300

Mt. Rundle, 34-**35**, 48, 73

Sawback Range, 71

Selkirk, 38

Stony, 78

Sulphur, 74, 212

Three Sisters, 48

Tunnel, 51, 74

Turtle, **75**

Wallace, 78

Mt. Wilson, 28

Mythology of constellations, 10-16

N

Napi, Blackfoot hero, 288

National Museum of Canada, 122

Natural gas (*see* Oil and gas fields)

Natural history:
  methods of study, 266
  newsletters, 268
  observations, making and reporting
    of, 266, 268-71
  plants, mounting of, 266-67
  publications, 268-70
  societies, 265, 268
  teachers of, 265-66

Naturalists:
  early, 299
  rôle of, 265, 268-70

Nelson, S. J., 28

Nevis, 45

New Norway, 30

Newbrook Meteor Station, 6, 8-9

Newton, Isaac, 17

Noctilucent clouds, 9, **10**

Nordegg, 75-76, 85

North American Boundary Commission,
  300-01

North Star (*see* Polaris)

North Star of Thuban, 14

North West Company, 297-99, 305-08

North-West Mounted Police, 112, **303**,
  310-11

Northern Cross (*see* Cygnus)

Northern Lights (*see* Aurora borealis)

Northwest Territories, 58, 136

Nor'westers, 305-08

Nutrient salts, 223-25, 233-35, 237

O

Obed, 31

Oceans:
  Arctic, 21
  Atlantic, 29
  Pacific, 54, 58, 67

Oil and gas era, 315-19

Oil and gas fields, 29-30, 34, 39, 41, 43,
  316-17

Old Copper Culture, Wisconsin, 280

Old Women's Buffalo Jump, 285-88

Olds, 81

Oligocene Epoch, 95, 119, 122
  Gravels, 122

Ordovician Period, 27-29

Orion, 10, 11
  Nebula of, **11**

Oxygen, 232, 238, 241, 246, 249, 252,
  259-60
  demand, 259, 261

Oysters, 38, 42, 44, 99

P

Pacific:
  air, 55, 60, 66
  winds, 54, 67

Pakowki dunes, **82**

Palaeozoic coral reefs, 39
Palaeozoic Era:
  Cambrian, 24
  Carboniferous, 24, 33-35
  Devonian, 24-33
  Ordovician, 24, 27-29, 31
  Permian, 24, **35-36**
  Silurian, 24, 29
Paleocene Epoch, 119
Palliser, Captain John, 118, 122, 299-301
Palliser Expedition, 103, 309
Palliser's Triangle, 118
Parks, **186**, 254, 267
  Banff National Park, 26, 28, 34, 154
  Dinosaur Provincial Park, 45
  Elk Island National Park, 81, 104, 170
  Jasper National Park, 24, 26, 31, 34, 48, 58, 70
  Nemiskam National Park, 106
  Waterton Lakes National Park, 23-24, 34, 47, 60, 71, 73
  Wood Buffalo National Park, 104, 171, 178
  Writing-on-Stone Provincial Park, 288
Peace River region, 27, 29-31, 33, 35-36, 38-39, 41, 55, 62, 77-79, 82-85, 89, 96, 98, 283, 290, 297-98, 315
Pedlars, 304
Pegasus, 15
Penhold, 61
Perseus, 15
Petitot, E., 301
Petroglyphs, **277**, 288
Photosynthesis, 159-60, 232-34
Phytoplankton, 240
Pictographs, 288, **293**
Pincher Creek, 58, **95**
Pine Point lead-zinc deposit, 30
Place names of Alberta, map, **94**
Plains or Equestrian Culture, 291-92
Plant Life:
  in lakes, 227, 234
  in limnetic zone, 227, 231
  in littoral zone, 227
  in streams, 237
  on land, 29, 33-34
Pleiades, 10, **19**
Pliocene Epoch, 96
Pluto, 9
Points, stone, projectile, 279-86
  Agate Basin, **282**
  Alberta, **283**
  Avonlea, 284-**85**

Besant, 284, **285**, 286
Clovis, **279**, 282
Duncan, 284-**85**
Eden, 282-**83**
Fluted, **282**
Folsom, **279**, 282
Hanna, 284-**85**
Hell Gap, 282
leaf-shaped, **286**
Lerma, 282
McKean, **284**
Milnesand, 282
Oxbow, **284**-85
Plainview, **282**
Recent, **285**
Scottsbluff, 282-**83**, 285
Wetaskiwin, **285**
Polaris (see North Star), 12-14
Pollution, 259-62, 265, 270
Pond, Peter, 297-98, 305-06
Population growth, 314-17
Prairie, 93-115
  climate, 99-100
  fescue, 125
  fire, **101**
  in bloom, **93**
  mixed-grass, 98, 103, 111, 125
Prairie Farm Rehabilitation Act, 319
Prairie Nest Record Cards, 269, 271
Precambrian Era, **21**-27
  Archaeozoic, 21
  Azoic, 21
  Basement, **22**-24, 27, 49, 69
  Proterozoic, 21-24
Precambrian rocks, **21**-22, 48, 69, 83
  Churchillian, 23-24
Precipitation:
  annual variation, 60, 62
  autumn, 64-**66**
  mean annual, **60**
  showers, 62
  spring, 59-**61**
  summer, 61-**63**
  winter, 58
Preglacial river valleys, **72**
Prehistoric mammals, 26, **48**, **50**, 95-96, 98-99, 278-82
Productivity, 222-26
  in lakes, 224-253
  in ponds, 225
  in reservoirs, 225
  in rivers, 225
  in saline lakes, 225
  in streams, 225
  in saline sloughs, 225

Profundal zone, 223, 227, 235
Provincial government rat control, 114, 133
Provost, 88

Q

Qali, **174**-176, 179-80
Qaminiq, **176**, 178
Quasars, 18-19
Queen Elizabeth Planetarium, 9

R

Radiocarbon dating, 278-80
Rain:
  autumn, 64-**66**
  effect of topography on, 62
  spring, 59-**61**
  summer, 61-**63**
  winter, 58
Ralston, 55
Ramparts, 71
Rare species, 269
Red Deer, 27, 29, 63, 81, 284
Red Deer River Crossing, 312
Red River revolt, 309
Red River settlement, 136
Red Rock canyon, **197**
Reforestation, 190-91
Regulus, 12
Reptiles:
  Lizard:
    Horned toad, *Phrynosoma douglassi,* **107**, 111, 120
  Snake:
    Bull, *Pituophis catenifer,* 107, **126**-27
    Gopher (see Bull snake),
    Hog-nosed, *Heterodon nasicus,* 120
    Rattlesnake, *Crotalus viridis,* 107
    Wandering gartersnake, *Thamnophis elegans vagrans,* 128, 131
    Western plains gartersnake, *T. radix haydeni,* **97**, 107, 127, 128, 131
Reservoirs, 225, 262-63
  Bearspaw, 262
  Brazeau, **262**
  Ghost, 262
  Kananaskis, 262

Reservoirs (Continued)
  Spray, 262
  Spruce Coulee, 130-131
  Waterton, 262
Ribstones, 288
Richardson, John, 299
Riel Rebellion, 292, 312
Rigel, 10-11
Rivers:
  drainage systems, 51, **85, 86**, 99, 253-54
  life in, 242-47
  northern drainage, 155, **157**
Rivers:
  Assiniboine, 297
  Athabasca, 59, 62, 65, 69, 73-77, 83-85, 290, 297-98
  Battle, 81, 138-39
  Belly, **45**, 251
  Bow, 73-74, 77, **84**-85, **91**, 249-51, 260-61, 286, 297, 315
  Brazeau, **262**
  Clearwater, **76**, 85, 297-98
  Cline, 75
  Driftpile, 83
  Hayes, 303
  Heart, 83
  Hotchkiss, 84
  James, 85
  Kananaskis, 73, **247**
  Keg, 27
  Lesser Slave, 78
  Little Bow, 287
  Little Smoky, 77
  Mackenzie, 55, 305
  McLeod, 65, 85
  Meikle, 84
  Milk, 83, 252-54, 288
  North Saskatchewan, 73, 75, 85, 138, 249-51, 261-63, 284, 297-98, 304-07, 309, 311, **314**-15
  Notikewin, 84
  Oldman, 59, 73, 75, 249, 284, 287
  Paddle, 83, 87
  Peace, 43, 49-50, 59, 65, 77-79, 82-85, 253, 263, 305
  Pembina, 83, 87
  Prairie, 83
  Ram, 77
  Red, 297
  Red Deer, 45, 77, 85, **195**, 250, 252
  Sheep, 77
  Slave, 21, 69, 83, 85, **154**-55
  Smoky, 27, 39, 43, 77, 84, 193
  Snake Indian, 75, **193**
  South Saskatchewan, 59, 65, **81**, 99, 138, 250, 263
  Sunwapta, **74**, 75
  Swan, 83
  Wabiskaw, 78, 84
  Whitemud, 84
Road construction, 258
Robertson-Ross, Colonel, 310
Rocks, 21-26, 28, 33-34, 47, 138
Rocky Mountain House, 250
Rocky Mountain subalpine zone, 154
Rooted plant communities, 228
Routes of early explorers, 295-**96**
Rowan, Dr. William, 184
Royal Astronomical Society of Canada, 8
Royal Canadian Mounted Police, 310
Rupert's Land, 295, 297, 299-300
Russell, L. S., 124
Rutherford, R. L., 41

S

Salamander (see Amphibians)
Saskatchewan Sands and Gravels, 50, 281
Sandstones, 24, 71-75
  Cambrian, 71
  Precambrian, 71, 157
Saskatchewan, 26-27, 29, 31, 33-34, 38, 41, 49, 51, 136, 139, 262, 279, 284, 286, 288, 290
Saunders, William and Charles, 313
Saville, D. B. O., 266
Scorpio, 14
Seas, early, 21, **23, 28**
  Arctic Ocean, 21
  Atlantic Ocean, 29
  Black, 27
  Carboniferous, **33**
  Cretaceous, **42, 43**
  Dunvegan, **42**
  Gulf of Mexico, 21
  Jurassic (Logan's Sea), 37-**38**
  Mowry, **41**-42
  Pacific Ocean, 21
  Permian, **35**
  Triassic, 36-**37**
Seismic lines, 258
Selwyn, A. R. C., 301
Settlers, 311-14
Sewage treatment, 261
Shaw, Angus, 305-06
Sheran, Nicholas, 314
Shortgrass plains, 98-104, 111-12
Sifton, Sir Clifford, 313-14

Silurian Period, 29
Sirius, 11
Skiff, 283
Sky:
  autumn, 14, **15**, 16
  spring, 12-**13**
  summer, 13-**14**
  winter, 10-**12**
Sloughs, **148, 225**, 258
Slumping, 79
Smallpox, 303, 310
Smith, 84
Smoking Star Legend, 16
Snake (see Reptiles)
Snake Indian Falls, 75
Snow, 172
  autumn, 66
  effect on forest life, 175-80
  how made, **174**
  shadows, **176**
  spring, 60
  winter, **57**, 58
Soil:
  erosion, **85**, 187
  profile, **89**
  zones, **88**
Soils, **88**
  alkaline, 139
  Black, 89, 124, 139
  Brown, 87, 103, 124, 139
  chernozems, 87
  Dark Brown, 88, 103, 124, 139
  Dark Gray, 89
  Dark Gray Wooded, 89
  Gray Wooded, **89**, 124, 156
  Podzolic, 87, 89
  prairie, 101
  solonetzic, 103
  Thin Black, 89
Solar system, **18**
Spica, 12
Sputnik I, 6
St. Albert, 309-10
Stalker, A. M., 282
Stephen Shale deposit, 26-27
Stettler, 45, 282, 285
Steveville, 45, 111
Stone Age, 282
Stone rings (see Teepee rings), **286**-88
Stream:
  erosion, 258
  fluctuations in flow, effect of, 226, 262
  headwaters, **199**
  mountain, 198, **225**
  prairie, **225**

Streamflow, **86-87**
Summer Triangle, 13-14
Sun Dance, 291
Sundre, 34, 77
Sunshine:
    annual, **58**
    spring, 59-60
    summer, 64
    winter, 58
Surveys, 300-01
Sustained yield, 185
Sweetgrass Arch, 49
Swift Current, 124
"Swimmer's itch" (*see* Dermatitis,
    Schistosome)

T

Taber, 82, 281, 283
Taiga, 151-54, 157-58, 169
    definition, 151-53
    extent in Alberta, 153-58
    transitional:
        Lower Foothills section, 158
        Upper Foothills section, 158
Tar Sands (*see* Athabasca oil sands)
Tathlina uplift, 29
Taurus, 10
Teepee rings, **286**-88
Temperature:
    April, **58**
    autumn, 64-65
    changes of, 54, 60
    diurnal variation, 61
    ·effect of topography on, 56, 61
    in lakes, **222**
    inversion, 56-68
    January, **56**, 57
    July, **61**
    lowest, **57**
    maximum, 61, **62**
    Medicine Hat, 99
    October, **65**
    range of, 62
    rapid changes of, **55**
    spring, 59-61
    summer, 61
    winter, 56-59
Tertiary Period, 46-51, 73, 77, 95-96,
    119, 138
    Eocene, 46-48, 95
    Miocene, 46
    Oligocene, 46
    Paleocene, 46
    Pliocene, 46

Thales, 16
Thermal stratification, 222, 224
Thermocline, 222, 251
Thompson, David, 85, 135, 297-99,
    301, 305
Three Hills Weather Station, 56
Thuban, Old North Star, 14
Thunderstorms, 62-**63**
Till plains, 79
Timber:
    quota, 185
    volume, 186, **189**
Toltecs, 280
Tombaugh, Clyde, 9
Tonquin Valley, 71
Tornado, 64, **66**
Trees (*see* Vegetation, trees)
Triassic Period, 36-38
    animals, 36
Tundra, 65, 151-52, 182
    alpine, 217, **218**, 219
Turbidity, 260
Turner Valley, 34, 39
Turnor, Philip, 297
Turtox Service Leaflets, 266, 271
Tyrrell, J. B., 41

U

Universe, age of, 17-18
    origin of, 19
University of Alberta, 8, 301, 315
University of Calgary, 9, 301
Ursa Major, 11, 14-15
Ursa Minor, 12

V

Valley of the Ten Peaks, 71, 75
Vanguard I satellite, 9
Vega, 13-14, 19
Vegetation:
    Algae:
        Amphipora, 31, 33
        Aphanizomenon, 233
        Asterionella, **232**
        Chaetophora, 231
        Chara, Stonewort, 230-**31**, 235
        Characium, 231
        Chlamydomonas, 234
        Cladophora, 31, 33, **229-30**, 235, 237
        Cocconeis, 231
        Coleochaete, 231

        Cosmarium, 233, 236
        Cymbella, 237
        Draparnaldia, 237
        Gloeotrichia, 231
        Gyrosigma, 237
        Microcystis, 233
        Navicula, **230**
        Nostoc, **230**, 234
        Oscillatoria, **230**-31, 234, 236
        Pediastrum, 236
        Phormidium, 237
        Pinnularia, 237
        Rivularia, **237**
        Scenedesmus, **232**, 234, 236
        Spirogyra, 229-**30**, 234
        Stigeoclonium, 231, 237
        Synedra, 231
        Tabellaria, 231
        Vaucheria, 237
    Anemone:
        Canada, *Anemone canadensis*, **167**
        Crocus, Prairie, *A. patens* var.
            wolfgangia, 103, 140-**41**
        Cut-leaved, *A. multifida*, 140
        Western, *A. quinquefolia* var.
            interior, **213**
    Arnica, heartleaved, *Arnica
        cordifolia*, 127, **131**
    Arrow-grass, *Triglochin maritima*,
        148
    Aster:
        Creeping white, *Aster laevis* var.
            geyeri, 140
        Eaton's, *A. eatonii*, 127, 160
        Lindley's, *A. ciliolatus*, 128, 142
        Showy, *A. conspicuus*, 127
    Avens:
        Purple, *Geum rivale*, **130**
        Three-flowered, *G. triflorum*,
            143, 218
    Baneberry, *Actaea rubra* var.
        arguta, 127
    Bean, golden, *Thermopsis
        rhombifolia*, 126
    Bearberry, *Arctostaphylos uva-ursi*,
        127, 214
    Bedstraw, northern, *Galium boreale*,
        142
    Bilberry, dwarf, *Vaccinium
        caespitosum*, 127
    Bishop's cap, *Mitella nuda*, 127, 160
    Bistort, *Polygonum bistortoides*, 131
    Bladder pod, *Lesquerella arenosa*,
        127
    Bladderwort, small, *Utricularia
        minor*, 130

Vegetation (Continued)

Bluebell, *Campanula rotundifolia*, 126, **143**

Blueberry, *Vaccinium* spp., 210

Brooklime, American, *Veronica americana*, 130

Brown-eyed Susan (*see* Gaillardia)

Buckbrush, *Symphoricarpos occidentalis*, 98, 128

Buffalo-berry, *Shepherdia canadensis*, 107, 127, 160

Bulrush, *Scirpus* spp., 130, 148, 228
    Small-fruited, *S. microcarpus*, 130

Bunchberry, *Cornus canadensis*, **123**, 127, 142, 160

Buttercup, heart-leaved, *Ranunculus cardiophyllus*, 131

Cactus:
    Pincushion, *Mammillaria vivipara*, **105**, 120
    Prickly pear, *Opuntia* spp., 101, **105**

Camas:
    Death, *Zygadenus gramineus*, 126
    White, *Z. elegans*, **126**

Campion, Moss, *Silene acaulis* var. *excapa*, **213**

Cattail, *Typha latifolia*, 148, **221**, 228, 231

Cedar, ground, *Lycopodium complanatum*, 127

Chokecherry, *Prunus virginiana* var. *melanocarpa*, 128, **142**, 204

Cinquefoil:
    Early, *Potentilla concinna*, 126
    Shrubby, *P. fruticosa*, 126, 140

Clematis, purple, *Clematis verticellaris* var. *columbiana*, 127, 131

Clover, 131
    Alsike, *Trifolium hybridum*, 125
    Prairie purple, *Petalostemon purpureum*, **105**
    Red, *T. pratense*, 125
    White, *T. repens*, 125

Club moss, **125**-27
    Little, *Selaginella densa*, 103, 126
    Stiff, *Lycopodium annotinum*, 125, 127

Columbine, *Aquilegia* spp., **167**

Comandra, northern *Geocaulon lividum*, 161

Coral root, (*see* Orchid), **123**

Corydalis, golden, *Corydalis aurea*, 131

Cottongrass, *Eriophorum* spp., **167**

Cowberry, *Vaccinium vitis-idaea*, 161

Cow parsnip, *Heracleum lanatum*, 128

Cranberry:
    Low-bush, *Viburnum edule*, 127, 142

Crane's bill, *Geranium viscosissimum*, 131

Cress, rock, *Arabis hirsuta*, 140

Crowfoot:
    White water, *Ranunculus subrigidus*, **227**
    Yellow water, *R. flabellaris*, 130, 227

Currant:
    Black, *Ribes hudsonianum*, 127
    Red, *R. triste*, 160

Daisy, ox-eye, *Chrysanthemum leucanthemum*, 125

Dandelion, *Taraxacum officinale*, 125, 131, 141, 202, 207

Dewberry, *Rubus pubescens*, 142

Dock:
    Narrow-leaved, *Rumex mexicanus*, 130
    Sand (veined), *R. venosus*, **105**

Dogwood, red osier, *Cornus stolonifera*, 142, 160

Dryad:
    Yellow, (Mountain avens), *Dryas drummondii*, 195

Duckweed, *Lemna minor*, *L. trisulca*, 130, **229**

Everlasting, *Antennaria* spp., 103
    Showy, *A. pulcherrima*, 126

Fairy bells, *Disporum trachycarpum*, 128

Fern, fragile, *Cystopteris fragilis*, 127

Fireweed, *Epilobium angustifolium*, 131
    Broad-leaved, *E. latifolium*, 131, 195

Fleabane, Canada, *Erigeron canadensis*, 149

Gaillardia, *Gaillardia aristata*, **123**, 126, 201

Geranium, wild (sticky), *Geranium viscosissimum*, 201

Goldenrod, *Solidago* spp., 126, 131, 140, **167**

Gooseberry, wild, *Ribes oxyacanthoides*, 128

Grasses:
    Blue grama, *Bouteloua gracilis*, **96**, 98, 100-01, 103, 124, 126

Bluegrass, *Poa interior*, 101, 126

Bluejoint (Marsh reed), *Calamagrostis canadensis*, 96, 98, 160

Brome:
    Awnless, *Bromus inermis*, 125, 128, 131
    Fringed, *B. ciliatus*, 142

Fescue, *Festuca* sp., **95**, 125, 139, 149
    Bluebunch, (Idaho), *F. idahoenis*, 126, 131, 140
    Rough (Bunchgrass), *F. scabrella* **95**-96, 126, 140, 200

June, *Koeleria cristata*, 98-**99**, 101, 103, 126, 140

Needle and thread (Spear grass), *Stipa comata*, 98, 100-01, 103, 124, 126, 140

Manna, *Glyceria grandis*, 130

Marsh reed, *Calamagrostis canadensis*, 130

Parry oat, *Danthonia parryi*, 139, 200

Peppergrass, *Lepidium densiflorum*, 149

Porcupine, *Stipa spartea* var. *curtiseta*, 140

Quack, *Agropyron repens*, 125, 131

Reed, *Phragmites communis*, 228

Salt, *Distichlis stricta*, 148

Spike trisetum, *Trisetum spicatum*, 127

Timber oat, *Danthonia intermedia*, 126, 140

Wheatgrass: **98**, 100-01, 103, 124
    Bearded, *Agropyron subsecundum*, 126
    Northern, *A. dasystachyum*, 126
    Slender, *A. trachycaulum*, 140
    Western, *A. smithii*, 126

Wild barley, *Hordeum jubatum*, **143**

Wild rye:
    Giant, *Elymus cinereus*, 128
    Hairy, *E. innovatus*, 142

Hawkweed:
    White, *Hieracium albiflorum*, 127, 131

Hazelnut, beaked, *Corylus cornuta*, 142

Heart rot fungus, *Fomes ignarius*, 145

Hedysarum, yellow, *Hedysarum sulphurescens*, 219

Vegetation (Continued)

Honeysuckle:
Bracted, *Lonicera involucrata*, 160
Twining, *L. glaucescens*, **167**
Hornwort, *Certophyllum demersum*, 229
Horsetail, *Equisetum* spp., 130
Water, *E. fluviatile*, 157, 160, **228**
Hypoxylon canker, *Hypoxylon pruinatum*, 145
Juniper:
Creeping, *Juniperus horizontalis*, **123**, 126
Ground, *J. communis* var. *saxatilis*, 107, 126
Kittentails, *Bessaya cinerea*, 131
Knotweed, *Polygonum aviculare*, 125, 131
Lady's-slipper, yellow, *Cypripedium calceolus*, **213**
Lettuce, blue, *Lactuca pulchella*, 141
Lichens, **132**
Alectoria spp., **125**-26, 128
Caloplaca, **125**
Lecidea, **125**
Yellow-branched wolf, *Letharia vulpina*, 127
Usnea spp., 128
Lily-of-the-valley, wild, *Maianthemum canadense* var. *interius*, 142, 161
Lily, tiger, *Lilium philadelphicum*, **140**
Liverwort, *Marchantia polymorpha*, 130-31
Locoweed, yellow:
Late, *Oxytropis campestris*, 140
Lungwort, hairy, *Mertensia paniculata*, 160
Lupine, perennial, *Lupinus sericeus*, 201
Mallow, scarlet, *Sphaeralcea coccinea*, **105**
Marigold, marsh, *Caltha palustris*, **167**
Mare's tail, *Hippuris vulgaris*, 130, **146**
Meadow rue, western, *Thalictrum occidentale*, 127, 131
Meadow-sweet, white, *Spiraea lucida*, 131
Milfoil, water, *Myriophyllum exalbescens*, 130, 229
Mistletoe, dwarf, *Arceuthobium americanum*, 127
Mitrewort, *Mitella* spp., **143**

Monkey-flower, yellow, *Mimulus guttatus*, 130-31
Mooseberry, *Viburnum edule*, 160
Mosses, Class Musci,
Aulacomnium palustre, 127
Bryum pseudotriquetrum, 130
Ceratodon purpureus, 142
Cratoneuron, spp., 130
Dicranum spp., 127
Drepanocladus aduncus, 130, 148
Encalypta procera, 131
Eurhynchium pulchellum, 142
Funaria hygrometica, 131
Hylocomium splendens, 127, 160-**61**, 207
Hypnum patientiae, 130
Lescuraea stenophylla, 131
Mnium cuspidatum, 142
M. marginatum, 131
Philonotis, spp., 130
Pleurozium schreberi, 127, 160-**61**
Ptilium crista-castrensis, 127, 160-**61**
Pylaisia polyantha, 142
Thuidium recognitum, 127
Timmia austriaca, 131
Mustard, *Brassica* spp., 125, 131, 149
Naiad, *Najas flexilis*, 130
Onion:
Nodding, *Allium cernuum*, **127**
Prairie, *A. textile*, 126-27
Orache, lance-leaved, *Atriplex patula* var. *hastata*, 148
Orchid:
Calypso (see Venus'-slipper)
Coral root, *Corallorhiza* sp., **123**
Northern green, *Habenaria hyperborea*, 130
Round-leaved, *Orchis rotundifolia*, **130**
Venus'-slipper, *Calypso bulbosa*, 127, **213**
Paintbrush:
Common red, *Castilleja miniata*, 126, **213**
Common yellow, *C. septentrionalis*, **167**
Pea vine, *Lathyrus ochroleucus*, 128, 142
Pea, wild, *Lathyrus* spp., 160
Phlox, moss, *Phlox hoodii*, 103, 126
Pigweed, *Chenopodium* spp., 149
Pincherry, *Prunus pennsylvanica*, **123**, 128, **142**

Pinedrops, *Pterospora andromedea*, 131
Plantain, water, *Alisma* spp., 147
Pondweed, *Potamogeton*, spp., 130, 146, 229, **231**
Primrose, evening, *Oenothera biennis*, 131, 149
Prince's pine, *Chimaphila umbellata* var. *occidentalis*, 127
Puccoon, *Lithospermum ruderale*, 126
Pussy-toes, *Antennaria* spp., 103, 126-27, **140**
Raspberry, *Rubus strigosus*, 131, 160
Dwarf, *R. pubescens*, 160
Rose:
Common wild, *Rosa woodsii*, 107, 127
Prairie, *R. arkansana*, 107, 140-**41**
Prickly, *R. acicularis*, 128, 142, 160
Rush, *Juncus ensifolius*, 146
Wire, *J. balticus*, 130
Sagebrush, *Artemisia* spp., 98, 101, **103**, 107, 120
Pasture sage, *A. frigida*, 101, **139**-40
Samphire, *Salicornia rubra*, 148
Sarsaparilla, wild, *Aralia nudicaulis*, 160
Saskatoon-berry, *Amelanchier alnifolia*, 107, 128, **142**, 160
Saxifrage, *Saxifraga* spp., **213**
Sea blite, *Suaeda depressa*, 148
Sedges, *Carex* spp., 101, 127, 130, 140, 146
C. eleocharis, 140
C. heliophila, 140
Shooting Star, *Dodecatheon conjugens*, **123**, 126
Smartweed, water, *Polygonum amphibium* var. *stipulaceum*, 130, **239**
Snowberry, *Symphoricarpos albus*, 107, 140, 142, 160
Western, *S. occidentalis*, 98, 107
Solomon's seal:
False, *Smilacina racemosa* var. *amplexicaulis*, 127
Star-flowered, *S. stellata*, 128
Spike rush, *Eleocharis palustris*, 130
Spring beauty, western, *Claytonia lanceolata*, 130-31
Squaw-root, *Perideridea gairdneri*, 131
Stinkweed, *Thlaspi arvense*, 149
Stonecrop, *Sedum stenopetalum*, **105**, 126

Vegetation (Continued)
Strawberry, wild, *Fragaria virginiana*
var. *glauca*, 128, 160
Tansy, *Tanacetum vulgare*, **143**
Thimbleberry, *Rubus parviflorus*, 131
Thistle:
Bull, *Cirsium vulgare*, **143**
Canada, *C. arvense*, 149
Russian, *Salsola kali*, 149
Sow, *Sonchus arvensis*, *S.*
uliginosus, 141, 149
Trees:
Alder:
Green, *Alnus crispus*, 160
River, *A. tenuifolia*, 146, 198
Ash, Green, *Fraxinus campestris*,
190
Aspen (*see* Poplar)
Birch:
Paper, *Betula papyrifera*, 155,
157-58, 166
Swamp, *B. pumila* var.
glandulifera, 130
Water or Western,
B. occidentalis, 130, 146, 158,
168-69
Cottonwood (*see* Poplar)
Fir:
Alpine (Subalpine), *Abies*
lasiocarpa, 154, 158, **205**, 207
Balsam, *A. balsamea*, 151, 154,
157-58, 166, 168
Douglas, *Pseudotzuga menziesii*,
190, **214**
Larch, *Larix* spp.,
American, *L. laricina*, **154**
Lyall's, *L. lyallii*, 154
Maple, Ash-leaved (Manitoba),
Acer negundo var, *interius*, **190**
Oak, bur, *Quercus Macro*
carpus, 190
Pine:
Scotch, *Pinus sylvestris*, 190
Jackpine, *P. banksiana*, 117, 154,
157, **168**
Limber or Rocky Mountain,
P. flexilis, **214**, 216
Lodgepole, *P. contorta* var.
latifolia, 117, 124, 125, **127**,
131, 154, 158, **187**, **205**
Monterey, *P. radiata*, 190

Poplar:
Aspen, *Populus tremuloides*, 100,
107, 127, **128**, **135**, **138**, 142,
144, 154, 158, 161
Balsam, *P. balsamifera*, 127-30,
146, 154, 157-58, 168, 202, **205**
Cottonwood:
Black, *Populus trichocarpa*,
107, 146, 154
Narrow-leaf, *P. angustifolia*,
107, 146
Spruce:
Black, *Picea mariana*, 155,
157-58, 166, **191**
Colorado blue, *P. pungens*, 190
Engelmann, *P. engelmanni*,
205, 207
White, *P. glauca* var. *albertiana*,
124, 127, 130-31, 146, 154,
156-58, **163**, **191**, 207
Umbrella plant, yellow,
Eriogonum flavum, 126
Venus'-slipper, (*see* Orchid)
Vetch, *Hedysarum alpinum*,
Cushion milk, *Astragalus*
triphyllum, 126
Milk, *A.* spp., 140
Wild, *Vicia americana*, 160
Violet, western Canada,
Viola rugulosa, 128, 142
Willow, *Salix* spp., 107, 130, 146, 148,
195, 198, 203
Arctic or Snow, *Salix arctica*, 218
Beaked, *S. bebbiana*, 142
Peach-leaf, *S. amygdaloides*, **146**
Sandbar, *S. interior* var.
pedicellata, 146
Yellow, *S. lutea*, 146
Wintergreen, *Pryola* spp., 127, 160
One-flowered, *Moneses uniflora*,
127
Pink or Rose-coloured,
P. asarifolia, 207
Silverberry (Wolf willow),
Elaeagnus commutata, 107, 127
Yarrow, *Achillea millefolium*,
126, **140**
Vegetation types, map, **102**
Vegreville, 139
Venus, 11, 17
Volcanoes, 23-24, 42-43

W

Wagner Weather Station, 66
Wainwright, 83, 139
Walcott, C. D., 27
Walker, E. M., 212
Warren, P. S., 41
Wastes:
domestic, 260-61
industrial, 258, 260-61
mine, 258
oil refinery, 258
pulp mill, 258
Water birds, 270
Water blooms, **229**, 233
Water conservation, 256-63
Wates, Cyril G., 8
Wates Observatory, **8**
Weather:
autumn, 53, 64-66
Medicine Hat, 99
spring, 59-60
summer, 61, **63**, 64
winter, **56-58**
Western Alberta ridge, 29, 31, 33
Wet peatland, **156-57**
Wetaskiwin, 139, 284
Wheat, 313
"White dwarf" stars, 11
Whitecourt, 84
Wildlife conservation, 319
Williams, M. Y., 124
Williston Basin, 27, 34
Winds:
autumn, 66
Chinook, 57-58, 99-100, 125
spring, 60
summer, 64
winter, 58

Y

Yellowhead Pass, 23
Yellowknife, 22-23
York boats, **307**
York factory, 303-04
Yukon, 58, 253-54, 277-78, 282, 288

Z

Zooplankton, 240-42, 251